TEST OF GREATNESS

Test of Greatness

Britain's Struggle
for the Atom Bomb

BRIAN CATHCART

JOHN MURRAY

First published in 1994
by John Murray (Publishers) Ltd.,
50 Albemarle Street, London W1X 4BD

The moral right of the author has been asserted

A catalogue record for this book is available from the
British Library

ISBN 0-7195-5225-7

Typeset in 11/13 pt English Times by
Colset Pte Ltd., Singapore
Printed and bound in Great Britain by
The University Press, Cambridge

*For Ruth, Thomas
and Patrick*

Contents

Illustrations ix

Acknowledgements xi

Maps xiii

Abbreviations xv

Prologue 1

1. A New World Order 7
2. Penney 26
3. First Steps 48
4. To Work 65
5. The Task is Doubled 84
6. Lightning Strikes Twice 98
7. Annus Horrendus 115
8. Aldermaston 127
9. Trial 145
10. Final Preparations 164
11. The Voyage Out 184
12. The Core 202
13. Rehearsals 212
14. The Event 236
15. The Aftermath 261

Contents

Notes   278
Bibliography   289
Index   293

Illustrations

(*between pages 112 and 113*)

1. Operation Epicure
2. William Penney in 1932
3. Penney in 1952
4. Atomic summit in Washington, November 1945
5. Lord Cherwell
6. Sir Henry Tizard
7. Viscount Portal of Hungerford
8. Klaus Fuchs
9. The plutonium processing building at Aldermaston
10. Senior scientific staff on Operation Hurricane, aboard the *Campania*
11. HMS *Campania* at the Monte Bello Islands
12. The laboratory on board the *Campania*
13. Landing craft in service at the Monte Bello Islands
14. Waiting to set off in a landing craft
15. Cocoa Beach camp on Trimouille
16. A cinema show at Cocoa Beach
17. Establishing the unauthorized Press observation post at Mount Potter
18. An RAAF plane flies over Mount Potter
19. Ieuan Maddock at the control desk during the countdown
20. HMS *Plym*, with the bomb on board

21. Admiral Torlesse and Penney on 3 October 1952
22. The crew of the *Campania* turn to witness the eruption
23. Winston Churchill leaves 10 Downing Street on 23 October
24., 25., 26. and 27. 'The vastness of the upheaval'
28. A model of the atomic bomb
29. The first British nuclear weapon

The author and publishers would like to thank the following for permission to reproduce photographs: Plates 1, 9, 10, 12, 13, 14, 15, 19, 20, 24, 28 and 29, © British Crown copyright/MOD, reproduced with the permission of the Controller of Her Britannic Majesty's Stationery Office; 2, Alfred T. Goble; 3, 5, 6, 7, 8, 17, 18 and 27, Hulton Deutsch Collection Ltd; 4, 21, 22, 23, 25 and 26, Associated Press; 11 and 16, Noah Pearce.

Acknowledgements

Many people helped with the preparation of this book, but there is one group without whose co-operation it could not have been written: the veterans of the atomic bomb project who allowed me to draw on their memories of events forty-odd years ago. I must thank them first: Leonard Bunce, Pat Cachia, John Challens, John Corner, John Davies, David Deverell, Geoffrey Ellis, Frank Hill, James Hole, Edward Howse, William Lord, William Moyce, Noah Pearce, Herbert Pike, the late Roy Pilgrim, Frank Roberts, Sir John Rowlands, John Tomblin and Aubrey Thomas. I believe they represent as fair a cross-section as is possible of William Penney's staff, although I am conscious that there are likely to be some individuals and activities that I have neglected. That I was able to make contact with them, and that they felt free to talk to me – within certain security constraints – I owe to Michael McTaggart of the Ministry of Defence, who was most generous with his assistance. I must stress, however, that this is not an official history, and neither Mr McTaggart nor the Ministry – nor indeed the veterans themselves – bear any responsibility for the final text. All inferences, interpretations, opinions and errors are entirely my own.

I also received help from others who were not on the staff of High Explosive Research but who were none the less directly involved in some of the events the book describes. These were: Rear Admiral David Torlesse, Charles Scott, Dan O'Sullivan,

Acknowledgements

Derrik Littler, Lord Sherfield, Lady Penney, Sir Rudolf Peierls, the late Lord Cheshire and Alfred T. Goble. Other historians of the period provided help and guidance: Margaret Gowing, Ferenc Morton Szasz, Peter Hennessy, Denis Richards, my colleague Robert Milliken and, above all, Lorna Arnold, whose kindness knew no bounds and whose observations on the work in progress were always shrewd and enlightening. The staffs of several libraries and archives assisted, notably those of the Public Record Office, the British Library, the library of the Australian High Commission in London, the archives of the Los Alamos National Laboratory, the library of the Royal Society of London, the Centre for Kentish Studies and the archives of Imperial College and of the 1851 Commission. I am not a scientist, and relied heavily on others for scientific and technical guidance. Professor D. M. Edwards of Imperial College helped me on Penney's early scientific career, while my colleague Tom Wilkie, Science Editor of *The Independent*, saved me many times from confusion. Bill Lord, whose memoir was among my most valuable sources, also devoted much time and effort to reading the manuscript and suggesting changes. Again, however, the responsibility for any errors in the final text is entirely my own. Help and support of various kinds was given by David Tyte, Neill Griffiths, Patrick Ahmat, Dr G. Hooper, Wyn Llewelyn, Margaret St John, Hilda Morgan and Michael Roscoe (who drew the maps), and by Peter Wilby and Ian Jack, respectively Deputy Editor and Editor of the *Independent on Sunday*. To all I offer my thanks. To my father I am doubly indebted. He read the manuscript and suggested some significant changes, but more importantly it was he who taught me the love of history. Finally and above all others, I must thank my wife. This project would never have reached completion without her generous advice, encouragement and assistance. These she provided despite my poor judgement in starting out just as our sons were arriving on the scene. To her and to them, with love and gratitude, the book is dedicated.

Brian Cathcart
London, 1994

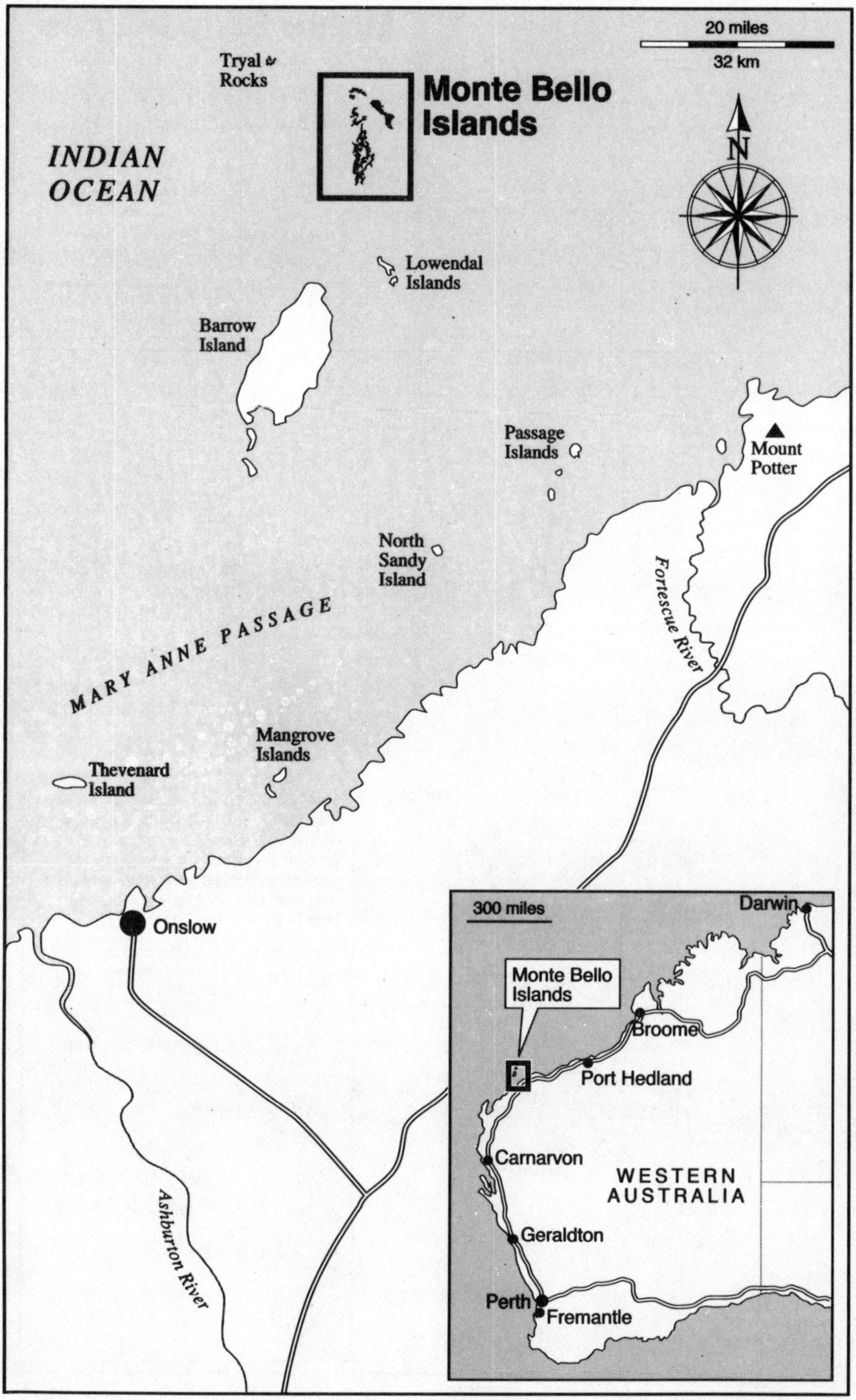

20 miles
32 km
Tryal Rocks
Monte Bello Islands
INDIAN OCEAN
N
Lowendal Islands
Barrow Island
Passage Islands
Mount Potter
North Sandy Island
Fortescue River
MARY ANNE PASSAGE
Mangrove Islands
Thevenard Island
Onslow
Ashburton River
300 miles
Darwin
Monte Bello Islands
Broome
Port Hedland
Carnarvon
WESTERN AUSTRALIA
Geraldton
Perth
Fremantle

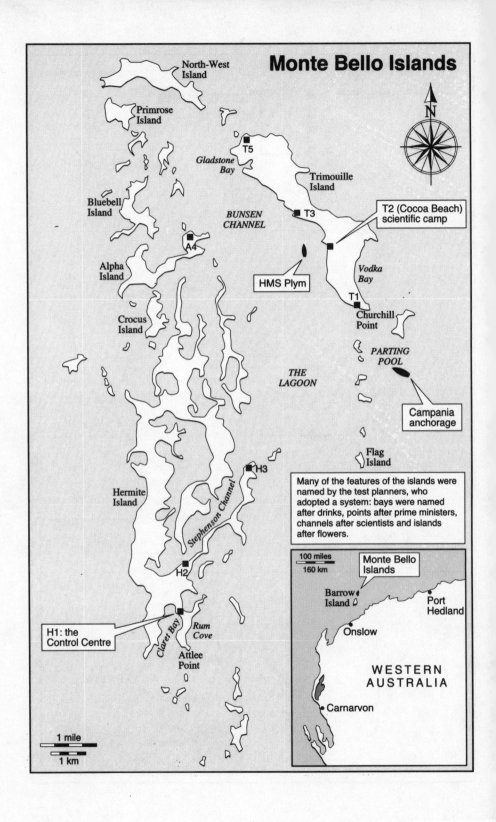

Monte Bello Islands

North-West Island

Primrose Island

Gladstone Bay

T5

Trimouille Island

Bluebell Island

BUNSEN CHANNEL

T3

T2 (Cocoa Beach) scientific camp

Alpha Island

A4

HMS Plym

Vodka Bay

T1

Churchill Point

Crocus Island

PARTING POOL

THE LAGOON

Campania anchorage

Flag Island

Many of the features of the islands were named by the test planners, who adopted a system: bays were named after drinks, points after prime ministers, channels after scientists and islands after flowers.

H3

Hermite Island

Stephenson Channel

H2

100 miles

160 km

Monte Bello Islands

Barrow Island

Port Hedland

H1: the Control Centre

Claret Bay

Rum Cove

Onslow

Attlee Point

WESTERN AUSTRALIA

1 mile

1 km

Carnarvon

Abbreviations

AEC	Atomic Energy Council
AERE	Atomic Energy Research Establishment (Harwell)
ARD	Armament Research Department
ARE	Armament Research Establishment (ARD's title after 1948)
ASIO	Australian Security and Intelligence Organization
BHER	Basic High Explosive Research
CSAR	Chief Superintendent, Armament Research
CSHER	Chief Superintendent, High Explosive Research
HER	High Explosive Research (shortened form of BHER)
HMAS	Her Majesty's Australian Ship
HUREX	Hurricane Executive
RAAF	Royal Australian Air Force
RAF	Royal Air Force
RE	Royal Engineers
REME	Royal Electrical and Mechanical Engineers

'The discriminative test for a first-class power is whether it has made an atomic bomb and we have either got to pass the test or suffer a serious loss in prestige both inside this country and internationally.'

William Penney, 1951

Prologue

ON a clear day in the middle of October 1950, a lone Mosquito aircraft of the Royal Australian Air Force flew low over the Monte Bello Islands, off the north-west coast of Australia. When it had completed one pass, the aircraft banked over the sea, turned and crossed back over the islands. Then it returned again and made another pass. The manoeuvre was repeated, and repeated, a dozen times or more before eventually the pilot broke off and headed back to the mainland.

There were no eyewitnesses to this event, for the islands were uninhabited. Once, on a spring day, pearl divers would have been at work in the shallows round about. Later, for a time, a handful of people camped on the islands for a few months each year to hunt turtles. But by 1950 those days were gone and the islands rarely saw a visitor. This was as had been hoped, for the Mosquito's mission was part of a secret operation, a matter so sensitive that although the prime ministers of Britain and Australia had exchanged letters about it, they had chosen not to mention it to their Cabinets. In Australia the number of people who knew about this operation could be established precisely: there were twenty-six, and not one of them was out in the far north-west. The Mosquito aircrew had no idea why anyone had wanted them to take aerial photographs of the Monte Bellos.

A few weeks later another unusual event occurred in the area, this time before an audience. On the afternoon of 8 November an

1

RAAF Dakota landed at the airstrip outside Onslow, the nearest port to the Monte Bellos on the Australian coast. It brought a party of five visitors, all dressed in Australian army bush gear. They were a curious collection. In charge was Air Vice-Marshal Edward 'Dizzy' Davis, a tall figure of considerable girth who as a young man had fought at Gallipoli. He was now retired from the RAF and working as a senior official at the Ministry of Supply in London. Next to him in seniority was a lanky, angular man in his forties with a large nose and prominent front teeth. This was Charles Adams, a scientist from a little-known Ministry of Supply establishment in Kent. His speciality was the development of equipment to observe and record events which lasted for only a tiny fraction of a second. With Davis and Adams were two young naval officers, Lieutenant Charles Scott of the Royal Navy and Lieutenant-Commander Tony Cooper of the Royal Australian Navy. Both were hydrographers, or makers of navigational charts. Last of the group was Max Phillips, representing the Australian Security and Intelligence Organization, his country's equivalent of MI5. They had come from Perth, a flight of several hours, and after disembarking and stretching their legs they made their way down into Onslow, where they were to spend the night.

Onslow in 1950 had one dusty street and about 350 inhabitants. The hotel, the Beadon Arms, built of concrete and standing two storeys high, was among its principal attractions, the others being a post office, a general store, a tea-room known as The Snifter and a cinema where, one recent traveller had noted, if you wanted a good seat you had to bring it with you. Down the middle of the street ran a line of red gum trees whose pungent odour lent a little freshness to the hot, dry air. On one side the tin-roofed bungalows backed on to the sea, their rears propped up over the shore. During the war allied submarines had used the bay as a base but since then little had occurred to disturb a rhythm of life which depended on the regular arrival of the supply ship from Fremantle and its equally regular departure loaded with the merino wool that was the local mainstay.

In such a place, a party of strangers in military attire could hardly fail to arouse curiosity, and indeed tongues had been wagging ever since their accommodation had been reserved. It was known that a naval vessel was due at Onslow jetty on the following day. This

2

was doubtless a rendezvous, the locals deduced, and the visitors were heading somewhere by sea. Better still, someone had a good idea of their destination, for on the day that the Mosquito had flown over the Monte Bellos, the radio operator at Onslow airfield had picked up the unusual traffic and eavesdropped. He was able to add his titbit to the others. So it was that when the visitors pushed through the Beadon's swinging half-doors and presented themselves at the bar, a couple of locals were on hand to remark: 'So you're going out to the Monte Bello Islands, then.'

There was no point denying it, but this was not how things had been planned. Their destination, like everything else about their journey, was supposed to be top secret. All that could be done was to take steps to ensure that the gossip did not travel. That evening, while his companions enjoyed a few beers on the Beadon verandah, Max Phillips paid a number of calls around town. The town's postmaster and his assistant acted as the local representatives of two Western Australian newspapers. Another resident was on the books of the Australian Broadcasting Commission, the national radio station, and the radio operator from the airfield represented a second radio station. Phillips visited all four, informing each in turn that the operation related to secret defence matters and asking them not to pass any information on to their associates in the Press. The story went no farther.

The next morning HMAS *Karangi*, a small vessel designed for laying harbour booms, embarked the five visitors at Onslow jetty and set out for the islands. These were dangerous waters, with shoals and coral reefs all about, so it was somewhat gingerly that they steamed into the Mary Ann Passage and made their way northwards between the scattered islands. A night was spent at anchor on the way, and the following morning the Monte Bellos were sighted.

They have never presented an inspiring spectacle. Long, low and dull brown, these are literally desert islands, the final afterthought of the great Australian desert which dips beneath the waves at the coast fifty miles away. There are about two hundred of them in all, but only three of any size and of these the biggest, Hermite, is just six miles in length and half a mile across at its widest. The loftiest point in the group is a sand dune some 140 feet high, and other hills stand out here and there, but for the most part the terrain is flat and little more than ten or twenty feet above the sea level. The shorelines are mostly low cliffs, and broad rocky shelves stretch out at or under the waterline in most directions.

These last were worrying the captain of the *Karangi* as his vessel drew close to its destination. His chart, which dated from 1840, showed a channel running into the lagoon at the centre of the archipelago and it was there that he had been asked to drop anchor. Rocks and coral, however, could be seen breaking the surface here and there, and in places the sea bottom could be glimpsed over the side. A boat was lowered to make soundings in the approaches to the channel and the results were not encouraging. It was decided not to risk the vessel in such restricted space. This caution was justified a few nights later when a gale blew up and the *Karangi*'s anchor cable broke, forcing the ship to put to sea. For the moment, though, conditions were no more than choppy and the landing party set off in a motor boat.

The visitors had a lot to do. Almost everything about the islands required close inspection, from the beaches to the rocky hilltops, from the vegetation to the temperature range and from the insect life to the geology. They needed to know whether there was sufficient flat land for an airfield, which there was not. They searched for fresh water, of which there was none. They examined the approaches to the beaches to see if flat-bottomed craft could land and whether jetties or piers would have to be constructed. They took samples of soil and gravel. They considered the possibility of building concrete structures and roads and they pondered the difficulties of living on the islands for several months at a stretch. Above all, they were interested in the high ground. Every hill, dune and crag was scaled, paced, measured, viewed from all possible angles, and photographed.

Gradually, the visitors formed an impression of the islands as a working environment for an expedition involving hundreds of men and many tons of equipment. In their little boats they rode the choppy sea both inside and outside the lagoon, and saw the menacing variety of sharks, stingrays and sea snakes that abounded in the waters. They got wet and occasionally cold – although they lie in the tropics, the Monte Bellos offer no shelter and the ocean wind can be sharp. Of shade there was none, for the tallest trees stood no more than four feet high. As on the adjacent Australian mainland, the terrain is dominated in all directions by one distinctive plant: spinifex. A type of grass, it grows in tight clumps to slightly more than knee-height and its shoots are stiff, sharp-edged and prickly. A field of spinifex forms an unyielding barrier to movement on foot and the survey party had frequent cause to curse it.

They saw some signs (and missed others) which showed that these islands, though uninhabited, were not completely without history. There were a few ruined buildings, remnants of pearling activities in and around the islands over half a century or more. There was a well, cut fifteen feet down through solid rock, and a disused oyster-bed fashioned from a mangrove swamp. There were also rats and large cats, the tenacious legacy of nineteenth-century shipwrecks. This was not a place that humankind had altogether passed by.

While Davis, Adams and Phillips were busy on the islands, Scott and Cooper surveyed the waters round about. They sank tide poles, measured the flow in the tidal channels and set up trigonometric posts. When an echo-sounding boat arrived – late – they got to work charting the sea bottom. This was to take some time, and when *Karangi* pulled out on 17 November, after a week at the islands, Scott had to stay behind to complete his task. With his departure ten days later ended Operation Epicure, as this secret expedition was codenamed. The *Karangi* returned to Perth with its crew under the impression that they had been surveying a site for experimental missile firings. A similar rumour got about in Onslow, linking the islands with the British-Australian Long Range Weapons Organization at Woomera in the heart of the continent. This story, artfully disseminated by Max Phillips, was quite untrue.

By mid-January of 1951 Davis, Adams and Scott were back in Britain and had prepared their reports. The shortcomings of the islands were laid bare: the heat, the glare, the lack of shade and water, the spinifex, the sharks and the sea snakes. 'Living conditions ashore for a prolonged period would be somewhat severe and the islands can only be called inhospitable', they concluded.[1] The tidal range and the rocky shoreline would make access a problem; radio reception was erratic and there were white ants on Hermite which would devour anything made of wood. Onslow offered no recreational facilities, no water supply, no building materials, insufficient accommodation and poor harbouring for ships; Fremantle, almost eight hundred miles away, should be considered the nearest port. The Australian authorities, and particularly the armed services, were praised for their co-operativeness, but there was a cutting reference to the civilians, who were thought too prone to strikes. Despite all this, the main conclusions were positive: the channel through the lagoon was, in the right circumstances, navigable; appropriate observation sites had been located on land and preliminary meteorological data was encouraging. In the words of Air Vice-Marshal Davis: 'Though there will undoubtedly be many difficulties to overcome, I am of the opinion that, from the administrative aspect, the site would prove suitable.'[2]

It was some months before the fate of the islands was sealed; an Australian election had to come and go before the necessary approval could be secured and in the meantime other sites, under American control, were discussed and rejected. But the Epicure report was ultimately decisive, providing as it did the practical confirmation of what the British authorities had hoped to find. So it was that the Monte Bello Islands, a place of pearls, spinifex and shipwrecks half a world away from London, were chosen to be the scene of an atomic explosion. There, on the morning of 3 October 1952, Britain became a nuclear power.

1

A New World Order

THE bomb that was tested in the Monte Bellos was a genuinely independent British deterrent, fashioned by British hands, using British materials, in British workshops and laboratories. The design had been borrowed in the first instance, but it had been adapted and improved by British scientists. This Britishness, however, like much else about the weapon and its development, was a matter, not of choice, but of necessity.

The story of the making of Britain's first atomic bomb is one of improvization and struggle, of hesitation and last-minute rush, of high stakes and low cards. No particular event marks its beginning, but the Epicure expedition to the Monte Bello Islands forms the cusp between two distinct phases. Before Epicure, the atomic project had been characterized by a somewhat evolutionary approach to organization and by a desperate struggle for resources. The right man had been put in charge and he began to build his team and start the work, but he found his path obstructed by many obstacles, from official secrecy to bureaucratic obstinacy. It did not help that everyone involved kept one longing eye trained on the United States in the hope that a lapsed partnership might be renewed. Nor did it help that this period saw the successive scandals of the British 'atom spies', although at least one of those spies made an important contribution to the British project. After Epicure the mood changed. There was a headlong rush to ensure that there would be a weapon to be tested and that it would explode on command. Matters of management and policy took second place to technology and logistics, but many mistakes were made and it was by luck as much as judgement that failure was avoided. All this confusion and haste was owed in large part to the circumstances of the country, exhausted by six years of war and groping to define its place in a changed world. It also flowed from the unusual circumstances in which the weapon project was conceived, which were far from conducive to clear-sighted planning.

ON 28 AUGUST 1945, Clement Attlee sat down in his office in Downing Street and tried to make sense of the whirlwind of thoughts turning in his mind on the subject of the atomic bomb. He had been prime minister for barely a month, and in that time it seemed as though the world had been turned upside-down. The election victory itself had been remarkable enough – even Attlee was unable to conceal his surprise at the result when he presented himself to the King at Buckingham Palace. Within days, the first of the new weapons was dropped on the city of Hiroshima, to be swiftly followed by a second on Nagasaki. Japan surrendered and the Second World War came to an end. With astonishing suddenness, many months before most people in Britain had dared to hope, there was peace. But it was a peace unlike any that had gone before: a peace made by nuclear weapons. For a newly elected government, and particularly one with limited expertise in defence and foreign affairs, this was as perplexing as it was welcome. To discuss what should be done about this new phenomenon, Attlee had called a meeting of senior ministers on the following day. Now he was composing a memorandum to set before them.

'A decision on major policy with regard to the atomic bomb is imperative', he wrote. Until this decision was taken, civil and military planning would be worthless, for the emergence of the new weapon had made nonsense of all previous thinking about the future defence of Britain. Far-flung strategic bases were now irrelevant since the heart of the Empire was acutely vulnerable to devastating attack; in a country as small as Britain, moreover, a dispersal of industry, airfields and arms factories would be useless; bomb-proof basements and ARP services were now 'just futile waste', Attlee wrote. 'It is difficult for people to adjust their minds to an entirely new situation . . . Even the modern conception of war to which in my lifetime we have become accustomed is now completely out of date.'[1]

Certain things were clear. First, within a few years other countries, including the Soviet Union, would discover for themselves how to make the bomb. Second, this was a weapon against which there was no defence; bombing could only be answered by counter-bombing, so the answer to an atomic bomb on London would have to be an atomic bomb on another great city. Third, no voluntary international agreement to abstain from using the weapon would work, and any attempt to bully the Russians would probably lead to world war. It was a terrifying situation; what was to be done? Attlee wrote: 'The only course which seems to me to be feasible and to offer a reasonable hope of staving off imminent disaster for the world is joint action by the USA, UK and Russia based upon stark reality. We should declare that this invention has made it essential to end wars. The new World Order must start now.'

A completely different framework of political thinking was required, Attlee wrote. The 'whole conception of war' must be 'banished from people's minds and from the calculations of governments'. As every nation must submit to the rule of law, so every international dispute must be settled peacefully, be it Palestine, India or the Ruhr. The Soviet Union must abandon its dreams of revolution and Britain and the United States must similarly abandon any hopes they might harbour of overthrowing Communist governments. 'This sort of thing', he wrote, 'has in the past been considered a Utopian dream. It has become today the essential condition of the survival of civilization and possibly of life in this planet.'

That this most matter-of-fact of British prime ministers should have found himself committing such thoughts to paper is a measure of the moral and political impact of the explosions at Hiroshima and Nagasaki. Everywhere, people were struggling to understand the new phenomenon, to find their bearings in the new order. Here was a single bomb, delivered by a single aeroplane, that could destroy a whole city; would the United States now use it to dominate the world? Would Stalin submit, or would there be a new war? If the Soviet Union got the bomb, could anything stop it obliterating Britain? If not Russia, could somebody else do it? Would all future wars be atomic wars? Were armies and navies now

9

useless? The certainties of generations were now dust in the wind. Attlee felt on his shoulders the dreadful weight of his responsibility to give leadership. 'No government', he wrote, 'has ever been placed in such a position as is ours today. The Governments of the UK and the USA are responsible as never before for the future of the human race.'

Britain shared this burden with the United States because Britain had shared, as a junior partner, in the development of the new weapon. Although it had been made in America and dropped from a US bomber, it was in some respects the fruit of British initiative and British scientists had gone to the United States to help design and build it. Agreements, both formal and informal, existed between the two governments about the further development and use of atomic energy. So it was not only as the prime minister of a victorious great power that Attlee felt himself obliged to act, but as the leader of one of the countries which had unleashed this new force. Britain and the United States, he felt, had the responsibility to guide the world into the new order, and they must enlist the co-operation of the Soviet Union. 'I believe only a bold course can save civilization', he concluded. Such were the views that Clement Attlee presented to his senior colleagues at the end of August, and he found them no less at sea than himself.

A little less than four months later, on 18 December, he convened his Cabinet committee on atomic energy again in Downing Street. On this occasion, the nature of the business was very different. Each minister had received a copy of a report by an advisory committee which had been investigating what Britain's policy should be in the atomic field. Attlee, in the chair, drew their attention to what he saw as the most important recommendation in the report, that either one or two nuclear reactors should be built in Britain. Reactors, or 'piles' as they were then known, might serve a variety of purposes: to generate electricity; for research or to produce materials for use in atomic bombs. Attlee was clear about which he had in mind. 'How many piles should be built', he explained, 'depended in part upon the output of bombs which the Government thought necessary.'[2]

The meeting was also told that 'the Chiefs of Staff had not yet been able to make a full study of our strategic requirements for bombs and the possibility of making reductions in other forms of armament production. Fuller study might well show, however, that in the light of possible production rates in other countries, the building of a second pile in this country would be justified.' After a discussion of the cost of the piles, both in terms of cash and of equally scarce manpower and materials, the ministers reached an agreement. One pile should be built, but the groundwork should be prepared at the same time for a second pile in case it proved necessary. Meanwhile, the Chiefs of Staff were instructed to submit a report on Britain's requirements for atomic bombs.

Here, then, was the first step on the path to the British atomic weapon. The pile, which was in due course constructed on the site of a wartime ordnance factory near Sellafield in Cumberland, was wanted for the large-scale production of plutonium, seen as the vital nuclear explosive material of the future. That Britain wished to go down this path was not at issue. The record of the Cabinet committee indicates that ministers did not discuss whether this pile should be built, but whether Britain needed two piles rather than one.

From the Utopian thinking of August to the strategic military planning of December seems an extraordinary leap. The man who wrote in his August memorandum that 'steps must be taken to prevent the development of this weapon in any country' was now establishing arrangements for the production of that same weapon in his own country. The man who declared that 'this invention has made it essential to end wars' was preparing to equip Britain to fight an atomic war. How did this change come about?

In many respects, the contrast is illusory. Attlee did not see any direct conflict between the policy of August and that of December. At the December meeting, once the decision about the nuclear reactor was taken, ministers went on to discuss the state of the negotiations for the establishment of a regime of international control over atomic energy. The objective here was to remove atomic matters from the hands of national governments and place them under the auspices of the new United Nations Organization. This was an idea to which Attlee was sincerely committed. The boldness of his determination to transform the entire basis of relations between states may have diminished with the passage of four months, but the desire to chain up the atomic monster remained and that alone was an ambitious, possibly a Utopian, goal.

11

By December it was widely accepted that international control offered the best hope of preventing a cataclysmic war. The idea was that a United Nations body, by such means as the regulation of the supply of nuclear raw materials and the inspection of factory sites, would ensure that governments could not develop the new weapon independently. It was recognized that this would be difficult since no such regime had been created before. The picture was complicated, moreover, by the high hopes held out by scientists that nuclear fission could be harnessed to produce cheap electricity. The peaceful uses of atomic energy, they said, might be every bit as revolutionary as its warlike application. But if countries were to develop this new resource for generating power, could they be prevented from making weapons at the same time? Plans were by now taking shape for a United Nations Atomic Energy Commission which would tackle this and other problems, and Britain was conscientiously supporting the preparations. For Attlee, this was the practical form of the 'bold course' he had searched for in August.

It would be wrong, however, to infer that the British Government was confident of a successful outcome to these negotiations. For one thing, an investigation of the possibilities of control, conducted by British officials on Attlee's instruction, had concluded, to his dismay and irritation, that it was not really practicable. No amount of international policing, it seemed, could prevent countries from making atomic bombs if they wished to. The best bet, the officials said, was to bind nations together in a collective security arrangement under which any nation that attacked another with atomic weapons would itself be attacked by all the others. Attlee did not think much of this. As to British policy, the report said bluntly: 'The United Kingdom Government should itself undertake the production of atomic weapons as a means of self-defence as soon as possible.'[3]

Alongside the doubts about workability ran another concern: Josef Stalin. Suspicion of the motives and intentions of the Soviet leader, never far below the surface in the final stages of the war, had become a public fact since the peace. For a Labour government under pressure from its supporters to eschew the despised 'power politics' of the past and follow a foreign policy based on ideals, this was an awkward matter. Ernest Bevin, the Foreign Secretary, was

12

no great idealist and by Christmas 1945 he was already at odds with many Labour backbenchers. The post-war negotiations over the settlement of Europe had given no grounds for hope that Stalin was disposed to any bold schemes for setting international affairs on a new footing; there had already been unpleasant clashes with Molotov, the Soviet foreign minister. Nor, on the ground in eastern Europe, the Middle East or the Far East, did Soviet foreign policy appear to be based upon anything other than old-fashioned power politics.

Further, the Government knew – although the public had not yet been told – that the Soviet Union had spied on British atomic work even while the two countries had been allies. The defection of a cypher clerk, Igor Gouzenko, in Canada in September 1945 had led to the discovery that Allan Nunn May, a British scientist engaged in nuclear research in Montreal, had passed information and materials to a Soviet agent. Nunn May had worked on the British-Canadian research reactor at Chalk River in Ontario and had visited the Argonne Laboratory in Chicago, one of the centres of the American work. He was by no means an important figure but it was clear that his information would have been most helpful and interesting to the Russians. His arrest was deferred to give relations with the Soviet Union a chance to improve, but the hope was vain and he was taken into custody in London in March 1946. Thirteen others implicated by Gouzenko were arrested in Canada. Such cases later became almost commonplace, but in 1945 the discovery that the Soviet Union was actively interested in atomic research, at a time when it had been thought to know nothing about it, was depressing and alarming.

Attlee's enthusiasm for international control of atomic energy was thus tempered by a growing conviction that it would only be established with great difficulty and great patience. The hope of success remained, but while it was only a hope, Attlee and his senior ministers took the view that they could not afford to take risks with Britain's defences and must therefore prepare the ground for the development of its own atomic weapon by embarking upon the large-scale production of plutonium. Fateful as this decision was, it was only the formal implementation of a widely shared assumption that the country, as a world power, must inevitably arm itself with the latest and most powerful of weapons. As we saw, the ministers gathered together in the December meeting did not discuss whether to produce plutonium, but how much should be produced. They were in no doubt that Britain should have the bomb, although ultimately they might be prepared to surrender it, or abandon its development, if a convincing regime of international control were agreed.

To build a pile, moreover, was not an unambiguous or irrevocable step towards a weapon. Ministers and their advisers were as committed to the notion that Britain must have a fully-fledged atomic research programme to probe the peaceful possibilities of the new discoveries as they were to the idea that the country should have a bomb. Atomic energy was already being portrayed as a potential panacea – Attlee himself had publicly spoken of the possibility that it might become 'a perennial fountain of world prosperity'.[4] A few pounds of uranium, the newspapers were by now constantly repeating, could yield as much power as thousands of tons of coal. Even if this was an exaggeration, and even if it took many years to produce results, a solution to Britain's desperate fuel shortage at last seemed possible. There was no doubt that this was a field in which British science and industry must not fall behind. In the autumn of 1945 Attlee had already approved the creation of the Atomic Energy Research Establishment (AERE) which was to be the focus of this work; a large-scale atomic pile would be another useful and practical way of taking the research programme forward. Not only would it point the way towards a pile capable of generating power, but much could also be learned from the study of the plutonium it produced. The decision to build a pile, then, could be presented in all honesty as one aspect in the development of a peaceful atomic research programme. And that is precisely how it was presented. The British public and the international community were not told of the pile's other purpose, which was without doubt its primary purpose.

By the opening of 1946, Attlee and his ministers had set things in motion. The task of implementing their instructions naturally fell to others. Chief amongst these was Air Marshal Viscount Portal of Hungerford, whom Attlee personally persuaded to take the post of Controller of Production, Atomic Energy. Portal was a hero of two wars. In the First World War he had served four years in the Royal Flying Corps, rising to the rank of Lieutenant-Colonel and winning the Military Cross, DSO and bar, all by the age of twenty-five. In the Second World War he briefly directed Bomber Command and then, from 1940 onwards, he was the Chief of Air Staff and one of the handful of military men closest to Churchill. He was, in Churchill's words, 'the accepted star of the Air Force', but he was more than that.[5] He was a gifted administrator, inclined to fairness but capable of the ruthlessness that Churchill always wanted in his generals. He was intellectually a match for Whitehall's finest minds, a deft handler of politicians and above all – in Churchill's eyes – a positive thinker. When, in 1940, Churchill wrote that 'the Navy can lose us the war, but only the Air Force can win it', he might have been thinking of Portal.[6] In strategic terms, Portal's first thought was always attack. He, just as much as his subordinate Arthur 'Bomber' Harris, was responsible for the strategic bombing offensive against German cities. In 1945, as one of the architects of victory, he was showered with honours, becoming a Viscount, a Knight of the Garter and a member of the Order of Merit. He was naturally drawn into the discussions about the atomic bomb and future defence, and he quickly formed the view that Britain should make as many bombs as it could, as quickly as possible. When the Cabinet committee meeting of 18 December asked for a more detailed report on this from the Chiefs of Staff, he helped to write the reply. This declared: 'We must have a considerable number of bombs at our disposal. It is not possible now to assess the precise number which we might require but we are convinced we should aim to have as soon as possible a stock in the order of hundreds rather than scores.'[7] To achieve this, the Chiefs of Staff concluded, two atomic piles would be better than one.

When Attlee asked him to take on the new job, Portal was reluctant. Although still only fifty-two, he was exhausted. He had retired from the RAF only days earlier and was eager for the relative calm and the higher financial rewards of City boardrooms. But the Prime Minister persisted, and Portal yielded, insisting, however, that he would work only part time and would stay for two years at most. The project was to benefit enormously from his influence and his ability to make Whitehall work for him, but he was never able to embrace the atomic energy programme as he had the RAF; it was always a dispassionate and rather weary hand on the tiller.

Portal's was one of three important appointments announced at the end of January 1946. John Cockcroft was named Director of the Atomic Energy Research Establishment, which found a home on a former airfield at Harwell on the Berkshire-Oxfordshire border. Cockcroft was a Cambridge nuclear physicist who had helped create the first machine to split atoms, an achievement which was to bring him the Nobel prize. He had subsequently worked on the development of radar before taking charge of the British-Canadian nuclear reactor research project in Canada towards the end of the war. The other appointment was of Christopher Hinton, a senior ICI engineer who had spent the war building factories to produce bombs and shells. He was chosen to lead the team which would design and construct the atomic pile. All three men would work within the framework of the Ministry of Supply, a department which, during the war, had combined responsibility for the production of food and military materials, and which was now deemed to have the spare capacity and the most appropriate experience to handle atomic affairs. Cockcroft went to Harwell and Hinton to Risley in Lancashire to build up their respective establishments. Portal, meanwhile, set up his office on Ministry of Supply premises in London, in the Shell-Mex building on the Strand, which had been the headquarters of 'Tube Alloys', as the British atomic project during the war was known. Here, for security reasons, a corridor of offices was closed off with steel bars to create what became known as the 'Cage'.

Although he had technical abilities, Portal was no scientist, and one of his first steps was to appoint another ICI man, Michael Perrin, as his technical adviser. Perrin had performed much the same function in Tube Alloys. One further figure had an important role at the outset: Sir James Chadwick. Chadwick, another Nobel physicist from Cambridge and undoubtedly one of Britain's greatest living scientists, had directed the British team working on the bomb in America during the war and became an influential voice in British policy-making in the atomic field. Like Portal, he was in no doubt that Britain should make bombs in large numbers and as quickly as possible. Portal, in the early months, leant heavily on him for advice.

Those early months were dominated by a single concern. Slowly but surely since the end of the war, co-operation between the

United States and Britain in the atomic field had withered. Even in wartime it had been a turbulent relationship beset with suspicion and misunderstanding and on occasions it was kept alive only by the personal rapport of Churchill and Roosevelt. After the victory over Japan, with Roosevelt no longer on the scene, the Americans could see less and less reason for sustaining such a difficult partnership. This was a cause of great alarm in London, for practical as well as diplomatic reasons. British scientists had been involved in a wide range of work on the development of the bomb, but they had nothing like a comprehensive knowledge of what was required. For security reasons the Manhattan Project had been 'compartmentalized' and as a result, to take one instance, no British scientist had ever laid eyes on the American plutonium piles. Building piles in Britain would be infinitely more difficult and expensive if the Americans did not share their knowledge.

On the face of it, there seemed at first to be grounds for optimism, for during the war the two countries had negotiated a series of written agreements pointing towards post-war collaboration. In 1944, for example, Churchill and Roosevelt had agreed that: 'Full collaboration between the United States and the British Government in developing Tube Alloys for military and commercial purposes should continue after the defeat of Japan unless and until terminated by joint agreement.'[8] The words appeared to be a guarantee, but they were not. It was symbolic of an ill-starred partnership that Roosevelt failed to tell any of his relevant advisers and officials of this promise, and that the only American copy of the memorandum was lost – the code words 'Tube Alloys' fooled the filing clerks, who assumed the document must relate to naval torpedo tubes. As a result, when the British tried to invoke the agreement, nobody on the American side had heard of it. It had been, in any case, an over-ambitious commitment for any president to have made without consulting Congress and, while Roosevelt himself might have been able to ensure that it was honoured, Harry S. Truman would not.

Like Attlee, Truman had found that victory in the war confronted him with daunting decisions about his country's place in the new order. Unlike Attlee, he was actually in possession of the new weapon, and this brought with it many distinctive pressures. Americans were proud of the bomb, on which their government had spent the extraordinary sum of $2 billion, and which had so spectacularly ended the war. They were also jealous of it, and from the earliest days after Hiroshima there was a strong current of public opinion which felt that the United States should keep the secret of this new invention to itself. Even when it was explained that there was no specific scientific secret which could be kept, and that other countries would be certain to master the science and engineering of bomb manufacture within a few years, the view remained that the United States should keep its monopoly as long as possible. This view naturally found favour with isolationists and anti-Communists, but it also had a strong attraction for the ordinary run of representatives in Congress and among the public at large.

Truman was slow to declare any policy on atomic weapons, and in the first months it was only under pressure from Congress and from Attlee that he expressed any opinions at all. He too wanted to see a regime of international control, and was ready for a 'bold course', but he was careful to reassure his electorate. On 8 October 1945, during a fishing trip in Tennessee, he invited some journalists for a chat on the front porch of his lodge. Talking about the bomb, he carefully drew a distinction between scientific knowledge, which was accessible to all, and technical knowledge. This technical knowledge, he promised, would not be shared; any other country wishing to develop the atomic bomb 'will have to get it on their own hook, just as we did'.[9] The remarks were made on the record, and so were headline news the next day. They caused deep despondency in London. A month later, and more or less at his own request, Attlee flew to Washington for a meeting with both Truman and the Canadian prime minister, Mackenzie King. Despite the myriad international problems confronting the three former allies, only one subject was on the agenda: the atom.

The meeting fully conformed to the wartime pattern of Anglo-American diplomacy in the atomic field. Two agreements were made, one public and one private. The public agreement was simple enough, and laid the groundwork for the creation of the United Nations Atomic Energy Commission. The second, secret accord was extremely short, and included the declaration: 'We desire that there should be full and effective co-operation in the field of atomic energy between the United States, the United Kingdom

18

and Canada.'[10] On paper at least, the Truman administration had promised what Attlee wanted, and the British party returned to London in buoyant mood. Within weeks, however, it was plain that the Americans would not deliver. The precise definition of 'full and effective co-operation' had been left to a tripartite committee in Washington, and that committee made no progress. Worse, a bill began to take shape in Congress which promised to set a legal block on any future exchanges of atomic information with foreign countries. In the spring of 1946 matters came to a head. Britain informed the US government of its decision to build an atomic pile and asked for technical information under the terms of the Washington agreement. At first the Americans procrastinated; then in April they said no. This was a watershed. Although the British never lost hope, it was to be years before the Truman administration could be persuaded to think again.

Three main factors lay behind the American decision. First, there was the desire of many in the United States to keep such an expensive and extraordinary invention for themselves. Second, there was a view that a bilateral arrangement with Britain would be resented by other countries and would make more difficult the task of establishing United Nations control of atomic energy. And third, there was the complex American attitude towards Britain. In Washington a suspicion had prevailed since the war years that Britain intended to cash in on the civil possibilities of atomic energy without having paid its share of the huge development costs. The US taxpayer had built the great atomic installations which proved the potential of the atom, so it was felt that the US taxpayer should reap in full whatever commercial reward there might be.

It should be said that Britain's contribution to the wartime effort was not adequately recognized in the US, and that many of the people most active in protecting the American interest, as they saw it, were not aware of the debt that was owed to the British, or of the written commitments that had been given. Senator Brien McMahon, the young Connecticut Democrat who was the prime mover behind the bill in Congress banning the sharing of atomic information with foreign powers, admitted years later that if he had known of the depth of the nuclear relationship with Britain he would have acted differently. Others in Washington who knew the whole story were more than content to see Britain cut out.

19

General Leslie Groves, for example, who had directed the Manhattan Project during the war, believed that Britain should not build piles or have bombs because it was too vulnerable to Soviet attack, and that it should not be given classified information because it could not be trusted to keep it secret. The Nunn May case, revealing that a scientist cleared by the British security services had been working secretly for Moscow, came at just the right moment to lend support to such views.

All these various pressures came to bear on President Truman and, since he lacked Roosevelt's sympathy for the British, he saw no reason to resist them. When the McMahon Bill passed the Congress in July 1946, he signed it into law. In the development of atomic energy and the atomic bomb, the British were left to 'get it on their own hook'.

This meant a vast increase in the burden carried by Christopher Hinton and his team, by now beginning to assemble. They already knew that they would have to design and construct not one but three distinct industrial complexes: one, to extract and refine uranium metal from ore, which was to be built at Springfields, near Preston in Lancashire; the pile itself at the Sellafield site, soon to be named Windscale; and a third to extract and refine the plutonium which was manufactured in the course of the nuclear reaction inside the pile. This last was also built at Windscale. They scarcely knew where to begin. Leonard Owen, Hinton's deputy, recalled years later: 'At the start, of the twelve of us at Risley, only one person knew anything about atomic energy. He was Dennis Ginns, an engineer who was home on sick leave from Chalk River . . . The only written information we had was the Smyth Report, a general account of the American wartime atomic energy project which we had all read from cover to cover. While there was some criticism in America that the report gave too much information away, it was remarkable to us for what it didn't give away that one was anxious to know.'[11] It was an unpromising beginning.

To compound the difficulties, in the course of 1946 a consensus arose among scientists and officials that a fourth plant should also be built, which would employ an extremely complex technology known as gaseous diffusion to enrich uranium in the rare isotope

U-235.* This would allow more efficient use both of the raw material, natural uranium, which was then in short supply, and of the pile itself. More plutonium, and ultimately more bombs, could be produced. When the proposal went before Attlee's Cabinet committee in October there was dismay at the cost, but according to Michael Perrin, who was present, an outburst from Ernest Bevin settled the matter. 'We've got to have this', Bevin said. 'I don't mind for myself, but I don't want any other Foreign Secretary of this country to be talked at, or to, by the Secretary of State of the United States as I have just had, in my discussions with Mr Byrnes. We've got to have this thing over here, whatever it costs . . . We've got to have a bloody Union Jack flying on top of it.'[12] Bevin's colleagues gave their approval for the first stage of work on the gaseous diffusion factory, which was to be built at Capenhurst in Cheshire.

By October 1946, Portal's mind was turning to another matter. Although he and everyone else involved at a senior level assumed that they were working towards the production of a British atomic bomb, there was no formal basis for such an assumption. Bevin's exclamation that 'we've got to have this thing over here' illustrates the point. The subject on the agenda was a new uranium processing factory, but when he spoke of 'this thing', he undoubtedly meant the weapon. If the new factory was needed to make a British bomb, Bevin was saying, then it must be built. Yet neither the Prime Minister, nor the committee, nor the Chiefs of Staff, nor anyone else had actually given the authority for the development of a bomb. So long as he was dealing only with the factories which would produce the fissionable material for the weapon, Portal did not need such authority. When the moment came to begin the design and development work on the bomb itself, he did. By the autumn of 1946, with Hinton beginning to show confidence that his chain of factories could be built and would successfully produce plutonium, that moment was drawing near.

---

*Each of the chemical elements has a variety of forms, known as isotopes, which are identical except that their nuclei contain different numbers of neutrons, or neutral particles. Most uranium is U-238, but it was found that there were advantages in increasing the proportion of U-235.

More is required to make an atomic bomb than a mere lump of plutonium. It takes a dozen important components, electronic, explosive and nuclear, to set in motion the fission chain reaction. Not one of these components was available off the peg in Britain; indeed to design and produce each would require a substantial scientific effort. If Hinton was satisfied he could make the plutonium, then the time had come to think about how some of these other components should be developed. In September, Michael Perrin wrote: 'All those who have been connected with the American work on bomb design and production have . . . stressed the need for a strong team to carry out research and development on this subject here.'[13] There had at first been a plan that this could be done by Cockcroft's team at AERE Harwell, but Perrin said that for political and security reasons this would be unwise – many of the Harwell team had expressed a clear desire not to be involved in weapons work, and in any case it suited the Government to be able to present Harwell as an establishment dedicated to peaceful research. Instead, Perrin suggested, the job could be given to the Armament Research Department (ARD), an establishment under the wing of the Ministry of Supply dedicated to improving the weaponry available to the British forces. The current Chief Superintendent of Armament Research (CSAR), William Penney, had been one of the British scientists sent to the United States during the war to work on the atomic bomb. 'It would seem advisable', wrote Perrin, 'to set up a separate organization to work on the military applications of atomic energy which would bring together the expert knowledge associated with AERE and with CSAR, to arrange for selected parts of the work to be farmed out to existing research and development establishments and to have a separate establishment for the co-ordination of the work and the execution of some of the most secret parts of it.'[14] Here was the first written outline of an official organization for the design, development and manufacture of a British atomic bomb, as distinct from the production of its main nuclear component, plutonium.

Portal took the matter up in October, commissioning from Penney a description of how he would carry out the work at ARD. In November he took this to the Chiefs of Staff. 'I do not suggest that there is the slightest doubt that the atomic bomb should be developed here', he told them.[15] What he wanted, and received, was their approval for his proposed method of making it. Six days later he saw the Prime Minister who asked him to submit a written proposal. Then Attlee convened a Cabinet committee meeting for the afternoon of Wednesday, 8 January 1947. This was not the same committee which had been dealing with atomic matters since August 1945, and which had carried the title GEN.75. It had a slightly different membership and a different title, GEN.163. Present were Attlee's closest confidants, Bevin and Herbert Morrison, the Lord President of the Council, and three other ministers: Lord Addison, the Dominions Secretary; Albert Alexander, the Minister of Defence, and John Wilmot, the Minister of Supply. The GEN.75 members who were conspicuously excluded were Hugh Dalton, the Chancellor of the Exchequer, and Sir Stafford Cripps, the President of the Board of Trade. We do not know the reason for their absence. It may simply reflect the fact that money, an important element in the GEN.75 deliberations about plutonium production, was not expected to play a large part in the discussion. On the other hand, Attlee may have regarded this as an exceptional occasion meriting particular security measures and a status apart from the previous meetings.

Before them, the ministers had an eight-page memorandum from Portal which could hardly be bettered as a case study of committee management. It opened: 'I submit that a decision is required about the development of atomic weapons in this country. The Service Departments are beginning to move in the matter and certain sections of the Press are showing interest in it.'[16] Portal offered the ministers three options and made it quite clear that only one was workable or desirable. The first was not to develop the weapon at all, a course which he imagined 'would not be favoured by H. M. Government in the absence of an international agreement on the subject'. The second option was to develop the weapon using the normal agencies employed to provide the armed forces with equipment. If this course were followed, Portal pointed out, a great many people would soon find out about it, including the Americans, and 'this might well seem to them another reason for reticence over technical matters'. The third option was 'to develop the weapon under special arrangements conducive to the utmost secrecy'. The work would be done at the ARD under Penney, who, Portal observed, 'knows more than any other British scientist about the secrets of the American bomb'. The project would be camou-flaged behind the cover name Basic High Explosive Research, and under a special arrangement Penney would answer for the work to Portal rather than to his usual superiors on the armaments side of the Ministry of Supply. This scheme, Portal added for good measure, already had the blessing of the Chiefs of Staff.

The minutes of the meeting do not record anything that could be described as a debate. Bevin repeated, in moderated language, the views he had expressed in October about the need for Britain to acquire its own atomic bomb; Alexander concurred, and Wilmot, the Minister of Supply, stated in response to an inquiry that the task would require about 180 people. If Attlee offered any views, his words were not minuted. The meeting concluded exactly as Portal had wished, agreeing 'that research and development work on atomic weapons should be undertaken', and that the third option, involving the 'special arrangements conducive to the utmost secrecy' should be adopted. There followed a brief report by Bevin on the slow progress in the talks on international control of atomic energy, including the observation that 'we could not afford to be dependent upon other nations' in the development of atomic power. After that, Cabinet committee GEN.163 broke up, never to con-vene again.

That short discussion on 8 January was undoubtedly the occasion on which the decision that Britain should make nuclear weapons was given formal voice, but it was not the moment at which that decision was made. Long before then it was understood by ministers, senior officials and scientists that the path they were following led to this destination. Some, such as James Chadwick, had made up their minds before the war ended. Others, including Attlee himself, took a few weeks after the shock of Hiroshima. Certainly by the time the first pile was ordered, at the GEN.75 Cabinet committee meeting in December 1945, the consensus existed. Britain was a world power with a great empire and vast strategic and commercial interests to defend; if any other world power had this weapon, or might acquire it, it was unthinkable that Britain should be without it for long. This consensus was largely unspoken, but in Whitehall there was hardly a single dissenter. Attlee, Bevin, Portal, the Chiefs of Staff, Chadwick and many others were of one mind. Churchill too, although he was not consulted, had made no secret that this was his view. Had some form of partnership been offered by the United States, or had a convincing regime of international control been framed, the plan could have been changed. Time was allowed for these options to be explored, and to ensure that it was actually possible for Britain to go it alone, but when the time for waiting had passed and there was a practical reason for making the commitment, it was made.

Years later, Attlee was asked why. 'It had become essential', he explained. 'We had to hold up our position *vis-à-vis* the Americans. We couldn't allow ourselves to be wholly in their hands, and their position wasn't awfully clear always.' He went on: 'At that time we had to bear in mind that there was always the possibility of their withdrawing and becoming isolationist once again. The manufacture of a British atom bomb was therefore at that stage essential to our defence. You must remember that this was all prior to Nato. Nato has altered things. But at that time although we were doing our best to make the Americans understand the realities of the European situation – the world situation – we couldn't be sure we'd succeed. In the end we did. But we couldn't take risks with British security in the meantime. We had worked from the start for international control of the bomb. We wanted it completely under the United Nations. That was the best way. But it was obviously going to take a long time. Meanwhile we had to face the world as it was. We had to look to our defence – and to our industrial future. We could not agree that only America should have atomic energy.'[17]

2
Penney

ATTLEE'S GEN.163 committee not only determined the conditions under which a British atomic bomb would be made, it also chose the man who would make it: William George Penney. A Los Alamos veteran of distinction, Penney had the qualifications and was in the right place at the right time, but he did not come to the task easily or with any great enthusiasm. He had been, to use his own words, 'dragged into' atomic weapons development.[1] Before this occurred, he had proved himself a shining young talent in the world of fundamental scientific research. It was the war that diverted him to military work and ultimately towards the development of atomic bombs, and then his abilities and his sense of patriotic obligation made him indispensable. Although he cast many a regretful backward glance, he never returned to university science.

In one way he was born to armaments work, for his father, also called William, was a sergeant-major in the Ordnance Corps, that branch of the Army charged with keeping the guns supplied with ammunition. Young William spent his early years in a world of soldiers, bullets and shells. His mother Evelyn, before marrying, had been a bookkeeper in a department store, so there was some mathematics in his blood as well. When he was born, on 24 June 1909, they were stationed in Gibraltar, but by the time he began school the First World War had started and they were in Egypt. There he got into trouble for playing truant, not, he said later, because he disliked schoolwork but because he found it insufficiently demanding. This was a bright, independent-minded boy, the apple of his mother's eye but a cause of exasperation to his father, who wanted his family to fall into line just like his men.

In time Sergeant-Major Penney was posted back to Britain, and young William began a more formal schooling. In 1924, aged fourteen, he was sent to the Junior Technical School in Sheerness, his father's home town in Kent. He had been good enough for grammar school but his parents were going abroad again and could not afford a boarder's fees – at Sheerness the boy was able to lodge with an aunt. He had the good fortune to find an exceptional teacher in Albert Bell, the principal, who saw in the boy a rare talent waiting to be drawn out. Boredom and truancy were no longer a problem; under Bell's supervision Penney threw himself into his work with total concentration. In time, he took the university qualification exams, achieving, at the age of sixteen, a first-class mark. What would he do for money? Bell put his star pupil forward for a scholarship to the Royal College of Science, a part of Imperial College, London. Penney took physics and scored the highest mark in the country. In the autumn of 1927 he enrolled for a degree course in mathematics.

While still in his teens, he had found the life he wanted. Nothing for him would ever surpass the delight of confronting, with pencil in hand, a mathematical problem. William Penney had the gift of equations, the mind's eye that runs far ahead of the written figures, the instinct for an answer that makes calculation a matter of confirmation rather than inquiry. He was to prove himself able, even brilliant, in other fields, but mathematics was his true calling, a pleasure when much else was a chore. Half a lifetime later, when he had risen high in the public service, his staff still knew that the way to interest him in a humdrum matter was to draw his attention to some mathematical complication. The eyes would brighten, a pen would twitch into life and the whole subject would suddenly acquire importance and urgency.

Imperial College soon came to see that it had a prodigy on its hands. The degree course was telescoped into two years for him, so by 1929, at barely twenty, he had a first-class B.Sc. His scholarship was good for another two years, so he went straight into research, working with a visiting Dutch professor, R. de L. Kronig.

When Kronig returned to Groningen that autumn, Penney followed him to complete their project. In November of 1929 they submitted a joint paper to the Royal Society for publication, entitled 'Quantum Mechanics of Electrons in Crystal Lattices', a piece of work which, it was observed in the 1970s, 'achieved an extraordinary reputation'[2] and was still being cited in innumerable works decades later. Penney, now back in London, had made a spectacular debut. Other papers followed and in 1931 he was awarded the first of three doctorates.

Not only had he found the subject he was made for, but it was opening up for him in a particularly thrilling fashion. Penney was one of those who identified early the potential of a new technique, known as quantum mechanics, to influence theoretical thinking in both physics and chemistry. Quantum mechanics offered different ways of understanding the behaviour of particles inside atoms. In a series of papers in the 1930s, usually working with a collaborator, Penney employed this to explore the way in which solid substances are made up. Looking closely at the composition of specific materials, he was able to provide mathematical models for predicting how other materials would behave. It was pathfinding work, of great value both to chemists and to physicists.

This was science's last decade of innocence; perhaps not the intellectual idyll it has sometimes been painted, but certainly a time when secrecy, national rivalry and money had not yet taken hold of academic research. Penney worked in the Netherlands; he took an MA in the United States; he fed on, and fed, the thinking of famous scholars in Germany, the Soviet Union, France and Italy. And, having no difficulty in winning scholarships, he thrived. After his two years at the University of Wisconsin his supervisor reported that the young Englishman was 'an exceedingly promising research man' with a 'native ability in mathematical physics' and 'an unusual gift for absorbing new developments'.[3] His output of research papers was prodigious. When he applied for his next scholarship, to go to Cambridge, this twenty-two-year-old was able to submit no fewer than eleven published articles to support his case. His referee at Imperial wrote: 'W. G. Penney is, in my opinion, an extremely strong candidate. His progress and achievements since he left school, less than six years ago, seem to me remarkable. His undergraduate instruction and examinations were completed in two years . . . and in the subsequent period of less than four years to the present date he has not only mastered a wide range of mathematics, physics and physical chemistry, extending to the borders of existing knowledge, but he has also made many important original contributions to knowledge . . . I might add that, apart from his excellent academic qualifications, Penney is a man of attractive personality, a good athlete as well as a good scholar and investigator. I feel sure he has a distinguished career ahead of him.'[4]

The scholarship was duly awarded and in 1933 Penney went to Cambridge. The research papers poured forth: in the first year there were five; in the second, seven and a short book; in the third and final year he slowed to four published papers, but there was also a second Ph.D. and, as his scholarship drew to a close, the offer of an academic post at Pembroke College, Cambridge. Imperial, however, had never quite let him slip away, employing him as an occasional lecturer and recognizing his achievements with a D.Phil. – his third doctorate. Just as he took up his post at Pembroke, a vacancy arose for assistant professor of mathematics at Imperial. It was offered to Penney, and he accepted.

Where, in the world of science, did Penney now stand? At Imperial he was plainly a favourite son, a jewel in the college crown, and they had conferred on him every distinction they could. Now at twenty-seven he had a salaried post with a title, no small matter in the 1930s, particularly as he was by now a married man. In the wider world, although his work was gaining in reputation, he still had plenty to prove. Academic prodigies are not so rare in mathematics or physics; it is a discipline in which the young are expected to produce the most imaginative work. Penney had chosen his postgraduate teachers well and impressed them without exception, but he was still one of a generation of young men feasting on the new quantum mechanics. He had done some distinguished work but he would certainly, and cheerfully, have expected much more of himself in the future.

If Penney was a specialist in an esoteric field of science, this did not mean that he was out of touch with life. He was not just a theorist, but a teacher, indeed he loved to lecture and loved the company of students. Although he was modest and unassuming by nature, throughout his life Penney would have the gift, with a few words, a little joke or a question founded on genuine curiosity, of putting people at their ease. He had no class complexes, no airs and no sense of position. A big, broad-shouldered figure whose face fell naturally into a wide, boyish smile, he radiated calm and good humour. Students found him understanding, approachable and entertaining, and if they had the talent nothing was easier than to be swept along by his enthusiasm. He was also a natural sportsman, one of those lucky people who excel at every game they attempt. As a new boy at Sheerness he surprised everyone by defeating the school boxing champion. On the football field he developed into a muscular centre forward, playing in a school team which, he was proud to recall later, included four future professionals, one of them an international. At cricket, his combative style at the crease earned him the nickname 'six-or-nothing Penney'.[5] He continued to play football and cricket as an undergraduate and at Wisconsin dabbled in American football. To all he applied the 'six-or-nothing' approach, committing every muscle to the effort. Later in life he became a golfer and from the tee would launch the ball into the ether with ferocious energy. His short play would never match his driving.

As war approached, then, Penney was happy and successful, with every prospect of a distinguished academic career before him. In 1939 he doubtless followed with interest the debates among physicists prompted by the discovery, in Germany, of nuclear fission. Could this lead to a fission chain reaction? Was it the key to cheap power? Might it be used to make a nuclear bomb? There was a frenzy of argument, experimentation and publication. But Penney was not directly involved in this field so these were not his problems. Nor was he among the many university scientists drawn into the development of radar for Britain's air defence. Like many of his colleagues he registered as a scientist available for military work and, when war broke out, waited for the call. 'One day,' he recalled later, 'after several months of hearing nothing, I met Sir Geoffrey Taylor, a world authority on fluid mechanics, and he told me he was being asked by Government departments lots of questions about explosions and that sort of thing. He could not deal with all the questions and therefore asked me to have a go at the pressure wave caused by an explosion under water.'[6]

Taylor was one of the most senior academic scientists brought in by the government in the late 1930s to help prepare for war. He took charge of some detailed research into the behaviour of the blast waves generated by high explosives, and it was this project which Penney now joined, becoming a member of the Physics of Explosives Committee (Physex). 'The meetings', a colleague wrote later, 'not infrequently resembled scientific seminars rather than formal business meetings; blackboards were often in use.'[7] The object was to tease out how a bomb did its damage, how the extent of this damage might be predicted, reduced or, in the case of weapons to be used by British forces, increased. It was a field little understood but requiring urgent attention.

While Penney contributed to Physex, the main thrust of his early war work was, as Taylor had asked, the examination of blast waves under water, reporting to a parallel committee called Undex. This research was valuable to the Admiralty, since it had a bearing on the design of mines, torpedoes and depth charges, as well as of ship and submarine hulls. Again, as Penney wrote, there was little previous work to go on: 'When I showed Taylor the results of my first calculation on the underwater blast wave, I asked if there were any experimental data. He looked a little sheepish and said he would try to get some for me. A few days later he produced a dirty piece of tracing paper. I had seen better drawings, but what it showed was the pressure-time record fairly close to an underwater explosion. A few days later, I was allowed to see the source. I was very surprised to find that it dated back to the end of World War One.'[8]

In July 1943 Penney was asked to help with the preparations for the Allied invasion of Europe. The plan was to surprise the Germans by seizing as a bridgehead not an established port but a strip of Normandy coastline. The harbour necessary to land men and equipment would be floated in sections across the Channel and set in place on the coast. This was the Mulberry harbour. The Navy wanted something to protect this structure from the pounding of the seas, and this was where Penney came in. He and a colleague were asked to study the behaviour of sea waves and report on the best possible arrangement. The result was the Bombardon, a floating steel breakwater 200 ft. long. Penney worked with the engineers who built it, and was involved in field trials off Weymouth in the spring of 1944. Two days after D-Day an array of Bombardons was set in place off Arromanches in Normandy, where for almost three weeks they sheltered the enormous landing operations which made possible the liberation of France. Penney, however, was not allowed to savour this success, for by now another project, bigger, more secret and even more momentous, had claimed him.

A REQUEST HAD come from the United States for Penney to be sent to New Mexico to assist with the development of the atomic bomb. Work had been proceeding rapidly in the mountain camp at Los Alamos which was the design laboratory for the weapon, and a small British team, mainly of senior physicists, was taking part. In the spring of 1944 Geoffrey Taylor paid a visit to give advice and saw that the project would soon have a use for a man such as Penney. Waves again: the atomic bomb would generate explosive shock waves on an unprecedented scale and work would have to be done to establish how the weapon might most effectively be used and what damage it could be expected to cause. Practical expertise in this field was vital, and Penney, with his Physex and Undex experience, was perfectly qualified. And he had something else to offer. One of the designs of bomb being worked on at Los Alamos involved detonation by implosion – the process of sending an explosive shock wave inwards on to a radioactive core. Penney would be able to advise on the behaviour of such a wave.

In London, Penney was spending most of his time on his war work, but he was still on the books at Imperial and lectured there for four hours a week. When the college was asked to release him for at least a year for an unspecified assignment abroad, it replied with a firm no. 'Dr Penney is actually instructing students in the fundamentals of radio engineering,' the college explained, 'and as such gives lectures to students in the physics, engineering and mathematical departments. If he goes, we cannot find a substitute for him . . .'⁹ Taylor, still in America, was asked whether anyone else would do, and his response was no less firm: 'He should be secured for us, if at all possible.'¹⁰ Arms were twisted at Imperial and Penney was released.

Once he was told why he was wanted in America, his own reaction to the American invitation was little different from the college's, for he had every reason to wish to stay in Britain.

Professionally, he was still caught up in the preparations for D-Day and remained devoted to his work at Imperial, while on a personal level the timing could hardly have been worse: Adele, his wife of eight years, was an invalid, and they had two small sons. Moreover, like many scientists confronted with working on the atom bomb, he was also fearful of the consequences of success. Someone who was close to him at the time has recalled asking him why he was going to America. He replied that he was not allowed to say, but he hoped that nothing would come of it.

Shortly before D-Day he flew to the United States and crossed the country by train. Alighting at Santa Fe in New Mexico, he was swiftly despatched up the twisting roads to Los Alamos, high in the mountains, thirty-five miles out of town. For William Penney this was not quite so foreign an experience as for the other British scientists sent to work there. Years before, while he was studying at Wisconsin, he had spent a summer touring the western United States in a Ford coupé. One of the stops he made along the way was in the New Mexico mountains at a ranch that belonged to a young physics professor at Berkeley, J. Robert Oppenheimer. Penney and a companion, Alfred Goble, spent a few days with Oppenheimer, riding the mountain trails, enjoying the breathtaking scenery and talking science. It was 1932, a year of sensational breakthroughs in physics, and there was much to discuss. Now he was back in the same country, just forty miles from the Oppenheimer ranch.

Los Alamos proved to be a dusty city hastily improvised upon a high, flat ridge and peopled by an astonishing collection of scientists. Many of the most senior figures were Germans, Italians, Hungarians and other refugees from Hitler and Mussolini. With them were the best brains in American physics and a British team which, though small, included men of some eminence. The laboratory roll call included Enrico Fermi, Hans Bethe, Edward Teller, Isidor Rabi, George Kistiakowsky, Otto Frisch, Rudolf Peierls, Niels and Aage Bohr, Geoffrey Taylor, John von Neumann, Richard Feynman, Emilio Segre, Luis Alvarez, John van Vleck and many more. In the words of General Groves, it was 'the largest collection of crackpots ever seen'.[11] The atmosphere was a unique mixture of the military and the academic, the industrial and the scientific, the urban and the frontier. The work proceeded at

breakneck pace and the approach chosen involved an almost
constant exchange of ideas, so that many remember Los Alamos
as a hectic, two-year brainstorming session. The average age was
twenty-five so Penney, arriving five days after his thirty-fifth
birthday, found he was one of the camp's greybeards.

Before long he was called to the office of the Director to be
briefed and there, after an interval of twelve years, he shook hands
once again with Robert Oppenheimer. Penney wrote later:
'Oppenheimer wanted somebody at the laboratory who had studied
explosive phenomena and blast in a theoretical way, but who had
[also] looked at bomb damage trying to connect theory with observation. He knew some of my work in London had been on such
matters and he would like me to follow all the papers arriving at
the laboratory from American and British sources on blast and
damage. If I would also join in progress meetings on other matters
where I might be able to contribute, that would be fine.'[12]

Penney spent just over a year at Los Alamos and the experience
was to alter the course of his life. When the year began neither he
nor anyone else expected that he would become a particularly
important figure. James Chadwick, who directed the British team
from Washington, had been keen to see as many British scientists
as possible working on the implosion bomb, but when Taylor
suggested Penney he was nonplussed. 'I think it very desirable to
have him,' he wrote, 'but I would not have given this request very
high priority.'[13] From Penney's account of Oppenheimer's instructions, it is clear that so far as the Americans were concerned his
principal assignment was on the blast side, and that if he made
any contribution to the implosion weapon it would be regarded
as a bonus. In the end, all parties were to be more than satisfied
with his work.

There was much more to the Manhattan Project than just
Los Alamos; it embraced more than a dozen university campuses
and industrial complexes scattered across America. These were
compartmentalized for security reasons, and scientists working in
one compartment often knew nothing of what was happening in the
others. But within the Los Alamos fence, where the end-products
of all this work were designed and made, there was little segregation
and scientists above a certain rank could move freely between the
various departments. At regular colloquia they would meet to

report progress and swap ideas, and Penney, the ingenious and likeable Englishman, found himself drawn steadily into the implosion work. Looking back later on his Los Alamos year, he wrote: 'I spent about half of my time working on some of the scientific phenomena going inwards into the bomb and the other half on scientific phenomena going outwards.'[14]

One of his early tasks was to give a paper to the senior staff on the theory and practice of bomb damage in the light of Britain's experience of Luftwaffe attack. This included some description of the injuries caused by different kinds of explosions. Rudolf Peierls, the senior member of the British team, recalled the occasion: 'His presentation was in a scientific, matter-of-fact style, with his usual brightly smiling face; many of the Americans had not been exposed to such a detailed and realistic discussion of casualties, and he was nicknamed, by Victor Weisskopf, "the smiling killer".'[15] Happily, the label did not stick and Penney soon won the respect and trust of the Americans. 'He was very knowledgeable and effective in the area of his speciality', recalls Peierls. 'He clearly had a sense of what was important and he preferred, and went after, simple solutions rather than complicated ideas.'[16] In a project where quick results were essential, these were valuable qualities.

By the spring of 1945, however, he was anxious to return home. Adele, his wife, had died and he felt it was a time when he should be with his children in England. As for the Los Alamos work, he had not yet made any really striking individual contribution to the project. He asked whether he might expect to be back in London by September. The Americans had other ideas. 'Groves has urged me strongly to arrange for Penney to stay', Chadwick wrote, 'for he wants him to see the job through. Penney is more valuable than he himself thinks. He is now going to be concerned with operational matters.'[17] It was the first intimation of the importance that the Americans attached to Penney's work, and of the trust they were to place in him.

The full weight of this trust soon became apparent. On 27 April, Penney found himself in a conference room in the Pentagon in Washington, the only Briton – and one of only two Los Alamos scientists – in a group of ten people charged with the task of identifying where in Japan the atomic bombs should be dropped. This was the first meeting of the Target Committee of the Manhattan

Project and the atmosphere was one of the utmost solemnity; Penney noticed that even his ebullient colleague John von Neumann was feeling the responsibility. They knew that in the coming weeks they must condemn whole cities to destruction. From a list of seventeen targets, they were to identify the four most suitable. Their choice would depend on many factors, including likely weather conditions and the progress of the conventional bombing campaign already under way over Japan. Penney was given the task of assembling data 'on the size of the bomb burst, the amount of damage expected and the ultimate distance at which people will be killed'.[18] His calculations would now influence at what precise altitude the atomic explosions should take place, and he would have responsibility for ensuring the safety of the bomber crews delivering the weapons. The difficulty at this stage was that, while Penney knew how to translate explosive power into numbers of casualties and buildings destroyed, he was still in the dark about just how powerful the bombs would be. The best he could do at this stage was to guess: he was fairly confident that the simpler of the two designs in preparation, the uranium 'gun' bomb, would have the explosive power of between 1,000 and 5,000 tons of TNT, while the plutonium weapon – the implosion bomb on which he had himself been working – could be anywhere between 100 and 5,000 tons.

Fortunately, he was given more to go on. The scientists were so uncertain about the implosion design that they insisted it must be tested before use over Japan, so on 16 July 1945 they staged the world's first atomic explosion at a site near Alamogordo in the New Mexico desert. This provided an opportunity to measure the scale and effects of the new force and Penney was closely involved. He acted as a consultant for many of the measurement teams and devised an instrument of his own, which Rudolf Peierls thought the most reliable of all. 'He had a number of wooden boxes prepared with circular holes of varying sizes, covered with paper. In a pressure wave of a certain strength, the paper over the larger holes is ruptured, while those over the smaller ones remains intact. The size of the largest holes still covered will therefore give a measure of the overpressure, and hence of the blast intensity.'[19] This was the first of many ingenious but simple ideas Penney came up with for measuring the power of atomic explosions; they were to become his star turn.

Penney did not, however, witness the Trinity Test, as it was called, for at the moment of detonation he was stranded at a distant air base. He had been due to observe the explosion from the air and found his plane grounded by unfavourable weather. But his wooden boxes, with their paper-covered holes, did their job, as did many other measuring devices. It was soon clear that the yield of the implosion bomb had been approximately equivalent to 20,000 tons of TNT, four times greater than Penney's highest estimate. He quickly digested this astonishing news and within a week presented to his Los Alamos colleagues another of his matter-of-fact but shocking analyses. 'He applied his calculations', wrote one American scientist. 'He predicted that this [weapon] would reduce a city of three or four hundred thousand people to nothing but a sink for disaster relief, bandages, and hospitals. He made it absolutely clear in numbers. It was reality.'[20]

Penney had become at this stage one of the most important people in Los Alamos. General Groves, who rarely gave much credit to the British scientists, was later to acknowledge this. 'Throughout the life of the project', he wrote, 'vital decisions were reached only after the most careful consideration and discussion with the men I thought were able to offer the soundest advice. Generally, for this operation, they were Oppenheimer, Von Neumann, Penney, Parsons and Ramsey.'[21]

After Trinity, events moved rapidly. Within ten days Penney was sitting in another US air base, this time far away across the Pacific on the island of Tinian, from where the B-29 bombers known as Enola Gay and Bock's Car would take off to deliver their bombs to the targets in Japan. He was there for two reasons: to advise on any changes in the detonation height which might be necessary as a result of what had been learned at the Trinity Test, and to watch one of the attacks. With him was Leonard Cheshire, the young RAF pilot who had won a Victoria Cross for his courage in 'marking' targets for the big bomber raids on Germany. Together they made up a British observer team. The Americans, having promised to take them on one of the bombing missions, had second thoughts, and the pair missed the Hiroshima attack on 6 August. Only after making a vigorous protest to Washington were they allocated places in one of the two planes accompanying the second mission. They took off before dawn on 9 August, flew to a rendezvous point off Yokohama, and waited for the other planes to join them. They were too high, and Bock's Car, carrying the bomb, flew on without them to the chosen target, the arsenal at Kokura. The cloud cover there was too dense, and attention switched to the fallback target, Nagasaki. The B-29 carrying Penney and Cheshire eventually followed the same path, and arrived just in time.

Penney later described what happened: 'We were about forty miles away from Nagasaki when we saw a flash, followed by the billowing mushroom cloud. There was little we could do except circle in the air, well away from the cloud, and try to see what was happening on the ground. Cheshire's experience enabled him to see things that were not apparent to the rest of us. The whole of the city was hidden in dust and smoke, but very few fires were visible. Cheshire drew a sketch of what he thought was happening, and the description he gave later, with the aid of the sketch, was remarkably accurate. The smoke pall seemed to be ever-increasing, and after watching for nearly an hour we left for Tinian . . . All of us were in a state of emotional shock. We realised that a new age had begun and that possibly we had all made some contribution to raising a monster that would consume us all. None of us could sleep. We argued well into the night, and in our talks were raised the same tremendous issues that have been debated ever since.'[22]

By the time ten more days had passed, Penney was on the ground among the ruins of Nagasaki, witnessing the destruction that the bomb had wrought. With two American colleagues, he had been sent to report on the physical damage to the two target cities. Penney took responsibility for calculating the yield of the two explosions, but it was not easy. At Trinity specialized instruments had been employed, but here in Japan there was just wreckage. For a couple of days he wandered aimlessly about with no idea of how to begin. Then he had an inspiration. He wrote later: 'The observers' attention gradually became focused on bent cylindrical flagpoles and other drag damage effects; dished or broken panels, one side exposed to the air pressure from the blast and the other side fully or almost protected; partially collapsed empty cans with little or no openings; and any other damage effects which might permit estimates of the blast to be made. Measurements were made on the spot and a variety of samples were collected.'[23] Penney then brought this collection of samples back by air to Britain for closer examination. From the US he flew on a civilian flight and on arrival in England he was presented with an excess baggage bill of £450. 'A Customs man asked me what I had to declare and the chap just would not believe me when I told him the bags were full of old pipes and concrete and things. He asked me to open them up and had a good look at the whole collection before finally deciding that I really must be crazy.'[24]

The next few weeks Penney spent at Imperial College and in his south London home preparing a report based on his observations in Japan and the examination of the crushed cans and bent poles. There was a great deal of calculation to be done, and the Government lent him two mathematicians from the Armament Research Department, John Corner and Herbert Pike, to help. The result of their work was an estimate that the uranium bomb dropped on Hiroshima had a yield equivalent to about 10,000 tons of TNT and that the plutonium implosion bomb dropped on Nagasaki had a much higher yield, probably even higher than the Trinity Test explosion. Warning that he might be wrong by as much as one-third, Penney suggested a provisional figure for the second explosion of 30,000 tons. (In his later researches he revised these figures to 11,000–13,000 tons for Hiroshima and 20,000–24,000 tons for Nagasaki.) The Americans were impressed and grateful, and it seems that they attempted at this stage to persuade Penney to return to Los Alamos for good. He had, however, received other offers.

Very soon after his return to Britain, probably in November 1945, Penney was approached by C. P. Snow, the novelist, who was a Civil Service Commissioner and an important influence on government scientific policy. Snow informed Penney that the post of Chief Superintendent of Armament Research was about to fall vacant and that if he applied he was certain to be appointed. It was, on the face of it, a most unattractive job for a man such as Penney. CSAR – the nickname was Caesar – was in charge of the Armament Research Department, which was based at Fort Halstead in Kent and had outstations scattered over the whole country. To the academic scientist its work was dull, a matter of guns and shells and explosives. It had been revitalized in the latter part of the war by an infusion of fresh talent from the universities, but the new CSAR would have the job of running it down to peacetime strength, always a demoralizing process.

Snow explained, however, that this was not what he had in mind. Britain had not yet decided to make an atomic bomb, he said, but that decision was likely to come in time. When it did, men with experience in the field would be vital. If Penney took the post of CSAR he would certainly be given an important role. As Penney later recalled: 'Snow said, "Look, you must come into the Armament Research Department, just in case. Will you do it?" '[25] Snow was not acting alone. Chadwick had already invited the outgoing CSAR, Sir John Lennard-Jones, to lunch at the Athenaeum to put forward the case that Penney should be his successor. Lennard-Jones had known Penney at Cambridge, and gave his support. It is likely that Lord Cherwell, who was scientific adviser to Churchill, was also involved. These were some of the most influential voices in the country on matters of scientific policy, and they wanted Penney on hand, in a government post with research and development resources, ready to take part in the design and manufacture of the British bomb they thought inevitable.

How did they select Penney? The field was a narrow one. Of the twenty or so members of the British team at Los Alamos, most could be disqualified because they were either too junior or because they lacked experience with the implosion weapon, regarded as vital. Of those who remained, Chadwick was too exhausted by his wartime efforts and Taylor was probably thought too eminent for anything other than consultancy work. That left Rudolf Peierls, William Penney, Otto Frisch and Klaus Fuchs. Of these, the first two were the more senior. Peierls, with Frisch, had drawn up the first practical blueprint for an atomic bomb in the early months of the war, and he had gone on to lead the British team at Los Alamos. He was, however, a German by birth, and had only taken British nationality in 1940; this may have counted against him. Moreover, he had already returned to university life and was soon to become involved in public campaigning for international control of atomic energy and for official openness about atomic matters. It is likely that Chadwick was already aware of his strong feelings, and he may have concluded that Peierls would not have taken the job. For whatever reason, he was never approached.

This left Penney, who had much to recommend him. At Imperial, at Cambridge, and through his war work in London he had impressed all the people who mattered in the government scientific establishment. He was the right sort of man, young but not too young, energetic, discreet and loyal, and he had a talent for explaining scientific problems to non-scientists such as servicemen and civil servants. Most of all, he had won the admiration of the Americans. His contribution on the Target Committee, at the Trinity Test and in the survey of Hiroshima and Nagasaki had impressed the leaders of the Manhattan Project to a degree that was quite dazzling in London. He was the obvious candidate. In his own words, 'accident had made me a suitable choice'.[26]

'You *must* come', Snow had said. It was an appeal to his patriotism and his sense of duty. Yet Penney hesitated. In his heart he wanted to go back to academic life, and he had received a flattering and tempting offer: the Sedleian chair of mathematics at Oxford University. To work on the British bomb would mean, in the first instance at least, repeating the scientific effort of the Manhattan Project rather than breaking new ground. It would mean secrecy; it would mean running a cumbersome bureaucracy; it would mean a great deal of work that would have nothing to do with mathematics. None of this held any appeal. And then there was the matter of conscience.

Penney was not immune from the moral anxieties that affected many of that first generation of atomic scientists, the men and women who, in the often-quoted words of Robert Oppenheimer, had 'known sin'.[27] His first thoughts on the bomb had been to hope that it would not work, and since then he had seen with his own eyes the effects it produced when used in anger. He had watched the mushroom cloud erupt over Nagasaki and seen the city disappear in dust and smoke. Then he had walked the blasted streets and examined the dark shadows on the ground where human beings had once stood. He had seen the raw, blistered bodies of the casualties and the scorched matchwood and rubble that had been homes and offices, schools and hospitals. He could not help conjuring up in his mind's eye the effects of a similar visitation upon a British city. He would not have been human if he had not been deeply disturbed. But scientists, by and large, are pragmatic people and Penney for one would not allow himself a purely emotional reaction. While some of his Los Alamos colleagues became convinced that the weapon should not have been used, or should at most have been detonated over an unpopulated region of Japan, Penney's view was different. He took no pleasure in the success of the weapon, but his personal qualms were neither here nor there. In a war in which soldiers and civilians were being killed, the scientist had an obligation to put his skills at the disposal of his country, and in a democracy it was up to the government to decide how those skills might be used.

There was another factor to be set in the balance. Leonard Cheshire, who discussed the bomb and its implications with Penney in the long nights at Tinian, believed that Penney was 'locked into' nuclear weapons development: 'We both witnessed the final act of a war in which fifty-five million people died. Bill Penney had played an integral part in building the bomb. One couldn't just go off then and return to private life.'[28] Undoubtedly, some scientists were affected in this way. They had, as one writer has put it, 'drawn a line across history' and it was difficult for them now to put down the pen.[29] With the promise of atomic electricity generation and of hydrogen weapons to come, it looked as though there might be further revolutionary discoveries ahead, further lines to be drawn across history. How far Penney was influenced by such feelings is not possible to measure, but he was not a vain man; if a part of him was caught up in the adventure of the bomb and flattered by his new-found influence, it was a lesser part.

In November 1945 Penney was married again, to the nurse who had cared for his children while he had been in America, Joan Quennell. For their honeymoon they spent a week in the Gloucestershire countryside and there he made the decision about his future. As Joan listened, he talked about the drawbacks and advantages of each of the different paths that lay ahead, and about what he should do. At length he made up his mind. He would accept the post of CSAR and, for a few years at least, become a civil servant and a bomb-maker. He made this choice for simple reasons. Like Chadwick, Cherwell and Snow, he believed that Britain, if it were to remain a first-class power, would almost certainly have to make atomic bombs of its own. He knew too that he happened to be the man best qualified for the job that was proposed. It was his duty, he thought, to accept. Penney and Joan Quennell were to enjoy a long and happy marriage, but after making his decision that week in Chipping Camden, and for all the years he worked in the field of nuclear weapons, he never again felt free to discuss his work with her.

A YEAR AND a half were to pass before Penney began work on the British bomb, but in the interval atomic weapons dominated his life. His appointment as CSAR was announced on 1 January 1946, by which time General Groves had already asked him to assist with the first American peacetime nuclear tests, to be held during the summer at the Pacific atoll of Bikini, in the Marshall Islands. From the Government's point of view, given the unhappy trend of events in Anglo-American nuclear relations, it was too good an opportunity to be missed. Penney sailed for the United States in March and did not return until October. Two of his British colleagues from Los Alamos, Ernest Titterton and James Tuck, also took part, as did five other British scientists including Roy Pilgrim, a blast expert from Penney's staff at the Armament Research Department. The tests took place in July, and provided the occasion for one of Penney's greatest coups.

Operation Crossroads, as the tests were called, was an enormous undertaking, involving 242 ships and 42,000 men. Penney was given the title of co-ordinator of blast measurement, although his principal task was to come after the explosions, with the interpretation of the results. At least two tests were planned, of which the first would be an 'air burst' comparable to Hiroshima and Nagasaki but this time over the sea, and with a cluster of redundant warships beneath. This would allow the US Navy to assess the effects of a nuclear Pearl Harbor. The second bomb would be detonated 100 feet beneath the surface of the sea. Penney participated in the elaborate preparations and before the first test he had an idea. He recalled later: 'It was all very impressive and carefully planned. But I could see that no one seemed to be allowing for the bomb to fall anywhere else but right on target, so I asked the Americans if I could make my own arrangements for recording the blast. I got one of the Americans to help me fill 1,000 empty petrol tins, the ordinary four-gallon type, with sea water. We sealed the hole in each tin and scattered them [on islands] across the proposed explosion area, allowing for the bomb to drop a few hundred yards away from the centre of the target.'[30] This was quite different from the boxes he used at the Trinity Test, and the idea may have been suggested by the crushed petrol cans he had found on his tours of Hiroshima and Nagasaki, which had proved so useful as measuring instruments. The principle was simple: the volume of the damaged can after the explosion could be used to calculate the maximum blast pressure it had suffered, and readings from several hundred cans could provide a picture of how the blast wave travelled over a wide area.

When 'Able Day', 1 July, arrived, an entire fleet of giant American and Japanese warships lay ready at Bikini. Soon after dawn a B-29 bomber flew high above and, at the appointed moment, released its heavy payload. As Penney had feared, the bomb exploded at some distance from its intended target point. Many of the more sensitive American recording devices arrayed beneath were either so close that they were destroyed or so far away they failed to register the shock. Penney's humble jerrycans, however, performed well. As he put it: 'I did a bit of a sum and was able to tell them about the blast.'[31]

The second test at Bikini, the underwater explosion, made a lasting impression on Penney. He was struck by a phenomenon he observed there which appeared to endow atomic explosions in water with a special menace, and which was called 'base surge'. He explained later: 'The explosion threw an enormous quantity of water up into the air. The water broke into fine drops, so that after the explosion there was an enormous cylinder of water drops in the air with a cloud at the top. The average density of the air and water in the cylinder was higher than that of the air outside so that it quickly fell down again under the action of gravity. Then it went rushing outwards across the surface of the sea like a foggy, contaminating gas. Its movement was for all the world like a thin pancake mixture spreading as it poured into a frying-pan.'[32] It was quickly recognized that this low-level cloud was spreading radioactive materials over a wide area in a way that an air or ground burst could not. Penney, imagining the same effect over a port city, could see that it might kill many more people than an air burst. The base surge was to fascinate him for years.

After Operation Crossroads he spent some time in Washington gathering together the data he would need for a full study of the blast effects generated by the two explosions. While there, he was asked by the leader of the British mission to the United Nations Atomic Energy Commission, Sir Alexander Cadogan, to provide him with technical assistance. This he regarded as a great honour, and it provided him with his first experience of atomic diplomacy. He found it instructive. 'I was completely disillusioned by the Russian attitude', he told a newspaper interviewer years later. 'I resolved that I would not leave Britain unequipped in the situation I knew would come.'[33]

In all this time, Penney had been only faintly aware of any progress in London in the planning for a British atomic bomb. This was, as we have seen, largely because there was very little progress to be reported, since the early emphasis was on Hinton's reactors and other factories. But Penney was not completely out of touch. Chadwick, after seeing Portal in May, had written to him to say: 'He seems to be very willing it should be put in your charge with a final responsibility devolving on him.'[34] This was reassuring, but it was some way short of a formal confirmation of his role. Later, Penney paid a short visit to the British-Canadian research reactor at Chalk River in Ontario and talked to John Cockcroft, then in the process of setting up Harwell. Cockcroft doubtless took the opportunity to bring Penney up to date, and he concluded that the younger man had 'all the right ideas'.[35] But still there was no firm go-ahead for the bomb project.

When Penney returned to London, however, matters advanced decisively, for this was the moment at which Lord Portal decided that he needed to set the bomb project in motion. On 2 October, Portal wrote to Chadwick, who was by now fretting about when the work would begin: 'Penney arrived yesterday and gave me a very interesting account of the Bikini tests. We are all agreed that he should be in charge of the ordnance work in this country and he seems keen to take it on.'[36] Three weeks later Penney was back at Fort Halstead, writing his reports on Bikini and informing Portal: 'I have also made some progress in that other matter which we discussed when I came to see you last and I hope to ask you for another meeting in the near future.'[37] 'Ordnance work' and the 'other matter' are both references to the atomic bomb.

Towards the end of October Penney gathered his thoughts and one day, abiding by Portal's instruction to maintain absolute secrecy, he sent away his secretary, closed his office door and began to type a report with his own hands. There were ten pages in all, plus two diagrams, setting out his scheme for the design and development of the conventional components of a British implosion bomb within the existing establishments of the Armament Research Department. When he had finished he scribbled a note to Portal on CSAR notepaper: 'Here are the results of my efforts. I hope to see you on Monday 4th Nov in your office at 3 pm. Your secretary is checking that this time is convenient for you.'[38]

There were a couple more meetings, but Portal was soon busy taking the proposal through the Whitehall hoops, from the Chiefs of Staff to Downing Street, and Penney again ceased to be involved. Hearing nothing, he returned to his Bikini work. He had by now received a request from General Groves to extend the scope of his report to include a general theoretical examination of the effects of underwater explosions, and he was setting up a small team at Fort Halstead to conduct experiments. In late December he felt the work was sufficiently advanced to justify his returning to Washington to report on progress. 'The calculations which I have made recently', he wrote to Portal, 'will be very well received by them and may go some way towards keeping alive the interchange of information between them and us.'[39]

Since the collapse of nuclear co-operation and the passage of the McMahon Act in mid-1946, Penney had become almost the last link between the British and American nuclear establishments. His visits to the United States and his continued contact with scientists and officials there were perceived to be of the utmost importance for Britain. This helps to explain a peculiar fact: Portal, who received the approval of the GEN.163 committee for the bomb scheme on 8 January, chose not to inform Penney, the man most immediately affected, until May – more than four months later. In the interval, Penney sailed to America in January to attend his symposium on the tests, reporting back enthusiastically about the access he was being given to classified data and to senior American scientists. 'I think I shall have a great deal of information to show you of considerable importance', Penney wrote.[40] Portal was anxious to make the most of this. Years later he recalled: 'I think that Bill Penney was told a lot by friends. It may well have been *sub rosa*, I suppose it would have to have been. The desire was certainly there on the part of individual American scientists to help us. We were getting a lot of stuff under the counter and it was all coming to one man on our side. The channel was almost entirely to Penney.'[41] In 1947 it seemed that this flow of information might save British scientists time and effort. When Penney returned to London at the end of February he remained in contact with Washington as he ploughed on with his fourteen-volume Bikini report. It took another two months to complete. Only then did Portal tell him to begin work on the British bomb.

3

First Steps

BASIC High Explosive Research, or BHER, came into being one hot afternoon in June 1947 when Penney gathered together in the library at Woolwich Arsenal the scientists and engineers whom he had selected as the nucleus of his team. There were thirty-four of them, and only the most senior had been told why their presence was required. The others, drawn from the Armament Research Department headquarters at Fort Halstead, from various ARD outstations scattered around the country and from laboratories and offices in the Arsenal itself, found much to arouse their curiosity as they arrived and surveyed the gathering. An odd cross-section of disciplines was represented, from small arms to big guns and from mathematics to explosives chemistry, and it was also not an audience selected by rank or experience, since some fairly junior figures were present. More intriguing still, security was unusually tight: the door was guarded, and although it was sunny outside the windows were closed and the curtains drawn.

When they were all in their seats, Penney took his place on the dais, looked up through heavy spectacles and began to speak in a characteristic drawl that still carried the accent of his parents' class and county. The first few sentences put an end to speculation: Britain was going to produce its own atomic bomb, he announced, and ARD had been asked to work on it. Those present had been chosen to join a new section which would carry out the design, development, manufacture and testing of certain components and would assemble the completed weapon. Aware that his audience had little idea what this meant, Penney then delivered a two-hour lecture on the principles of the bomb, a lecture which is remembered as a *tour de force* of clarity and simplicity; Penney the teacher at his very best.

The atomic bomb is made possible by one of the more peculiar properties of nature, only discovered on the very eve of the war. Atoms of the metal uranium, one of the heaviest of the elements, can split, and when they do so they release large amounts of energy. Not only that, they also expel particles known as neutrons, and as these fly out of the splitting uranium atoms they are capable in turn of causing other, adjacent uranium atoms to split and release more energy and more neutrons. A process of successive splits and releases of energy and neutrons is called a chain reaction, and so powerful is the cumulative release of energy from a chain reaction that very rapidly the uranium explodes, far more violently than any chemical, or 'conventional' explosive. This is an atomic explosion. But if uranium is a natural substance, why has it not all exploded long ago? First, because it does not occur in nature in its pure form, but needs to be refined to pure metal, like iron from iron ore, before it is in a fissionable state. Second, because even then only a rare variety of uranium, the isotope U-235, is capable of sustaining a chain reaction. Only 7 parts in 1,000 of pure uranium are U-235. It is by extracting a sufficient quantity of this substance from natural uranium – an extremely difficult procedure – that the raw material for an explosive chain reaction is created. This was the first important achievement of the Manhattan Project.

To possess enough of this fissionable material is one thing; to make a bomb which will explode at the desired moment is another. Here, the principle of 'criticality' comes into operation. To produce a nuclear explosion requires a certain minimum quantity of fissionable material known as the critical mass. In a quantity smaller than the critical mass, the neutrons released in each fission are more likely to escape harmlessly than to cause the further fissions which will result in an explosion. The result is a limited number of fissions, but no sudden release of energy and no explosion. This is known as a 'fizzle'. In a quantity that is greater than the critical mass, or 'supercritical', a sufficient number of neutrons will find atoms to split to ensure not only that a chain reaction is maintained but that the number of fissions multiplies extremely rapidly. This causes the huge build-up of energy that occurs in a nuclear explosion. Obviously, a supercritical mass is not something that can be assembled and left sitting around until needed. The bomb designer aims to create the supercritical mass only at the instant he wants the explosion to take place. At Los Alamos, the 'gun method' was developed to do this. The casing of the bomb was formed from a heavy tube resembling a gun barrel, sealed at each end. Within this casing, at the required moment, one 'sub-critical' lump of U-235 was fired at another. When they met, a supercritical mass was created, a fission chain reaction took place and vast amounts of energy in the form of light, heat and radioactivity were released. This was the design of Little Boy, the long, cylindrical bomb that was dropped on Hiroshima.

The bomb dropped on Nagasaki, which was known as 'Fat Man', was quite different in design and was the result of a separate line of research and development. Very early in the war it was predicted that a second fissionable material, plutonium, could be used effectively in bombs. Plutonium does not exist in nature; it is produced in a nuclear reactor, where the uranium chain reaction is created in controlled conditions. The effect is to set in motion changes in the structure of some uranium atoms, so that ultimately they are transmuted into atoms of the new metal, plutonium. Fissionable material was in desperately short supply, so when this possibility was recognized, huge atomic piles, or reactors, were quickly built in the United States to produce plutonium in sufficient quantities for a bomb.

Much of this was known to Penney's audience in Woolwich library, and indeed to the public at large if they cared to read the published literature on the Manhattan Project. But Penney now had some surprises to spring. First, plutonium was no mere alternative to U-235; it had properties which made it a much more efficient explosive, with a smaller critical mass. To illustrate this: Little Boy required 65kg of uranium-235 while Fat Man contained just 6kg of plutonium. The second surprise was that plutonium's special physical properties made it unsuitable for use in a bomb detonated by the gun method. At Los Alamos, another technique had had to be found for kick-starting the chain reaction. This was implosion. Although by 1947 the gun method was public knowledge, implosion remained top secret. Faster, more sophisticated, more efficient and more flexible, it was manifestly the atomic weapon technology of the future and as such, the Americans had decided, its secrets were not on any account to be shared. It was too late, however, to keep the secret from the British, for Penney and several others in Britain's Los Alamos mission had been involved in the wartime implosion work and had brought their knowledge away with them at the end of the war. That knowledge would now be the basis of the BHER project, for Britain's bomb would be a plutonium-implosion device on the Nagasaki model.

The best scientific ideas, it is often said, combine cleverness with simplicity. Implosion was certainly clever, but it was by no means simple. Compared with the gun method it posed technological problems of nightmarish complexity. This is how it worked. In the implosion design, the nuclear explosive core of the weapon took the form of two hemispheres of plutonium placed face to face to form a ball. In this state, given hemispheres of a particular size, the assembly was sub-critical and thus relatively safe. However, if the hemispheres were crushed together suddenly and with extreme violence into a single, extremely dense mass, the assembly became supercritical. Then the chain reaction occurred and the explosion was unleashed.

It was vital, however, that the crushing process should be an almost perfectly even, three-dimensional inward pressure of extraordinary force, compressing the core from every direction at once. If there was any weakness or flaw in the pressure wave, the plutonium would simply squirt out at the weakest point and the chain reaction would either not occur, or fizzle. It is like squeezing a lump of dough in your hands. Cup both hands and push, and the dough forms a ball. Push harder and it begins to ooze out through any gaps it can find, either between your hands or between your fingers. With the plutonium in an atomic bomb, no oozing at all could be tolerated. How could such perfectly even inward pressure be created?

Explosives – conventional explosives of the kind employed in shells and bombs – were the answer. The plutonium was surrounded with a jacket of high explosive which, when detonated, would send a powerful pressure wave inward on to the core. Here,

Penney explained, was the principal task of the BHER team: to make the explosive jacket and the means of detonating it. It would be completely different from any work previously undertaken by any member of the ARD staff, for the jacket would be a complex affair, not simply a large ball of high explosive fitted with a detonator and a hole in the middle for the plutonium. As Penney emphasized again and again, the inward pressure wave produced by the exploding jacket – the 'convergent wave' – had to be as near to perfectly spherical as physically possible. All of those present would have seen immediately the difficulty that this posed. When a block of explosive is detonated, the explosive wave begins at the point of detonation and moves through the block like a ripple from a stone thrown into water (except that it gathers force as it goes, rather than losing it). This has clear implications for implosion. If, say, the explosive jacket of the implosion bomb was detonated at a single point on its outer surface, no convergent wave would result; a single wave would radiate out from the detonation point and the plutonium core would be blown clear out of the assembly on the opposite side. For the implosion to work, there would have to be simultaneous detonations at many points on the outer surface of the jacket, each sending an explosive wave inward. This is called 'multipoint' detonation. But even this is not good enough. Say there were several dozen detonation points; this would produce several dozen detonation waves, or ripples, all moving at the same time towards the centre. Taken together, they would not form a single convergent wave; instead, the effect would be bumpy, and the pressure would strike the central sphere rather as the dimples on a golf ball. The plutonium might squirt all over the place. How could this be overcome?

Penney had the answer. The problem had been solved at Los Alamos by one of the most ingenious of all the many ingenious ideas dreamt up there. It was called the explosive lens, and it employed the same physical principle that makes everyday spectacles work. Spectacles distort the movement of light towards the eye to compensate for poor eyesight. The light takes longer to traverse the thicker part of the lens, so by the time it reaches the eye the image has assumed a slightly altered form – it has been 'corrected'. The scientists at Los Alamos who worked on the first plutonium bomb had the idea that each inward explosive wave,

THE IMPLOSION BOMB, NAGASAKI MODEL

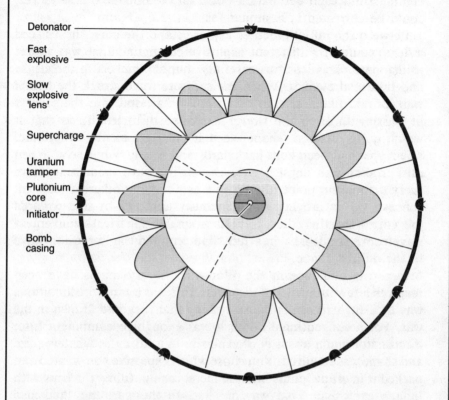

- Detonator
- Fast explosive
- Slow explosive 'lens'
- Supercharge
- Uranium tamper
- Plutonium core
- Initiator
- Bomb casing

How the slow explosive acts as a lens, 'correcting' the inward wave to the required shape

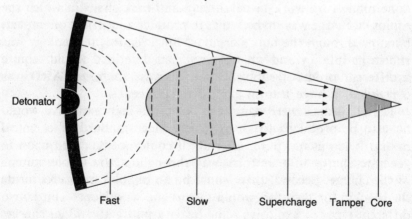

- Detonator
- Fast
- Slow
- Supercharge
- Tamper
- Core

coming from each detonation point on the outside of the jacket, could be corrected in a similar fashion.

Between the initial block of explosive and the core, they placed a 'lens' made of a different explosive compound that was slower to detonate. This lens was carefully shaped: thickest in the centre and thin at the edges. When the pressure wave struck the lens it was convex, like a section of a ripple in a pond, but the process of passing through the slower explosive distorted it, so that it was a quite different shape when it emerged on the other side. The ripple had been bent backwards and was now concave. When this process was applied to every single wave emanating from every detonation point, the result was a large number of identical concave waves moving simultaneously and side-by-side towards the core – together they formed a single, spherical, convergent wavefront. The lenses, in effect, had sculpted the implosion wave to the desired shape.

Here the audience in the Woolwich library might have been forgiven a few moments of disbelief. This was a far more ambitious way of using explosives than anything that they had known in the war. For a conventional bomb it was enough to combine a fuse, a detonator and a quantity of explosive in a casing of whatever size and shape was required. You chose which explosive you wanted and packed it in crude lumps into the metal casing, filling the gaps with molten explosive. That was old hat. In the war, they had also become familiar with the idea that explosives could be moulded into particular shapes to produce particular effects; ARD had done pioneering work in developing anti-tank shells in which the explosive charge was shaped so as to produce a jet effect on impact, bursting through the tank's armour. But even this technology was still in its infancy and what Penney had described would require a different order of sophistication; it was, so far as ARD was concerned, a huge leap in explosives science.

The challenges were daunting. First, the high explosive would have to be produced to an extremely high standard of chemical purity. If it was not pure, after all, it could not be relied upon to generate energy in a uniform way throughout the whole volume of the charge. Second, there could be no bubbles or cracks inside the blocks, for they too would distort the wavefront. Third, two different types of explosive – the faster kind for the initial charge, and the slower for the lens – would be used. These would have to fit together perfectly, as the slightest gap would affect the wavefront. Fourth, and perhaps most perplexing of all, it would be extremely difficult to get the shape of the lens exactly right. An optician working with a set of glass lenses can come to a conclusion quickly; the patient will say when he can read the letter-card. Explosives are rather more cumbersome to experiment with, and monitoring the wavefront produced by each test detonation would require new techniques. And fifth, to ensure that the multipoint detonations around the surface of the jacket took place simultaneously would require some extremely sophisticated electronics capable of recording events that lasted only for minute fractions of a second.

As his audience struggled to grasp the scale of the job that was being described, Penney turned to explaining how it could be done. For the moment at least, ARD's task was restricted to the outer components – they would not, for example, be dealing with the plutonium core. This left them with the electronics and the high explosives needed to create the implosion wave. Despite the effects of the McMahon Act, Penney said, a fair body of knowledge existed in Britain about implosion. He himself knew a good deal, and BHER would be able to draw on the expertise of some of the other British Los Alamos veterans. It is unlikely, for security reasons, that Penney actually named these individuals in his lecture, but the list was a reassuring one. James Tuck, a young Oxford physicist who had been instrumental in the development of the lenses and had taken part in the Bikini tests, was available to give advice. Penney's former mentor, Geoffrey Taylor, now knighted, would be able to contribute, as would Klaus Fuchs, now at Harwell, who had been involved with both the conventional and the nuclear aspects of the American implosion weapon. On the electronics side, Ernest Titterton had been in the team which developed the detonation systems and he would shortly be returning to Britain from Los Alamos, while Greg Marley, also at Harwell, was a specialist in high-speed observation techniques. Between them they commanded a wide range of knowledge of the plutonium weapon. There were important gaps, some of which were immediately obvious and some of which only became apparent over time, but the experience of these men at least gave BHER a starting-point.

Penney's audience at Woolwich would quickly have seen that much of their own expertise would be relevant: there were chemists to produce the explosives; physicists and mathematicians to predict and interpret its behaviour; blast measurement and photography experts to test its performance and engineers to make the moulds – the unusual guest list for the meeting was explained.

Penney made it clear that the British design should vary from the Los Alamos 'Fat Man' model as little as possible. He had already given this some thought. For the fast explosive the Americans had used a compound called Composition B, but the British had their own equivalent, RDX, which was in fact an ARD product – the initials stood for Research Department, compound X. It seems clear that this was chosen at a very early stage for use in the weapon. For the slow explosive in the lens, exactly the same compound was available as had been used in the American weapon: Baratol. The lens and the fast explosive would be moulded into blocks which, when fitted together, would form a large sphere with a hole in the middle where the plutonium and other core components would be placed. To demonstrate how this worked, Penney had tracked down a school geometry book dating from his Sheerness days, which showed that a combination of hexagons and pentagons together could form a sphere. With a flourish, he held aloft his battered brown textbook, open at the relevant illustration, to prove to his audience that it could be done. The geometry permitted two possible configurations, of thirty-two blocks or sixty-four. Each had its drawback: with the former the lenses would be large and awkward to handle, while the latter would require twice as many detonation points, making it more difficult to achieve simultaneity. Fat Man had contained thirty-two blocks, and that, apparently, is what Penney opted for.

The Woolwich library was by now oppressively stuffy, but the audience was spellbound. Penney drew his presentation to a close. The whole project, he stressed, must be the subject of the strictest possible security. This was the personal wish of the Prime Minister. The work would be carried out inside fenced compounds for which special passes would be issued. ARD colleagues who were not involved must be told nothing, and the BHER cover name must be used at all times. No one outside the BHER organization must be allowed to form the impression that there was any connection between ARD and atomic research of any kind. Within these constraints, Penney assured his staff, the project would enjoy the highest possible priority, as befitted an enterprise of great national importance.

When he had finished speaking a few questions were asked and answered, and then, according to one account, the session ended on a note of bathos. A 'military-looking gent' from Whitehall who had watched the proceedings throughout, possibly Air Vice-Marshal Davis, stepped forward and announced: 'You are given the tools, you have the fire in your bellies, go to it!'[1] With that exhortation began the work of BHER, or, as it was soon abbreviated, HER. After all the hesitation and delay, minds and hands were at last turned to the task.

THE FRAMEWORK FOR this enterprise – the administrative arrangements, the facilities, the division of labour – followed the scheme which Penney had drawn up in such secrecy the previous October. When he had first presented that document to Lord Portal the response was one of surprise. 'You're not asking very much', Portal remarked.[2] Penney's plan was deliberately minimal in conception, making the greatest possible use of existing ARD facilities and staff and allowing for some of the work to be subcontracted to outside bodies such as Chatham Dockyard and the Royal Aircraft Establishment. This economy was in the spirit of the times, for the country was in desperate straits, but it also reflected Penney's modest nature. The previous autumn Portal had suggested that BHER might be a new and discrete establishment in a separate location, rather like Harwell. He even proposed a site, an RAF base at Whitchurch in Somerset. Penney had said no. 'We can do much better at Woolwich and Halstead', he wrote.[3] He preferred to do the job with the minimum of upheaval, and his confidence that improvised arrangements would suffice must have been welcome to those with financial responsibilities who had approved the great investments at Harwell and Windscale. Penney's shopping list was short indeed. He had calculated that by the end of the first two years he would only need about ninety scientists, a further ninety skilled industrial workers and a number of draughtsmen. This would give HER a total staff of fewer than 220. He proposed to take over twelve buildings at Woolwich and Fort Halstead and ring them with security fences. Only three new buildings would have to be built.

In an interview many years later, Penney recalled going through his requirements one by one with Portal, who made notes and said simply, 'Fine.' 'How do I get these things?' asked Penney. 'I'll tell the Ministry of Supply you've got to have them', said Portal.

'What did you get, Lord Penney?' asked the interviewer.

'I got the fences!' said Penney, with a smile.[4]

It was not quite so bad as that, but certainly Penney very quickly became aware that for him the problems ahead would not only be technical ones. The principal challenge was to find staff of the right quality, and this he had foreseen in October. 'The two prime requisites of skill and silence will make difficult the assembly of sufficient numbers of suitable people', he had written.[5] He suggested then that higher salaries should be offered to entice good people into the work. But this was the civil service: all salaries, appointments and promotions had to be approved centrally in Whitehall and the machinery permitted very little divergence from the fixed ranks and pay grades applied throughout the government's scientific establishments. No special pay arrangements were made for HER, and in consequence Penney was to find recruitment an unending and exhausting struggle.

His first experience of the limits of civil service flexibility came within weeks and concerned not scientists, but secretaries. The senior management at ARD had a secretarial staff of four. Once Penney had received the official go-ahead from Portal, these women were vetted by security, briefed on the department's new assignment and swiftly set to work. Within weeks of the Woolwich meeting, however, it emerged that there was a problem. All four women were technically temporary wartime staff, and as the civil service was being slimmed down to peacetime strength, their jobs were under threat. Penney requested that they be allowed to remain in post, explaining that 'they are all now employed in work of a highly secret nature for which they have been cleared for security and of which they all have considerable knowledge'.[6] Moreover, he pointed out, they had all applied for permanent status. The response was a bureaucratic classic. 'Wartime temporary personnel must be replaced by established staff', Penney was told flatly. 'In our view the security aspect would be better safeguarded by filling such posts by permanent rather than temporary staff.'[7] What was more, while it was true that the four secretaries had applied for permanent status, this would not necessarily keep them at ARD, for even if they were accepted none of them would be given a sufficiently senior grade to do the work they were already doing.

The experience was to prove typical. In September all work on housing for the new staff at ARD was halted by a similar piece of official myopia. Houses, particularly in the south-east, were in painfully short supply in the post-war years. This was a time when it was those seeking accommodation, rather than those offering it, who placed advertisements in the press. If new staff were to be recruited, there was no alternative to building houses for them; indeed the houses themselves could prove the decisive factor in persuading the right people to join. It was clearly an urgent matter and one of Penney's first acts was to ask for seventy-two houses to be built near his headquarters at Fort Halstead and twelve near the explosives firing outstation near Shoeburyness on the Essex marshes. Sites were located and the first sods had just been turned when the Government, in one of its spasms of cost-cutting, issued a general standstill order on all public house-building across the country. Work stopped on the ARD houses as it did everywhere else. This time Lord Portal was persuaded to intervene, although the effect appears to have been limited, for five months later Michael Perrin was still grumbling that 'the urgency for this work was not fully appreciated'.[8]

These were irritations, but soon Penney had run into a difficulty which threatened the progress of the bomb work itself. He had spoken from the first of the need for a considerable number of draughtsmen to prepare vital engineering drawings. He needed six men immediately, but somehow they could not be found. It was true that there was a national shortage of skilled draughtsmen, but they were not so scarce that other research establishments were going without – at Fort Halstead alone, there were 200 draughtsmen engaged on other defence work. When Penney complained, he was told that a general review of Ministry of Supply resources was under way, and no transfer would be made until it was complete. He reported this to Dizzy Davis in the Cage, who took the matter up and was given the same answer. 'Weeks, if not months, will elapse', Davis lamented.[9] Again, Portal had to be brought in to apply his clout in the upper reaches of the Ministry of Supply. 'I understand that there is some delay in the Chiefs of Staff or Ministry of Defence organisation over setting up the machinery to review the programme of other armaments,' he thundered, 'but I do know for certain that the Chiefs of Staff attach enormous importance to the punctual progress of the BHER work and I am absolutely convinced that they would not wish this transfer of six draughtsmen to be held up pending the complete review which is intended.'[10] Even this drew only a grudging response and five months after the first complaint Penney was still waiting for the draughtsmen.

Secretaries, houses, draughtsmen: it is hardly surprising in the light of these setbacks that Penney's recollection of this period was that all he could get his hands on was the security fences. And yet it can have been no surprise to him or to Portal that the emergence of HER was resented and resisted elsewhere in defence research. This was a time when resources were tight and morale low; everywhere there was pressure to retreat to peacetime strength. Here was a new, secret outfit, gobbling up men, money and machines without pause or explanation – a mysterious, omnivorous cuckoo in the nest. Penney said later that his opposite numbers in other branches of defence research 'looked on me as a highwayman, picking their staff and this and that'.[11] And it was no good pointing to the modest and limited nature of the HER programme, for it soon became clear that Penney's original estimate of the staff he would need for the job was far too low. That had been an educated guess; by November 1947 enough work and enough thinking had been done in ARD to allow him to re-calculate his needs with greater authority.

After just four months, the new figures showed, he was already employing eighty scientists on HER, close to the figure of ninety he had thought he would require at the end of two years, and yet a number of aspects of the bomb work had not been tackled at all. The need to expand was already pressing, with chemists and engineers in particularly urgent demand. Plainly, many more people would be required. By the middle of 1948, he now estimated, his total staff should be not 220 as he had originally guessed, but something approaching 500. In short, HER would require more than double the staff Penney had first thought, and in half the time. Until this point, he had covered his staff needs largely by shuffling people around inside ARD, his own domain. The new figures made plain that this would no longer suffice and that he required a fresh approach to recruitment. Staff would have to be begged, borrowed or stolen from anywhere they might be found, and with 300 vacancies to fill, the highwayman would have to range very widely indeed.

If the defence establishment had been sullen and uncooperative about the draughtsmen, it was positively obstructive about the new demands. Even Portal, with all his influence, found that he was unable to impress on Ministry of Supply staff the urgency of Penney's work and the importance of helping him meet his staff targets. As the hiring backlog built up over the first few months, Portal's frustration grew until eventually he decided that brutal steps were needed; picking off staff in penny-packets from among the 4,700 scientists engaged in defence research would never solve the problem. Whole projects would simply have to be scrapped to release men for Penney. Needless to say, this idea met an even stonier response than its predecessors. Just before Christmas 1947, Portal deployed his ultimate weapon and took his case to Downing Street. 'What I want, and apparently cannot get', he wrote angrily to Sir Edward Bridges, the Cabinet Secretary, 'is a perfectly straightforward review of the present research programme in relation to staff available, leading to the scaling down or abandonment of effort in less important items in order that the more important ones (and particularly the most important) can get on more quickly . . . Until this review is made and accepted, I cannot get the facilities I need for the weapon for which I am responsible.'[12]

His prayer was answered, following a general reorganization of the high-level committees in the atomic energy empire. What emerged was not a one-off redistribution of resources but a new, permanent body which had the formal title of Atomic Energy (Defence Research) Committee but quickly became known as the 'cake-cutting committee'. While its brief was bland and advisory – 'to keep under review and report on the relations between defence research programmes as a whole and atomic energy defence research' – Portal briskly took the view that it was there to do what he wanted: to curtail or shut down research programmes on the margins so that the central task of building the atomic weapon could be tackled properly.[13] This view he impressed forcibly upon the chairman, Sir Henry Tizard.

Tizard, a former rector of Imperial College and president of Magdalen College, Oxford, was a Whitehall figure of great importance. His chief distinction was to have chaired, before the war, the scientific committee which ensured that the new technology of radar was developed and deployed in time to help win the Battle of Britain. Despite this, he did not enjoy Churchill's favour and due recognition only came to him with the arrival of the Labour government in 1945, whereupon he accumulated a large number of posts and chairmanships in the field of defence science. He was later to form strong opinions about the wisdom of British atomic weapons development, but in 1948 those views had yet to take shape. Tizard did not in any case enjoy much direct influence in the field; it was Portal who had the Prime Minister's ear. For the moment he accepted this pecking order and bowed to Portal's wishes about the role of his new committee.

The cake-cutters met for the first time in February 1948 and devoted their first session to discussing a document prepared by Penney. This was a detailed breakdown of his staff needs, identifying posts which should be filled immediately and posts which could wait six months. It ran from the senior grade of Principal Scientific Officer, where three chemists were wanted immediately, down through lesser grades, including the six elusive draughtsmen, to welders, storemen and electricians' mates. The committee concerned itself with the scientists and engineers, of whom forty-five were wanted immediately and forty-three more by August.

If Tizard was the judge and his committee the jury in this case, the man effectively in the dock was Sir Ben Lockspeiser, the Chief Scientist of the Ministry of Supply. He had overall responsibility for the various defence research establishments and he had to show what was being done to meet Penney's needs. When he came to give evidence, he had a sorry tale to tell: only four recruits were in the pipeline for HER, leaving eighty-four outstanding vacancies. 'Great difficulty' was being experienced in finding staff, he explained, not least because many suitable people were reluctant to enter top-secret research.[14] He thought the vacancies could probably be filled, but only at a very high price. Other high-priority research projects would be undermined and some might even have to be abandoned. Expressing his dismay at this prospect, he asked whether it would not be best to create a 'special complement' for Penney, so that HER recruitment could proceed separately from the existing scientific establishments. Neither Portal nor Penney was likely to fall for such a manoeuvre, which appears to have been designed to cut them off from the ministry's substantial pool of specialized talent. They demanded action and the committee obliged. As a first step, a meeting was arranged which would bring together all the government departments which employed scientists and engineers with relevant skills. Each would be asked to prepare a list of the staff they could spare. The balance, Lockspeiser was told, would have to come from within the Ministry of Supply.

In the event, the trawl through the other departments produced a poor catch; eleven staff were promised from outside the Ministry of Supply, of whom only one ever materialized. A lot of scrounging was done elsewhere, but to little effect. Harwell suggested three staff but eventually came up with just two raw recruits. Two chemists were found at ICI and three mathematicians at the Military College of Science. Some REME and RAF sergeants were found to do electronics work. It was not nearly enough to take the pressure off Lockspeiser, who soon found Tizard's committee breathing down his neck again. By May, after some Herculean efforts, he was able to report better results: fifty-three of the eighty-eight posts had been filled or soon would be. But he received scant reward, for by this time Penney had progressed to calculating his needs further in advance and he informed the committee that he would need another thirty-nine scientists before the middle of 1949. The hapless Lockspeiser could only throw his hands in the air. He had done all he could, he said. The only avenue that remained open was for Penney to take his pick from the candidates in the next round of civil service entry competitions.

It was a wearisome business, and one can only guess at how much of Penney's time was taken up in the paperwork, the infighting and the interviewing. And yet great progress had been made. Lockspeiser and his colleagues may never quite have conceded the principle that other projects should be shut down, but more than fifty extra people had been found and Penney was firmly placed at the front of the queue for the best of the new recruits joining the civil service. After barely a year, more than 150 scientists and engineers were working on the atomic weapon programme and although more battles for staff certainly lay ahead, there were grounds for hoping that the worst of the Whitehall battle was over.

4

To Work

FORT Halstead, where High Explosive Research found its
home, is not identified on maps or indicated on local sign-
posts. As big as the campus of a minor university, it is hidden
among the woods at the crest of the North Downs, where they
overlook Sevenoaks and the Weald of Kent. The name suggests a
military establishment of some antiquity, but this is misleading; the
first 'fort', if it can be so called, was established there only in the
1890s. Little more than a round earth bank and moat protecting
an ammunition store, it was part of a chain of supply depots
planned around the south and east of the capital. The chain was
never completed and the fort was sold off after the First World
War. It returned to military use in 1937, when rocket designers
from the Armament Research Department in Woolwich needed a
new site for research and development. In 1942, after a vigorous
spell of building work, the department moved its headquarters
there, so when Penney took over as CSAR four years later, the
Fort was the centre of his domain.

Up the hill from Knockholt Station to the Fort, one morning in
early May 1948, walked a young Londoner by the name of Edward
Howse. Howse had been brought up in Greenwich amid some
hardship in a family of eight children whose father spent most of
the Depression out of work. He had been clever enough, and lucky
enough, to go to grammar school and win a state bursary to King's
College, London, which was evacuated at the time to Bristol. He

studied physics and electronics and graduated as the war ended. His bursary carried the condition that he must enter government service, so after an interview with C. P. Snow he was sent to the radar establishment at Malvern. From there he was seconded to a commercial firm, British Thomson-Houston of Rugby, to help develop radar equipment. It was not a happy place, so he was pleased, in April 1948, to be summoned for an interview in London.

'They didn't tell me what they wanted me for; they just said they were selecting people to work at Fort Halstead or Woolwich. I had been away from London since 1939, so I jumped at the chance of going back. I said I wanted to work at Woolwich, because I lived at Eltham, but they sent me to Fort Halstead.' This was a typical HER capture of the period, part of the trawl of defence scientists forced on Lockspeiser by the cake-cutting committee. Howse was well qualified and in the public service, but working on the fringe; radar could live without him and HER could undoubtedly make good use of him.

At the gate of Fort Halstead on that May morning, Howse was greeted by two men, John Challens and Bernard Hillan. Challens was the scientist to whom Penney had given the task of developing the electronic firing mechanisms for the bomb, and Hillan was his assistant. The team was still small. 'My arrival increased Challens's staff by 50 per cent', recalls Howse. He was set to work designing some fairly simple electronic circuitry. He had still not been told that he was working on components for an atomic bomb and he remained in the dark even when, after a couple of months, he was instructed to put his circuits to work firing some rather unusual detonators. Enlightenment came one day as he worked with a colleague, setting off the detonators by releasing an electrical charge through his circuits and photographing the results with high-speed cameras. This job generated long strips of black-and-white film which they had to develop themselves. 'We both hated messing about in darkrooms with this stuff, so we kept complaining that we wanted a lab worker to do it. One day a chap came up the stairs – a fat, jovial-looking man with patches on his elbows – and said: "Your lab worker has arrived!" Then he introduced himself as Dr Penney – he just wandered up to two junior staff with no senior person accompanying him, and asked us how we were getting on; that is the kind of person he was. And it was from him that we began to get an idea what we were doing. He was quite open: we were producing the firing circuits for firing the detonators for starting the atomic bomb.'

This informal approach was at the very least unconventional for so senior a figure in the scientific civil service at that time. It was a reflection both of the enthusiasm Penney felt for the scientific aspects of his job, as against the drudgery of administration, and of his democratic nature. One of his great gifts, which served him just as well in Whitehall as in the laboratory, was the ability to mix easily with all sorts, crossing both professional and class divides. It helped that he had a quick mind and a broad command of the science of the weapon, so that he could grasp rapidly what his staff were doing. He was also young for a man in such a position, and a follower of sports. His scientists recall bowling to him at lunch-hour nets and discussing the fortunes of Kent cricket club with him if they met on the train to work. This Penney was able to do without loss of authority, leaving no one in doubt that he was the boss. But his forays into the laboratories and workshops could irritate some of his senior staff, who felt at times that they were being bypassed, and he was reproached on occasion for assigning jobs to people without consulting their direct superiors.

After the explanation from Penney, Howse's work began to make sense. He had been intrigued by the detonators he was given to work with. Conventional detonators are usually made of especially sensitive and volatile 'primary' explosive which, when ignited, fires easily to trigger the main charge, composed of more stable 'secondary' explosive. The new detonators worked on a different principle: they were made of a secondary explosive called PETN, and inside the charge were two electrodes bridged by a filament of wire, rather like a light bulb. A sudden, powerful burst of electrical current was passed through the wire, causing it to vaporize, and this triggered the explosive surrounding it. The technique was known as the exploding bridge wire, or EBW, and Howse's work involved studying what happened when these detonators were fired. 'We were trying to reproduce the wave forms that someone had seen in America', he remembers. That someone, it was now clear, was Bill Penney.

John Challens, the man who had recruited Howse and was directing the electronics work, was to become one of the most important figures in HER. A tall, patrician figure with a sharp tongue, he had been a controversial choice. Penney had come under pressure to appoint Ernest Titterton, who with his Los Alamos experience was widely seen as the obvious man for the job. He and Penney were close friends and remained so for the rest of their lives, but Titterton was a garrulous, somewhat bombastic character and Penney was worried about how he would fit in at HER. 'I am a little nervous about recommending Titterton as the man for this job', he wrote in June 1947. 'He has tremendous energy and is willing to assume any amount of responsibility in a job where he himself is doing the work. What I am not so sure about is whether he can direct a large group of scientific civil servants.'[1] In John Challens, Penney found someone much better suited to his needs.

Challens had spent the war working in the ARD outstation at Aberporth, on the Welsh coast, on the problems of measuring the performance of rockets. He was in his mid-thirties, the son of an engineer from Peterborough, educated at grammar school and Nottingham University. As a leading rocketry expert he had been chosen at the end of the war to visit Germany and study the V1 and V2 establishments there. Afterwards he was sent to the United States to help with rocket research, and for his contribution was awarded the American Medal of Freedom. He was back at Aberporth when his record caught Penney's eye and he was called for interview at Fort Halstead. When they met, Penney observed the security requirement and never once mentioned the words 'atomic bomb', but unlike Howse Challens knew what the project was, since his superintendent at Aberporth had tipped him off. 'Secrets don't always stay put', Challens says. The job was offered and accepted, and he started on 1 January 1948.

It was an appointment Penney never regretted. He wrote two years later: 'Mr Challens has long been known as a most capable man with excellent personal qualities . . . He is very self-reliant and not perturbed by a job however heavy and complex it may be.' Challens, he went on, showed 'outstanding drive and leadership' and had 'imbued his team with an excellent spirit of co-operation'.[2] For his part, Challens liked the way Penney, who had no direct interest in electronics, allowed him to get on with his work with a minimum of interference. 'He would come around periodically and would sit down opposite you and ask how you were getting on, but he couldn't take much electronics before he started to get bored. He was such an able man that if he had to set his mind to something he could cope, but he very much believed in not keeping dogs and barking himself. If he trusted someone he let them get on with it.' Titterton, who took a job at Harwell, showed no signs of resentment at being left out. He paid a couple of visits to Fort Halstead to give advice, and made light of the task ahead. 'Firing systems are naïve', he said. 'You'll soon do that.'[3]

Naïve or not, the electronics of the bomb presented many difficulties and to achieve what Penney wanted they would have to go some way beyond the state of the art as then known in Britain. 'We had a rough idea of how the Americans had solved the problem, a very rough idea. Enough to kick us off in the right direction', recalls Challens. The challenge was to produce a detonation at the same instant at thirty-two different points on the outer surface of the bomb. The exploding bridge wire, it was known, had been the American solution. Power was built up in a bank of capacitors and then suddenly unleashed like a bolt of lightning. This bolt then rushed along cables to the detonators around the surface of the weapon and the implosion began. It was impossible, even with this technique, to achieve thirty-two perfectly simultaneous detonations, and calculation showed that a short time-lapse between the first and the last could be tolerated. This margin of error, known as the range, was just a few millionths of a second.

'We were up against an impossible problem in the sense that we were supposed to produce something that would work every time, 100 per cent, and would never go off at the wrong time', recalls Challens. 'The more you put in devices to make something safe, the higher the probability that it won't work when you want it to, because one of the safety devices will have gone adrift. One thing that made the job easier was that space and weight were not limited. My philosophy was to make everything as big as possible, because the chances of making it reliable are much higher than if you make it small.'

Many specific tasks were involved in creating the electronic array for the bomb, but two stand out: the development of the trigatron and of the detonator itself. The trigatron was a switch at the heart of the firing mechanism, which operated as the gate to release the electrical charge. It had to hold off the voltage reliably until the desired moment, and then send a very powerful current into the cables with a minimum of resistance. There was only one trigatron in the mechanism and if it broke down the weapon might fire early, something not to be contemplated. An embryonic trigatron design soon emerged, but reliability proved elusive. The team soon discovered what came to be known as the 'Tuesday Effect', a relative of Sod's Law which ensured that a trigatron would perform perfectly well until it was tested on a Tuesday, when for some reason it would release the charge prematurely. After that it was always back to the drawing board.

The design of the detonator was a joint project between Challens's team at Fort Halstead and the ARD explosives department at Woolwich Arsenal. Here the scientist principally involved was Cecil Bean, an avuncular figure who was popular throughout the project. A Norwich man with a London University Ph.D., he was of all things an expert astrologer and would happily write a horoscope for anyone if he was supplied with the required birth details. Bean was ably assisted by Stanley Napier, an engineer known for his down-to-earth manner and lurid language. They made an odd but effective partnership.

Penney and Titterton were able to supply enough information about the Los Alamos detonator to get things started: the principle of the bridge wire and the use of secondary explosive. The right wire and the right explosive had to be chosen and a good deal of experimentation – of the kind in which Eddie Howse was involved – was required to produce a satisfactory model. Even then, many difficulties remained. Vast quantities of detonators would be needed. First they would be the subject of experiments in their own right, then they would be used for experiments in conjunction with the high-explosive lenses, and finally they would be used in the weapon itself. In addition, random tests were conducted on every batch to ensure reliability, and these became steadily more rigorous as time passed, until as many as ninety per cent of any batch would be test-fired purely to create the highest mathematical probability of success with the remaining ten per cent. It was obvious that many thousands of detonators would have to be made, so an industrial production line was established at Woolwich.

Here rows of women worked with microscopes soldering together the electrodes and the platinum bridge wires – just two thousandths of an inch in diameter and a tenth of an inch long – inserting them into plastic moulds and filling the moulds with PETN explosive to exactly the right density. These techniques had very often to be invented, and then they had to be practised and perfected. The result at the end of the line was an object that came to be called the exploder, a little bigger than a tennis ball, rounded on one side to be set into the bomb and with two large connectors sticking out of the other side to be joined to the cables. Women were chosen for the production work because they were thought to be better at the delicate handling involved.

The equipment for testing and monitoring the performance of the detonators and the trigatrons was developed at Fort Halstead by Challens's number two, a Welsh miner's son by the name of Ieuan Maddock. Another of Penney's inspired appointments, Maddock was a small, intense man with a balding pate and a moustache who had a native genius for electronic instrumentation. Barely thirty years old, he had already been working on the measurement of very brief events at university and in the civil service for seven years. Penney came across him in the ARD instrument section, promoted him and gave him the job of producing oscilloscopes which could show when the required detonation range of a few millionths of a second had been achieved. An oscilloscope is a cathode ray tube, like a television set, which can translate a short-lived event into an electrical pulse and display it as a line on a screen. Maddock was required to design and manufacture oscilloscopes which were some way in advance of what was available in Britain at the time. Having left school believing he was destined to be a carpenter, Maddock became over the next ten years a linchpin in British atomic weapons development and went on thereafter to become a knight and a fellow of the Royal Society.

Another job tackled at Fort Halstead was what Penney called 'phenomenology', or the study of the physical phenomena surrounding an atomic explosion. This was a sequel to Penney's own work on the effects of the explosions in Japan and Bikini, and he took a very close personal interest in it. In charge was another former Aberporth man, a Scot called John McEnhill who proved an exceptionally talented and dextrous experimental physicist. With him worked Bill Moyce, a south London printworker's son who went through Cambridge on a scholarship. Like Challens, Moyce joined ARD in 1936, but his path into HER was quite different, as he spent the war at an outstation in the Potteries, working on the physics of rifles. There, during a formal tour not long after his return from Bikini, Penney spotted him, and in April 1947 Moyce was instructed to report to Fort Halstead. This was again a shrewd choice, for much about Moyce was deceptive. A tall, jug-eared man, morose of appearance and with a drawling delivery, he did not wear his intelligence on his sleeve. But he was a versatile and ingenious scientist whose apparently childlike inquiries usually struck at the heart of the matter in hand. He was also something of a wit.

The phenomenology work involved both theoretical research and scale-model experiments, particularly of explosions in water, and McEnhill, Moyce and the rest of the team were to contribute to a secret conference on the effects of atomic explosions which was held at the Royal Institution in late 1949 with the object of informing government departments about the latest thinking. Their research was not, however, directly relevant to the design of the bomb itself, and Penney would ultimately be obliged to close down the operation and switch the staff to more important work. Moyce in particular was to become a central figure in the years that followed.

Challens, Maddock, McEnhill, Moyce – these were the sort of men on whom Penney came to rely most in the development of the bomb. There were more senior staff and more junior, who made vital contributions, but it was at this level that the design and production techniques were settled and the project was seen through. In the early months, many of them lived in prefabricated homes near Fort Halstead while houses were built for them in the village of Otford near by. Moyce remembers an odd challenge they took up in their spare time which also involved a fifth man, Bill Ashworth. 'The thing that was exercising our minds was how to make a television out of surplus radar parts. This caused great excitement and much discussion. Each of us built one. McEnhill's was an exquisite piece in a nice polished cabinet with a lens; typical McEnhill, perfection in everything. Ashworth was an engineer and he wasn't interested in the pictures so much as the resolution. Challens's resembled a Christmas tree, with components hanging on by wires. He was the first to succeed and then he threw it away;

that was his way. Mine was on a card table. We watched it all right. I would come home at night and my wife would say, "I was dusting around there and this fell out", and she would give me a resistor. "Oh, that won't make much difference," I would say.'

FORT HALSTEAD WAS the headquarters of the Armaments Research Department, but Woolwich Arsenal was its heart. There, in buildings strung along the south bank of the lower Thames, could be found the country's greatest reservoir of skills and experience in the field of armaments and explosives. In military use since Tudor times, it had become the Royal Arsenal under George III. ARD was the descendant of a relatively recent arrival on the scene: the Experimental Establishment, created in 1902 amid concern at the poor performance of British weaponry in the Boer War. The establishment grew dramatically in the First World War, making outstanding contributions to the improvement of both guns and explosives, but sank into a quieter existence thereafter and lost some of its scientific edge. It was to rectify this that new talent from the universities was pumped in at about the time the ARD headquarters moved to Fort Halstead in 1942. Woolwich, however, had never lost its pre-eminence in engineering and craftsmanship. 'It's a big place: five miles of riverfront and almost any engineering technique up to wartime', recalls one veteran, Len Bunce. 'They had standards. When I was an apprentice I used to go to Woolwich Polytechnic three half-days a week and if you didn't do well enough you were kicked out.' The result was a strong sense of pride and solidarity; 'Woolwich men' respected and stood by each other.

ARD was only one of several military establishments active in the Arsenal, but it had a strong presence and so in turn did the atomic bomb project. In the explosives section, the vital personality for HER was Ernest Mott, distinguished by being the only man in the team with whom Penney regularly found himself in conflict. Things started well enough between them but after a couple of years they could not abide each other. Slim, dark, good-looking and a little older than Penney, Mott was a Londoner and a graduate of East London College. Like Moyce, he had been brought down from Swynnerton in the Potteries to join the project, and before long Penney was sufficiently impressed to promote him, professing himself 'delighted with the drive he has shown in getting work started'.[4] Mott was practical by nature – he had designed his own home before the war – but at work he preferred not to get his hands dirty. 'He used to sit in his office and think', recalls one of his staff. 'You went to see him and he heard what you had to say and gave a bit of advice, and then he sat back and waited. We never saw him on the range. He sat up there like a great big spider and heard what was going on.'[5] His advice was usually good, and among his juniors Mott came to command considerable loyalty. This he returned in full; it was Mott's seniors who found him a pain in the neck.

Every month there was a meeting of the leading HER scientists, with Penney in the chair, at which progress was reported, ideas exchanged and instructions given. If a sour note was introduced it was almost always by Mott, a sullen and sarcastic presence at the table. 'He hated authority', says another explosives man. 'If he could kick old Penney under the table he would do. It was just his way.'[6] On the surface his complaints were about equipment which Penney would not allow him to buy or orders which he thought misguided, but at root it seems that Mott was an angry soul who felt bitterly that his superiors did not understand his work or appreciate his difficulties. And there is no doubt that his task was difficult. As we have seen, the explosive lenses represented an enormous technological leap, even for an establishment that prided itself on its expertise.

At Los Alamos the lenses had been made by moulding molten explosive, and the design principles of the moulds used there were known, but these in themselves were dauntingly complex. In its solid state, TNT-based high explosive is heavy and inflexible, much like wood. It can only be moulded at high temperature and if it is then allowed to cool naturally it loses its consistency of texture – air bubbles or cracks will form. It also contracts. For the atomic bomb, only mouldings of even consistency throughout would do, and they had to be accurate in shape to within a few thousandths of an inch, so natural cooling inside the mould was out of the question. Instead the cooling process had to be controlled, and this was done by circulating water around the mould. Three different water systems were incorporated, allowing water of three different and closely regulated temperatures to be circulated at one time. The object of this was to ensure that the explosive solidified slowly and evenly from the bottom of the mould upward. Any shrinkage of the material would then leave a gap at the top, which could be filled by adding more molten explosive through a funnel. In this way, it was hoped, shaped high explosive could be produced to meet Penney's demanding specifications.

The difficulties did not end there, for the initial charge of fast RDX and the lens of slow Baratol had to be manufactured as a single unit. Following the Los Alamos precedent, they would be cast successively, one on top of the other, in the same mould. First, the liquid Baratol compound was poured in, cooled, topped up as necessary and set into the shape of a cone. Then a part of the interior of the mould would be removed and the full shape made by pouring the fast RDX in on top. This in turn would be carefully cooled and topped up. When that was ready, the end-product would ideally be a single piece, combining the two distinct substances without flaw or crack. The task might be compared to making a single ice cream confection that combined two flavours in an exotic shape without mixing them. With explosives it was naturally more difficult and rather more dangerous.

Behind all this, as ever, lay an enormous amount of research and design work. The properties and characteristics of the explosives had to be established with an accuracy never required before, and the moulds, with their elaborate cooling systems, had to be drawn, made in prototype and tested, then redrawn, remade and retested. Chemistry, physics and engineering were involved, as well as a great deal of basic explosives skill. The mould design work was carried out by a team at Fort Halstead – when enough draughtsmen could be found – to specifications worked out by Mott's department at Woolwich.

One member of the lens team at Woolwich was Pat Cachia, a Maltese seaman's son who had spent seven years in the Army before taking a degree in chemistry. Of all the reasons that brought people into HER, his was one of the oddest. After graduating he took a job in leather research in central London, and with great difficulty he and his wife found a flat in Lewisham. He commuted to and from his work by train, but he grew to hate the crowds and the bustle. One morning on his journey into town he looked out of the carriage window and saw another train heading in the opposite direction, out towards the suburbs. It was empty. He had the idea that he should find a job somewhere in that direction, which would allow him to travel to and from work against the commuter flow, in comfort. Acting on the idea, he applied to Woolwich Arsenal and before long found himself welcomed with open arms into HER.

Cachia recalls a feeling that in the early stages they were groping in the dark. 'Nobody had any experience in that kind of thing. Explosives were destructive. You used them to break things up. Nobody had ever thought of using them for precision engineering. You couldn't find anybody who had any experience. All you could do was find people who were used to making things out of explosive: filling shells or making lumps.' And once they had made some progress in mastering the techniques, other uncertainties took over. 'You didn't know how good it had to be. You did something and you thought, "Is that good enough? Or has it got to be better?" You had to get an implosion and compress this thing, but how good did it have to be? There were no criteria. When you saw that the composition wasn't uniform and the density wasn't uniform – because by definition it never is – you asked, "Was it uniform *enough*?"'

Besides the lenses, there was another high-explosive component to be made. After the detonation waves had passed through the lenses and had been turned inside out, merging to form a single convergent wave, the compression force had to be increased. To achieve this, the next layer of the onion was a thick jacket of RDX fast explosive. Upon striking this, the convergent wave would accelerate suddenly towards the centre, thus providing the necessary compression. This layer of RDX, which was known as the supercharge, would be comprised of six blocks, together forming a sphere inside the lenses, with a pit in the middle for the radioactive core. These blocks would be massive, single pieces of high explosive on a scale never cast before in Britain, and as always in HER they had to be as near to perfect in size, composition and density as was possible.

To begin, there was a sort of competition at Woolwich, with all suggestions welcomed as to how such a large lump of RDX might be made. One idea, probably dreamed up by one of Mott's assistants, the Scotsman George Gallie, was to create a big ball of explosive by a layering technique akin to making toffee apples.

Mott asked Cachia to give it a try. 'We got a plastic ball and rotated it, and poured the stuff on top. It was a mess. I went to see Mott and said we weren't getting on well.' He agreed that the toffee apple scheme should be abandoned, but the idea of making the super-charge pieces by a gradual layering technique survived to be incorporated into the method eventually chosen. This was to take a crude mould of approximately the right size and rotate it. Above and beside the mould was a vat of molten explosive, and a pipe would bring the liquid down into the mould. A layer would be poured into the bottom and the flow turned off. The liquid would be cooled beneath a jet of cold air until set; then another layer would follow, and another, until a large block was created. In principle this system reduced the risk of bubbles, cracks and shrinkage.

Once a block was complete, it would be broken out of the mould and machined. Again, this was a relatively new technology requiring a fair amount of experimentation and engineering work. One of the leading figures involved was Len Bunce, a plumber's son born in Woolwich who had worked his way up from an apprenticeship in the Arsenal. Bunce and his colleagues developed a procedure which turned a crude block into a precision-tooled piece to fit into the jigsaw of the weapon assembly. The first step was to cut off the cheeks with a bandsaw and test them for quality. Then the block was mounted on an ingenious machine nicknamed the Chorley, because it was made at the Royal Ordnance Factory at Chorley in Lancashire. This performed the difficult task of cutting the curved outer face of the block. Then the inner curved face was scalloped out, and the sides milled to a smooth finish. Manoeuvring these blocks was a delicate business, since it was vital that no mark or dent should be left in the explosive and equally vital that it should not be dropped. Bunce developed a system of vacuum suckers for this.

As for the straightforward danger of dealing with high explosives, that at least was nothing new at Woolwich. The work was carried out in large purpose-built buildings whose walls were surrounded by high mounds of earth and whose roofs were made of light materials. If something exploded, the force of the blast would be directed upwards and the damage would be contained. Woolwich explosives men prided themselves on their phlegmatic approach to danger and on their record of prudence, but with the machining of these big shapes they were in unknown territory. 'Nobody knew very much about the hazards', recalls Pat Cachia. 'The RDX was powerful, about the most powerful explosive used in conventional conditions, and they were chary of it. We tried to work on it remotely but equipment was a bit short and there were people there at times, drilling and so on. There were no accidents.' Len Bunce remembers that even scientists accustomed to radiation hazards used to be extremely nervous when they visited him in the mounded buildings. The regulars, however, grew accustomed to the dangers. George Gallie, a veteran explosives man who was one of Mott's senior assistants, used to joke to colleagues: 'You should be a chemist; they can throw their mistakes down the sink.'[7]

WHEN A LENS or a supercharge section had been completed, it would be tested. Usually, it would be X-rayed to look for bubbles and cracks. To make doubly sure, every now and then one would be chosen at random and sliced into one-inch cubes for closer examination. But the most important means of testing the quality of the product, and the only practical way of establishing whether it did the job expected of it, was to blow it up. This could not be done at Woolwich or Fort Halstead; instead, the test firings were carried out to the east, in the bleak, windswept and muddy wastes on the Essex shore of the Thames estuary. Here lay the domain of Roy Pilgrim.

During the war, Pilgrim had run an establishment at Millersford in the New Forest testing bombs, both British and enemy, and here he had met Penney on several occasions while Penney was pursuing his Physex work on blast effects. In 1946, when the Americans invited a British team to attend the Bikini tests, it was probably Penney who suggested that Pilgrim should be included. First in Washington and then in the Pacific the two worked closely together, and an enduring bond of mutual respect was formed. Pilgrim was a quiet and thoughtful man with an independent frame of mind who was devoted to the business of field experimentation. A couple of years older than Penney, he had been brought up in Aldeburgh on the Suffolk coast and won a scholarship to Liverpool University before joining the Armament Research Department in 1929. There he rose in little over ten years to a position of considerable seniority, with 400 men under his command at Millersford.

When the war ended, the New Forest range had to close and ARD decided to create a new establishment on the Essex coast, with Pilgrim in charge. The marshes and mudflats stretching north-east from Shoeburyness, adjoining the resort town of Southend-on-Sea, had been military firing grounds for many years, and the holiday-makers and landladies had become used to the occasional earth-shaking thud in the distance. Before the war Pilgrim had worked there testing explosives for ARD on the island of Havengore, but that was primarily a gunnery range and ARD had been guests of the Army. Now the department wanted its own facilities for test-firing quite large quantities of explosives. The location chosen was on the north-west of the island of Foulness, in a great, flat expanse of land bounded by dykes and shallow creeks. Here, from 1947 on, Pilgrim and his staff built a number of fixed test sites. These consisted of rings of buildings protected by earth mounds, each surrounding a central blast point. The larger rings were 150 yards in radius.

The Foulness range was not built specifically for HER, since ARD needed the facilities for its conventional explosives work in any case, but before long the atomic bomb work dominated. Mott began to send experimental shapes from Woolwich, either by road or on a barge down the Thames, for Pilgrim's teams to test. These would be set atop a pole at the centre of one of the rings of buildings, fitted out with electronics, and detonated. The various measurements taken by the equipment housed in the surrounding buildings would then be assembled and sent back to Woolwich for study. As the months and years passed, the tests became bigger, with steadily larger assemblies of explosive, the apparatus grew more complex and ever greater numbers of scientists from Woolwich and Fort Halstead descended on Foulness to take part. For many of them, the scenes on the Essex marshes provide their most vivid memories of HER.

John Davies, who was a physicist on Challens's staff, recalls regular trips down from Fort Halstead. 'We started off with, say, three lenses and gradually got to a hemisphere; then you were looking at the wave going into the centre. Usually you were down there for about a week.' With a seaside resort on the doorstep, accommodation was no problem out of season, but in summer it could be difficult to find somewhere to stay. On one occasion eight scientists shared one bedroom in a boarding house in Thorpe Bay. The three senior men – Maddock, Challens and Hillan – occupied the one double bed while their juniors slept on the floor. Eventually, an empty house on the Foulness range was refurbished and turned into a hostel.

For a variety of reasons, the firings seem very often to have taken place at night. 'We might plan the trial for the day,' says Eddie Howse, 'but equipment failure would delay it until the early hours. A lot of it was photography, so that was better at night anyway. It tended to be one or two o'clock in the morning. People used to get very tired. You would work all day and then perhaps be waiting for somebody else. You would sit there playing cards, drinking tea and waiting, but still getting pretty tired.' Another frequent cause of delay was the weather. In certain conditions, the blast wave could rebound off an atmospheric barrier in the sky and strike an inhabited area up to twenty miles away, something guaranteed to make the range unpopular with locals. John Challens believes that on one occasion a test firing broke windows on Southend Pier, although responsibility was never admitted. Pilgrim and his staff, however, became expert at reading the weather conditions and timing their shots to avoid frightening the neighbours.

There were occasions when the fright was closer to home. Scientists who came down by car were told to leave the car windows open, but there was always one who forgot and emerged after the firing to find all his windows shattered. More alarming were the trials that went wrong. John Davies remembers: 'When one assembly was fired, they had put a metal insert in the centre. It just came straight back at the firing building. It hit the mound on the outside, but the pressure wave jammed the door and we were stuck there for a while.'

Even a successful firing could end in tears. One of the most important pieces of equipment was a bank of oscilloscopes which would display their readings at the instant of the explosion. All these readings were photographed automatically, using glass plates, so that they could be examined at leisure afterwards. When a shot was fired, the plates would be developed on the spot and then placed in an aluminium can for safe keeping. Howse recalls: 'One evening after a nice successful trial, Challens picked up the can, went out the door and tripped over a cable. There was a terrific crash and all the plates were shattered.' All was not lost, however, for the pieces were gathered up and brought to Fort Halstead, where the jigsaw was painstakingly reassembled.

WILLIAM PENNEY'S ATOMIC bomb project would undergo many changes before it bore fruit, but the early choices made by himself and by Lord Portal established its essential character. This was not a gathering of brilliant minds like the Manhattan Project, nor was it a reconstitution of the British Los Alamos team; instead it was a part of the regular defence establishment. But it was an anomalous entity, a secret but official fifth column marching to music which it alone could hear. HER may have come under the umbrella of the Armament Research Department and shared its facilities and senior administrators, but in many ways the two were separate organizations. So far as was possible in the laboratories and workshops the atomic work was kept secret from the rest of ARD, while the lines of command upwards were quite distinct. Penney answered to Lockspeiser for conventional ARD work, but to Portal for HER, and Portal, although nominally (like Lockspeiser) subordinate to the Minister of Supply, had a direct line to the Prime Minister.

The soldiers in this fifth column were anonymous public servants who belonged to the culture of applied military research. Most of them were grammar-school men, often from families of modest means, who went to university on scholarships or as external students and wanted thereafter to make a career, rather than a reputation, from their skills. They were accustomed to secrecy and to the need for results, and they valued the scientific civil service for its steady ways and its meritocratic order. The best of them were very good scientists indeed, typically in their thirties or early forties, who had pushed their way forward as ARD changed and expanded during the war. If there were real-life equivalents of the 'new men' in C. P. Snow's novel of that name about a British bomb project, these were they.

For Penney, who in the early stages saw the job as primarily the technological one of mastering the methods required to reproduce the Nagasaki weapon, these orderly, practical and effective men were the ideal workforce. For the scientists themselves, the bomb work represented a professional challenge and a probable fast-track

81

to promotion. 'I thought it was grand, a most exciting project', says Bill Moyce. 'I was totally absorbed,' recalls Pat Cachia. John Davies was delighted to find himself working with 'a wonderful bunch' of people at the cutting edge of electronics: 'In those days, microsecond pulses were quite a thing to try and monitor. A lot of the equipment you wanted just didn't exist; you had to make it yourself. Even oscilloscopes. We were at the forefront of the development of a lot of these things.'

The leadership of Bill Penney made the project all the more attractive. Herbert Pike, one of the ARD mathematicians who had helped Penney analyze the Hiroshima and Nagasaki data back in 1945, was an early recruit to HER. 'I had a very dull job doing internal ballistics, and then Penney came along', he remembers. 'It was a different world.' Youthful, breezy, informal and supremely competent, the Chief Superintendent was able to draw the best from his staff. Popping up unexpectedly in the laboratories wearing his loud undergraduate-style pullovers and his eternal grin, he would ask about progress and chip in with ideas. 'You would turn around and there he was', says Davies. 'Not criticising, but wanting to know what you were doing. You didn't feel he was out to catch you out; he just wanted to know what was going on. Was everything all right? Anything you wanted?' Noah Pearce, who was on Pilgrim's staff at Foulness, recalls: 'He was very much one of us. He used to pull our legs a bit but you didn't mind; you were pleased that he took notice.' Even at Woolwich, where the *bonhomie* was restrained by the friction with Mott, HER had a distinct style. Len Bunce, who transferred from another branch of the Arsenal, remembers: 'The atmosphere was different there. Where I was used to working under a more disciplined regime, in the Research Department there were a lot of free spirits roaming around. It was peculiar and interesting; a lot of these people were great characters.'

The professional excitement at HER bears some comparison with wartime Los Alamos. The scientists at Fort Halstead and Woolwich, deprived of so many of the secrets of the Manhattan Project, were having to break the same ground and solve many of the same problems. But there was a big difference: unlike Oppenheimer's team, they knew that the principle of the bomb design on which they were working was sound. If they could produce components to the correct standard, their weapon would explode. Knowing this, and knowing the consequences of the attacks on Hiroshima and Nagasaki, did they have no moral doubts about making the weapon?

As we have seen, the scientists usually did not know what the job was until they were already doing it, but the discovery rarely prompted second thoughts. Pat Cachia's reaction to the news was probably typical: 'There were no bad thoughts. It was patriotic. It was a very important and worthwhile job.' Eddie Howse, hearing it from Penney's own lips, took the same view; he was pleased to be working on an important, high-priority project and he was not troubled by moral anxieties. In 1947 and 1948 nuclear weapons were not controversial in the way that they would be ten years later. The hydrogen bomb, a thousand times more powerful than the atomic bomb, still lay in the future, as did the understanding of the dangers of global fall-out. Dreadful as it was, the new weapon did not have the power to wipe out humanity. In these years there was no Campaign for Nuclear Disarmament and no unilateralist wing of the Labour Party. Partly, no doubt, through Attlee's systematic stifling of debate in Parliament and the Press, there was no focused national discussion at all of whether Britain should have an atomic bomb. Attitudes were often vague: in some quarters hope continued to rest upon international control, while in others there was a growing anxiety about the intentions and power of the Soviet Union. The loudest voices speaking out against a British weapon were either pacifist or on the far left.

The HER staff, with their background in government military research, were never likely to include many pacifists or Communists. Nor were they a polyglot collection of free-thinking intellectuals like Oppenheimer's senior staff at Los Alamos. They were loyal and practical men and women who took the view, just as Penney did, that if the Government wanted an atomic bomb, it was their job to make it.

5

The Task is Doubled

WILLIAM Penney, as we have seen, did not want a British Los Alamos. He had been urged from the first to consider setting up HER on a site of its own but he insisted instead on keeping the atomic bomb work inside Woolwich and Fort Halstead. In the first year of the project, as he struggled to find the resources for even this modest arrangement, he must have been grateful that he had not attempted something more ambitious. In the second year, however, he was forced to think again, for a decision was made that transformed the scope and scale of his responsibilities. The decision was that High Explosive Research should manufacture not only the outer parts of the bomb but also its inner components, including the plutonium core.

This important matter had been left unresolved by the GEN.163 meeting in early 1947 which approved the creation of HER. At that time, ministers had a simple view of the bomb project. Hinton and his big industrial teams at Risley, Springfields and Windscale were working towards a single objective: the production of plutonium metal. Penney and his far smaller teams at Fort Halstead, Woolwich and Foulness were given the jobs of producing the explosive jacket for the weapon, its attendant electronics and its metal casing. The question of who should have responsibility for manufacturing the metal components at the heart of the bomb, notably the finished plutonium hemispheres, was not considered.

It would be no simple matter. Like the high-explosive components, the plutonium would have to be cast to extremely exacting specifications, in precisely the right configuration and in the appropriate alloy form. Unlike high explosive, plutonium is a highly poisonous element and was little understood in Britain at that time; handling it would effectively be a pioneering project, requiring a large team of metallurgists, chemists, physicists and engineers. A special 'hot' laboratory, in which these people could work with the plutonium with the minimum danger of radioactive contamination, would have to be designed and built from scratch. It would be a project on a considerable scale. Moreover, the plutonium was not the only component involved. In the Nagasaki weapon, the model for the British design, the two hemispheres were encased in a shell of uranium metal known as the tamper whose function was to give additional intensity to the nuclear explosion. And at the very centre of the plutonium, between the two hemispheres, was a tiny device known as the initiator, which employed the rare element polonium to 'kick-start' the fission process. These parts would also require a great deal of research, design and development.

That the question of who should undertake this work had not been addressed earlier is perhaps surprising, but Portal and his staff may have felt that, since no plutonium was likely to be available for at least a couple of years, even for experimental purposes, they had plenty of time. Penney and Hinton, the two men most practically concerned, were left in the dark. Penney, whose project was for security reasons kept quite apart from the rest of the atomic energy empire, knew very little about Hinton's work and in the early months simply assumed that the inner parts would ultimately be delivered to him in time for assembly in the weapon. In November 1947 he wrote of 'special components which must come from another Establishment'.[1] Hinton, for his part, may not even have known at this stage that the HER project existed. Had the two men spoken they would probably have been dismayed to discover the grey area that fell between them. Such contact, however, was not permitted and it was only when, in early 1948, the security surrounding HER was eased a little, that the matter came to be addressed.

This easing of security was an important development. It had not taken long to discover that the intense secrecy covering all aspects of HER was threatening to suffocate the project. Attlee was obsessive and ill-tempered in his insistence that as little information as possible about the whole British atomic energy project should be made public. He did not want the Soviet Union learning anything from Britain; he did not want public controversy; he did not want the negotiations on international control to be compromised and he did not want the Americans to be upset or alarmed by any news from Britain. Grudgingly, he conceded that the existence of the larger sites must be acknowledged, so the names Windscale, Springfields and Harwell found their way into the Press. As to what went on inside them, absolute secrecy had to be maintained. The newspapers were naturally interested and did what they could – Cockcroft was surprised one Saturday morning to come across a reporter from the *Daily Graphic* lurking in his garden. But Attlee was adamant that such curiosity should not be rewarded and when he saw stories in the papers containing information he did not wish to see printed he was perfectly capable of sending a stiff personal note of reprimand to the Ministry of Supply, demanding an inquest. Understandably, officials became extremely sensitive and an atmosphere of near-paranoia developed.

If the rules about ostensibly civil aspects of the project such as Harwell were restrictive, those shielding HER from the public gaze were draconian. On this subject, after all, Attlee was so concerned about secrecy that he would not even brief the full Cabinet. The weapon work inside Woolwich and Fort Halstead, as we have seen, took place largely in special fenced compounds; staff were subjected to additional security vetting when they were recruited and the nature of the job could not be disclosed to them until they were cleared. When they did find out what they had been hired for, they were not even supposed to tell their wives (although many did). They developed a particular reticence in the canteen and on the bus home, which prompted no little curiosity and some jealousy among colleagues not employed in HER work.

This claustrophobic regime broke down at the point where HER needed to do business with the world outside the fences. Although Attlee had declared that atomic weapons work should enjoy the same high priority as the rest of the atomic project, his intentions were frustrated by the paranoia he himself had engendered. For example, there was a formal priority directive which was supposed to enable Penney to cut through red tape, but security officials were so assiduous in ensuring that it had the smallest possible circulation that many very senior officials in relevant government departments were completely unaware of its existence. At the Air Ministry, for example, no one below the Deputy Chief of Air Staff could be told of it. In the Ministry of Supply itself, the assistant secretary in charge of atomic energy was left in ignorance of the directive until a colleague in another ministry alerted him to its existence. Portal's own copy, which in theory was his ultimate weapon in pushing forward the atomic project, hardly ever left his safe. As Hinton was later to remark: 'Priority so secret isn't terribly effective.'[2] Certainly it is hard to imagine that, if Attlee's firm wishes had been more widely known, Penney would have had such difficulties over four secretaries or half a dozen draughtsmen.

By the beginning of 1948 it was clear in the Ministry of Supply that something must be done to get HER out of this quarantine. The minister, George Strauss, put forward a proposal that the Government, in some low-key fashion, should acknowledge publicly that work was under way on the development of atomic weapons. This, it was explained, would enable Penney to draw much more effectively on the resources of the country, in the civil service and outside. It would have the additional and paradoxical advantage of putting the security of the project on a sounder footing. Strauss feared that the Press would uncover HER and produce some speculative and sensational story about the British bomb. This was an imminent danger. Already, Chapman Pincher of the *Daily Express* had written drawing attention to the presence of Penney, a Los Alamos veteran, at the head of the Armament Research Department. 'He is said to know more about the atom bomb than any other British scientist', wrote Pincher. 'If Britain makes atom bombs, Dr Penney as CSAR will almost certainly be in charge of the project.'[3] Total secrecy, warned Strauss, carried the risk of total exposure, but there was an alternative. He wanted to impose a formal clampdown on reporting by the use of a D-notice, the voluntary ban on coverage which the Press accepts in matters of national security. The D-notice committee, on which Press representatives sat, would of course have to be told about the project before they could be sworn to silence, and they were likely to demand some sort of announcement in exchange for their assent.

In short, everything pointed to the need for some modest

disclosure, and after some grumbling from the Ministry of Defence, where Strauss's solution was thought excessive, the proposal was accepted. Before any announcement was made, however, it was felt necessary to inform the Americans; it would not do for them to learn such news from the newspapers. The British embassy in Washington was duly instructed and, on 19 March 1948, the diplomat in charge of atomic matters called at the US State Department. He explained that the work had been going on for about a year and a half, but because secrecy was now impeding progress the government in London had decided on a casual announcement. The State Department, he said, was being informed first as a matter of courtesy. The British diplomat performing this act of courtesy was Donald Maclean, who by this time had been a Soviet agent for almost fifteen years and was approaching the end of a Washington posting that was his most active period in Moscow's service. It is more than likely, therefore, that by this route, if not by others, Stalin knew about the British bomb project before the British Parliament did.

With the diplomatic formalities out of the way, the Minister for Defence, Albert Alexander, was able to make his statement. This he did in a most oblique manner. In the House of Commons on 12 May, Hansard records:

'Mr George Jeger asked the Minister of Defence whether he is satisfied that adequate progress is being made in the development of the most modern types of weapon.

The Minister of Defence: Yes, Sir. As was made clear in the Statement relating to Defence 1948, research and development continue to receive the highest priority in the defence field, and all types of weapons, including atomic weapons, are being developed.

Mr Jeger: Can the Minister give any further information on the development of atomic weapons?

Mr Alexander: No. I do not think it would be in the public interest to do that.'[4]

And that was that. The question had been 'planted' with Jeger, a compliant Labour backbencher, by the Ministry of Defence, and Alexander had answered it according to his side of the same script. The matter was discussed no further. In the Press, the statement was recorded with conspicuous economy, because by the time it was made editors had received their copies of D-notice number twenty-five. Thus *The Times* devoted just a few short lines to it on page four; the *Daily Telegraph* gave it three paragraphs on page one and the *Daily Express* appended two paragraphs on the announcement to another story on atomic matters on page one. Attlee must have been pleased. Perhaps the most striking example of discretion is to be found in the *Atomic Scientists' News*, the journal of an association dedicated to increasing public awareness of nuclear issues. Its June issue carried four lines on Alexander's remarks, and offered no comment whatever.

It was an extraordinary affair. Writing fifteen years later, Richard Crossman summed up the exchange in the Commons: 'It is the kind of question which is put to enable a Minister to conceal the true situation while being on record as having made an announcement.'[5] The Government had made a revelation with the purpose of improving the functioning of its own bureaucracy. Into the bargain, it had secured a ban on any Press investigation of the subject. The Americans, and probably the Russians, had been told, but among the British public only the more conscientious readers of the newspapers would have noticed anything at all and even then they were given no measure of the significance of the development.

For Penney, however, there were concrete benefits. He could at last step out of the shadows, if not into the public gaze at least into the corridors of Whitehall. He was promptly invited to join Portal's principal co-ordinating committee, the Atomic Energy Council, where the bigger problems of the atomic project were aired. And it was here that the question of the inner components of the bomb was finally tackled. Penney had by now begun to express concern about this, so Portal placed it on the agenda for his début appearance at the AEC on 2 July, when it could be fully discussed in the presence of Cockcroft and Hinton.

As this meeting approached it was clear to Portal, if not to Penney, that it would have a vital influence on the final shape of the weapon programme, and Portal had some ideas about what that shape should be. A few days beforehand he called Cockcroft and Perrin to his office at Shell-Mex House for a preparatory chat. There, in the absence of Penney and Hinton, the individuals most affected, they planned how the work should be divided up. Hinton's northern group, already responsible for producing the raw plutonium metal, should go one stage further and manufacture the plutonium hemispheres. They should also produce the uranium tamper, while Harwell should prepare the initiator. These three components should then be delivered to Penney at HER for assembly inside his explosive lenses. On the face of it this was the simplest and most logical arrangement, but it had its drawbacks, for it implied a rather diffuse organization, with components of the weapon under development in three or more establishments at once. Portal had the answer for this. To co-ordinate the work he proposed setting up a new committee with Sir Geoffrey Taylor in the chair. From this committee, he expected, a full-time atomic weapons directorate would naturally emerge which would have the authority and the scientific expertise to manage all the various strands of weapon development and production.

This scheme was a radical new departure for Portal's department. It was certain to meet resistance from Hinton, whose appearances at the AEC invariably entailed bitter laments about how over-worked and understaffed his group was and about the meagre level of salaries he was allowed to offer. Portal must have known that he would be very reluctant to take on the additional responsibility of designing and building the facilities to produce the plutonium hemispheres. Penney, for his part, was unlikely to be impressed by a proposal to create a 'Weapons Scientific and Technical Committee' to guide the atomic weapons work, for this would certainly restrict his role as the principal weapon designer and co-ordinator – the role for which he had turned down an Oxford professorship. A directorate for atomic weapons, if it emerged, would relegate him to the role of a components supplier while leadership of the whole project would probably pass to Taylor. Perhaps it was with this thought in mind that Portal, after concluding his discussion with Cockcroft and Perrin, decided: 'The desirability of forming such a committee would not be included in the agenda for the Atomic Energy Council as it was considered preferable for the subject to arise in the course of discussion.'[6]

In the event, this was one meeting which failed to conform to Portal's carefully laid plans. One by one each of the ideas worked out in advance were put to the council, and one by one they were firmly rejected in favour of a quite different course. Risley, it was decided, should not take responsibility for the plutonium hemispheres; that job would be done by HER. Springfields, the uranium plant, would not make the tamper; HER would make it. Harwell would not make the initiator, although it would help with research; HER would do it. The leading force in securing this result was almost certainly the hard-pressed Hinton. His staff was too busy to take on another raft of tasks, while Cockcroft, always reluctant to involve Harwell in weapons work, appears to have been only too happy to step aside. The full implications of the change for Penney became clear when Hinton observed that, since HER was now to handle these fabrication tasks involving radioactive materials, a 'special factory' would have to be built for the work.[7] Penney was asked to report back as soon as possible with specifications for such a factory. Here was the germ of Aldermaston. In all this rapid decision-making, the idea of a directorate of atomic weapons simply died. If Penney was making all the components he could do his own co-ordinating, and Sir Geoffrey Taylor's services would not be required.

More than three months were to pass before Penney felt ready to submit a scheme for the proposed 'special factory', and by that time he was having doubts about the idea. He was already very busy recruiting and training his staff at HER and he continued to have wide responsibilities on the conventional side of the Armament Research Establishment (ARD was renamed in 1948). Now he was being asked to design and build the facilities needed to handle plutonium, polonium and uranium, as well as to design the weapon core itself and create the team which would make it. He felt a bureaucratic thicket closing in upon him.

In October he duly presented the specifications he had been asked to draw up. If HER was to take over the production of the radio-active components, he said, then logic demanded a new site. All HER operations, with the exception of large-scale explosives trials, should be concentrated on this site. The first of the specialist buildings should be complete by early 1951 and the transfers from Woolwich and Fort Halstead should come in stages in the months that followed. Having put forward this scheme, Penney went on to urge the AEC not to adopt it. The scale of the changes was so great, he argued, that he and his staff would have difficulty seeing them through without disruption to the schedule for producing the first bomb; the construction work itself was likely to cause delays and scientists would have to be diverted from working directly on the bomb to designing buildings. This was surely too high a price to pay. Instead, Penney proposed taking a step backwards and splitting the bomb work very much along the lines that Portal and Perrin had originally envisaged, with Hinton taking charge of the plutonium.

The rest of the council saw it differently. Hinton sympathized, but not to the point where he was ready to take on the extra work himself. Other members saw great advantages in concentrating all the bomb work on one site; Cockcroft and Perrin spoke of a British Los Alamos, a home for long-term British bomb research and development. Penney retorted that at Los Alamos the director had the authority to hire his own staff, set their salaries, recruit consultants at generous fees and commission and design his own buildings. This was some way removed from his own experience in Britain. As for long-term research, he had no manpower to spare for it; it was all he could do with his present resources to replicate the American wartime weapon.

Another question was woven into this argument, which concerned the status of the proposed new site. Penney wanted to maintain the link with conventional armaments research, with both ARE and HER remaining under his umbrella. The others felt it should be a separate establishment in its own right. The atomic weapons programme needed its own organization if the job was to be done effectively, they said; it must be divorced from the old institutions and freed to develop at its own pace, in its own way. Penney insisted that the two bodies were complementary. He wrote: 'Having now a loyal, enthusiastic and competent establishment, making good progress in atomic and conventional work simultaneously and in complementary fashion, it seems foolish to split the establishment and unsettle the staff for many years while some of them are trying to make Mark I of our atomic bombs.'[8]

At the root of Penney's arguments was a desire to keep his administrative obligations within manageable bounds. He was already stretched by the perpetual trench warfare of recruitment: he had a hundred vacancies to fill in senior grades and that figure would be doubled if he took on the inner components. There had been another passage of arms with Lockspeiser, this time over transfers of electronic engineers from other projects, and there was a growing problem with a shortage of design engineers. To embark on the creation of an entirely new establishment on top of all this, he felt, would be sheer folly. His colleagues on the AEC were unsympathetic. Looking back on these debates some years later, Penney recalled: 'For many months the other members took the line that instead of them taking contracts from me, to make plutonium, uranium shells and so on, I should have my own facilities. They wanted to give me hunks of plutonium and I was to shape it. Instead of a small team I was going to get a big group. This grew quite rapidly so that in fact I was doing the lot . . . Cockcroft said "I'm not going to"; Hinton was too busy.'[9] The outcome was a compromise, agreed eventually in February 1949. The new, combined site was to be created, but it would remain part of ARE; Penney must take responsibility for the 'special factory', but he was to be spared the task of disentangling his two organizations.

IT MAY HAVE been part of the agreement – although if it was, it was an informal part – that Lord Portal should ease the burden on Penney in his expanded role by putting an end to all the haggling over recruitment. Certainly, Portal was anxious about Penney's mounting commitments: in January 1949 he had complained to the Chiefs of Staff that the chore of finding staff was diverting the CSAR from his real task of developing a weapon. Portal had also learned with irritation that Tizard's cake-cutting committee was not providing much assistance. As Dizzy Davis reported of the committee's sessions: 'Long discussions take place over filling CSAR's vacancies but nothing material seems to result, and discussion frequently declines into an argument between CSAR and Lockspeiser or his representatives.'[10] Portal now resolved to take the bull by the horns. He wrote to Tizard recalling the wishes of the Prime Minister and the Chiefs of Staff and demanding that urgent steps be taken to close down some lines of defence research to free men for HER. This had always been the purpose of the committee in Portal's eyes, but in a year of operations not a single project had been wound up; instead, Penney had been fobbed off with a few men here or there and otherwise had to rely on graduate recruits from the civil service entry examinations.

At the same time, Portal confronted Lockspeiser directly and in an even more aggressive tone, reminding him that in the previous summer he had promised a 'proportional forced levy' on all defence research establishments to meet Penney's desperate need for electronics experts. After eight months, Portal pointed out, 'this forced levy so far has produced only ten of the twenty-one extra men then needed by Penney, and of these only three arrived within three months of the date of your letter'.[11] Portal identified one man, a chemical engineer by the name of Alan Grange, whose transfer from another establishment had been blocked, and ordered Lockspeiser to release him within a week.

If this salvo from Shell-Mex House was expected to provoke a crisis around the corner in Whitehall, it succeeded. Lockspeiser delivered up Grange after four days, but with a furious protest that HER needs could only be met 'at the expense of work of the highest Air Ministry priorities in the fields of navigation, bomb sighting and so on'. This would undermine the bomber programme, he said. 'I feel we must preserve some balance between the weapon itself and the means of using it.'[12] Tizard, by now concerned about the demands of atomic weapon work, decided to act. He asked the Chief of Air Staff, Lord Tedder, to consider the whole matter. Tedder agreed and a meeting took place in March, but the moment was not an auspicious one for Tizard.

The previous month, Attlee had concluded a lengthy review of the country's strategic needs in the light of the deteriorating international situation. The Cold War had begun and West and East were in open confrontation over Berlin, while international control of atomic energy was a dead letter. The Prime Minister's response was to authorize an expansion of the British nuclear programme. The gaseous diffusion plant at Capenhurst, which had been approved as a pilot project in 1946 after Ernest Bevin's flurry of bombast, was to go to full production, and there was to be a third pile at Windscale. These measures would allow plutonium output to be increased sufficiently to enable the RAF to build up the stockpile of 200 bombs now thought necessary to provide an effective deterrent by the target date of 1957. To accompany this expansion, Attlee issued to the Minister of Supply a new priority directive for atomic energy. He underlined the 'importance and urgency' he attached to the programme and hoped that nothing would be allowed to interfere with its realization. 'The demands which the expanded programme will make on our resources (including the provision of any houses that may be needed) are not likely to be heavy and, with the sole exception of some skilled scientists, engineers and technicians who will have to be withdrawn from other important projects, the effect that these demands will have on other high-priority programmes should not be serious.'[13]

Coming so soon after this, Tizard's bid to clip HER's wings was doomed. Portal carried the day and a humiliated Tizard was obliged to pass on the bad news to all the leading figures in defence research. 'It is urgent to re-examine your staffs,' he wrote, 'and in consultation with Lord Portal's representatives to offer to transfer any members of the existing experimental staffs who would be suitable for the HER work . . . In making this offer, no regard should be taken at this stage of the effect of their possible transfer on other work of high importance.'[14] Perrin obligingly sent Tizard a new list of HER recruitment needs, identifying sixty-seven posts to be filled within three months.

This may have appeared a final victory, but it was not. Tizard and the defence research chiefs would not give up, and with good reason, for HER's appetite for scientists appeared insatiable. After the Tedder meeting there was quick progress and thirty or more recruits were found for HER, leaving a shortfall of thirty-three, but in June the staff requirements list was updated to include for the first time the specialists who would work on the inner components. Penney now wanted seventy-one more scientists within three months, and a further forty-five after that, taking his complement of scientists and engineers to 330. In response, the defence research chiefs produced for the first time a study of their own manpower problems which showed that they were 1,300 posts short of their full complement, or more than twenty per cent. The depredations of HER had already affected radio and guided weapons work and other conventional projects and now threatened to disrupt the gun research programme, they warned. Armed with these findings, Tizard now took his case directly to the Prime Minister and persuaded him to authorize a thorough review. Attlee, however, did not want to become involved further, and left the matter to the Chiefs of Staff. A fuse had been lit that was to burn for several months.

Meanwhile, Penney was looking for a place to build the new HER headquarters. Here, the example had been set at Harwell. It was a former RAF base, far enough from large towns to limit the dangers to local people but near enough to give staff some contact with civilization. Portal urged Penney to look at other airfields farther to the west. 'I've extra pull with the RAF', he said.[15] So in the spring of 1949 Penney toured the Cotswolds looking at airfields and found one which suited him: South Cerney, near Cirencester in Gloucestershire. It met the basic criteria and had additional advantages to boot: the existing buildings were of good quality and would be useful; it was near enough to Harwell to maintain liaison and there was a prospect that much of the initial labour force for construction could be found in Cirencester and Gloucester. The Ministry of Works approved, as did Portal, so a 'Cerney Committee' was set up to plan the building programme. Unfortunately, the RAF decided after some hesitation that it did not want to part with the site and Portal's 'pull' was not sufficient to change their minds. South Cerney was not available.

Penney started to look again. Fairwood Common and Pembrey in South Wales were considered, as were Atcham near Shrewsbury, a naval air station at Bramcote and a factory site at Yate, near Bristol. Each in turn was rejected. It was now summer; six months had passed since the new establishment had been approved and no progress had been made. Penney was becoming anxious. Then in August, the Ministry of Civil Aviation came up with a suggestion: Aldermaston in Berkshire, a former RAF base situated on high ground between Basingstoke and Newbury. Again it fitted the bill and this time the RAF were no longer using it, so they could hardly demand to keep it.

Aldermaston is an ancient manor which once belonged to the Anglo-Saxon King Harold. The airfield was built in 1941 on what had been the estate of Aldermaston Court, a Victorian pile that dominated the village. It was used by the US Army Air Force as a jumping-off point for troops heading for North Africa and, later, France. On D-Day fifty-two gliders carrying men and equipment of the 81st Airborne flew out of Aldermaston to land behind Omaha Beach in Normandy. After the war, the base was taken over by BOAC as its training headquarters, but that closed down at the end of 1948. Now it was available and, Penney thought, suitable.

He recalled later, in staccato style, how rapidly matters proceeded: 'Once we'd said yes, then he [Portal] really put his hat on . . . Dizzy Davis to me, we looked at it . . . back to Dizzy Davis, back to Portal . . . quick action through the Prime Minister; it was all done in two or three days. A damn great site bigger than Imperial College.'[16]

In fact it was not quite so clear-cut as that. Over the next few months a number of ministers objected to the choice. The Ministry of Health, then responsible for housing, declared that a worse area for housing could hardly have been chosen; the Ministry of Labour said the same was true for construction workers and the President of the Board of Trade, Harold Wilson, wanted the whole project transferred from the rural Home Counties to an industrial development area. He suggested somewhere near Manchester or Liverpool, whose strong university science departments could be employed to advantage. It was December before Attlee set these objections aside and gave his final approval, and even after that the unrest did not die down altogether. As late as May 1950 the Minister of Works was complaining that such 'atomic devilries' should only be located in very remote areas such as the highlands of Scotland, the Yorkshire Moors or Salisbury Plain.[17] By then, however, Aldermaston was set upon its course to international notoriety.

August 1949 was a high point in Penney's torrid progress towards the British bomb. He had been obliged to accept the task of producing the inner components, but in many ways that was no defeat, for it gave him complete control over the design and manufacture of the weapon. Moreover he had succeeded in keeping HER and ARE together under his authority. HER now had a scientific staff approaching 300 and was still growing, and its work appeared to be on course, so that a test explosion would be possible in the middle of 1952. Although recruitment remained a wearisome problem, he had at last, thanks to Portal, gained the upper hand in the contest with the other defence research chiefs. And there was another cause for satisfaction: the Americans, for so long closed to all idea of co-operation, were ready to talk. But if Penney permitted himself any feelings of satisfaction or confidence in August, he was to pay dearly for it in September.

6

Lightning Strikes Twice

SEPTEMBER 1949 was an animated month in the life of Michael Perrin. The Deputy Controller of Production, Atomic Energy (Technical Policy), as he was formally known, was an influential figure. His job, at Lord Portal's side, was to ensure that policy in the atomic field kept in step with scientific developments. Since very often this involved interpreting the science to politicians and civil servants and explaining to them what was likely to be possible and what was not, Perrin's own judgement was important and he had many opportunities to shape policy. This suited him, for he was something of a Whitehall animal. His background was in chemistry research at ICI before the war, where he played a leading part in the development of polythene. He rose to be assistant to the research director and in 1941 followed him into Tube Alloys. Portal kept him on when he took over in 1946, not only because he needed Perrin's background knowledge but also, perhaps, because the two men, both educated at Winchester and Oxford, spoke the same language. The appointment was made against the advice of Chadwick and Hinton. The latter, who had been senior to Perrin when they were both at ICI, thought little of his scientific ability and of the advice he gave on nuclear policy. Hinton's deputy, Owen, took the same view, only more strongly. Perrin himself, who enjoyed Portal's confidence, was unworried by this. Well known in Whitehall, he moved with perfect ease in the committee rooms and club dining rooms where so much of the business of government was done. His reputation was one of efficiency and discretion, if not great flair. If a senior official in another department needed to consult someone about a delicate matter relating to atomic energy, he would probably have chosen Perrin.

On 5 September 1949, Dick White, the deputy director and head of counter-espionage at MI5, invited Perrin to visit him in his office to discuss just such a matter. White placed before Perrin a top-secret communication that he had received from the British embassy in Washington. It contained the transcript of a message which had been sent from the Soviet consulate in New York to Moscow in the year 1944, giving information about the Manhattan Project. With it, there may also have been an FBI report, freshly drafted, on a British scientist who had worked at Los Alamos. Perrin, still familiar with the detail of the British contribution there, read the material with growing alarm. When he had finished he looked up and told White: 'It looks very much as if Fuchs has been working for the Russians.'[1]

As a Soviet spy, Klaus Fuchs could hardly have been better placed. He had been involved in the wartime atomic bomb project from its earliest days, he had made important contributions to the Manhattan Project and he had enjoyed generous access to its secrets. Where Alan Nunn May, operating on the fringe of the project in Canada, had provided Moscow with a couple of intriguing details of the atomic bomb, Fuchs was able to describe almost the whole weapon. In the words of Hans Bethe, his division chief at Los Alamos, Fuchs 'told the Russians exactly how to assemble the bomb; how to use implosion; how the explosive and nuclear material was arranged; how to calculate the yield of the bomb and the neutron diffusion, and he certainly told them about the critical mass . . .'[2] To make matters worse from Perrin's perspective, after the war Fuchs had become – and he still was – the head of theoretical physics at Harwell, intimately involved in the British nuclear programme. Worse still, he was one of the most senior external consultants advising William Penney on the design and construction of Britain's atomic bomb.

Perrin could see in an instant the nightmarish implications if the suspicions about Fuchs were substantiated: first, the Soviet Union knew much more about bomb design than anyone could have imagined and might well be much farther advanced in building their own weapon than had been assumed; second, the British project was probably an open book to Moscow; and third, the Americans would be outraged to learn that a British citizen, cleared by British intelligence, had betrayed their most precious secrets. It is ironic, although it can have been little comfort, that Perrin himself had in 1944 asked the security services to double-check Fuchs's background to ensure that 'we do not slip up in any way'.[3] On that, as on all other occasions save for the very last, Fuchs was given a clean bill of health.

Emil Julius Klaus Fuchs was born in Germany in 1911, the son of a clergyman of liberal views and a depressive mother who killed herself when he was nineteen. As a student at Kiel University he became involved in anti-Nazi activities and joined the Communist Party. In 1933 he fled to Britain, where he found a post as a research assistant in the physics department of Bristol University. After taking his Ph.D. he transferred to Edinburgh University, but on the outbreak of war was interned as an enemy alien and shipped to Canada, where he was held in a camp with other Germans. Friends in Britain secured his release and in 1941 he received the call to join the small British team investigating the feasibility of an atomic bomb. He moved to Birmingham to assist Rudolf Peierls, another German *émigré*. It was Peierls and his friend Otto Frisch who had first alerted the British authorities to the possibility that a bomb could be made and that scientists in Nazi Germany might well be making one. A number of scientists were then set the task of testing and elaborating the blueprint they had drawn up. It may seem odd that a German immigrant was chosen to help, but Fuchs was only one of several refugees involved. This made good sense. They were very often the best qualified, their hostility to Nazism was not in doubt and most of the good British-born scientists were already involved in other war work.

Fuchs was probably not an outstanding scientist of the calibre of Peierls or Frisch, but he was on the next level down and before long he was an indispensable part of the wartime British atomic effort. When this was transferred to the United States and attached to the Manhattan Project he went with it, working in New York and then at Los Alamos. Usually a quiet figure, he was reasonably popular and became particularly close to the Peierls family. When the war ended, Cockcroft was delighted to capture him for Harwell. There he thrived, for the first time developing a real affection for Britain and the British. Among the AERE staff he was known as a dedicated worker and a stickler for security. He once declared, in a moment of hubris: 'I suppose you could say that I *am* Harwell.'[4]

It is a measure of how good a spy he was that, when he was eventually arrested, those who knew him best were all utterly astonished. None of them had ever had the slightest suspicion. Peierls stubbornly refused to believe it until he heard it confirmed from Fuchs's own lips in Brixton prison. Here was a man who had for seven dramatic and intense years been able to commit himself completely to his work and his friends at one moment, and then betray them the next: and this without ever being able to share his secret with any confidant but his various and occasional Soviet contacts in Britain and the US. He himself attributed this ability to 'controlled schizophrenia'.[5] Others, notably the writer Rebecca West, who attended his trial, would put it down to an undeveloped personality, incapable of connecting actions with consequences. Of his motivation there is little doubt: he probably never ceased to be a Communist after joining the Party as a student in Kiel, and he took the view that the secret of the bomb should not be kept from the Soviet Union.

How was he unmasked? The message which Perrin read in September 1949 had been passed to the British embassy in Washington by the FBI, which had been alerted by its code-breakers. During the war, the US had intercepted radio traffic between Soviet diplomatic missions and Moscow. This was in code and the code was unknown to the Americans, so the material was stored. When the Soviet Union came to be perceived as an enemy a new effort was made to break the code, and success came in 1949. The wartime files were reopened and the Los Alamos report soon came to light. Evidence that Fuchs was the author came from other decoded material which showed that the spy, known to Moscow as 'Rest', was a non-American scientist whose sister had attended a university in the United States. Fuchs had such a sister. An exhaustive trawl through the records produced two wisps of corroboration: Fuchs's name appeared in Gestapo documents captured at the end of the war which listed thousands of Germans suspected of being Communists, and it appeared again among hundreds of entries in the address book of a suspect in the Canadian spy ring exposed in 1945 by the defector Gouzenko.

Five months passed after Perrin's visit to MI5 before the suspicions about Fuchs were confirmed. For the few people who shared the secret, they were months of acute suspense. The intelligence experts did not doubt his guilt, but their evidence was not quite conclusive and, coming as it did from secret FBI radio intercepts of coded diplomatic messages, could not be produced in court. If he was to be prosecuted as a spy, Fuchs must either be caught in the act of contacting a Soviet agent, an unlikely eventuality, or persuaded to confess, which might be a long and delicate business. In the meantime many questions hung in the air. Was it an isolated offence, and if not, when did the spying begin? Was it the result of blackmail, or conviction? Who else was involved? Above all, how much had been given away?

In the end Fuchs confessed, was tried for treason the following March and sentenced to fourteen years in jail. The case caused a sensation. In Britain, attention focused on his betrayal of wartime atom bomb secrets and his high rank at Harwell. In the United States, where the question of whether to make a hydrogen bomb was on the agenda, the chief cause of concern was whether the spy had betrayed to Moscow details of discussions about this new super-weapon which had taken place at Los Alamos around the end of the war. Little or nothing was said on either side of the Atlantic, although much may have been suspected, about Fuchs's involvement with the British atomic bomb.

Penney employed very few external consultants at HER, and those he used were selected with considerable care. One was James Tuck, a Los Alamos veteran who, at Penney's request, wrote a handbook to introduce HER staff to the principles of implosion. Tuck emigrated to the United States in 1949, ultimately returning to Los Alamos. Another was Sir Geoffrey Taylor. Vastly experienced in a range of relevant scientific fields and with a formidable command of the literature, he was an obvious person to turn to when a particularly difficult problem arose. Besides these two, the list of scientists in the universities from whom Penney sought advice is short indeed. The main reason for this was undoubtedly security; permission was always required from inside Portal's security 'Cage' in Whitehall and there were complicated clearance procedures to be gone through. The rules were quite different, however, for Harwell scientists such as Fuchs. They were already under Portal's umbrella and were positively expected to help Penney wherever possible. They were also familiar with the secrecy regulations although, when contacts with HER began, additional precautions were still taken. AERE scientists who visited Fort Halstead, such as Titterton, the electronics expert, Marley, the high-speed photography pioneer, and Fuchs, did so amidst cloak-and-dagger arrangements intended to conceal their destination from their colleagues.

Penney and Fuchs knew each other well. At Los Alamos they had both been members of Bethe's theoretical physics group, known as T Division, and spent a good deal of their time on the problems of the convergent wave in the implosion design. They worked, however, in different specific areas. Fuchs studied multipoint detonation in some detail and was familiar with the problems of timing that were involved. He was also the scientist in charge of liaison between T Division and X Division, the department responsible for conventional explosives, so he was able to observe closely the development of the implosion lenses. Later, with Tuck, he helped to design the initiator, the little device at the very centre of the bomb, and in his final months at Los Alamos, he studied possible alternative configurations of implosion bombs to the one dropped on Nagasaki. Such a breadth of knowledge was of obvious value to Penney as he strove, without access to American files or scientists, to replicate the American implosion weapon as closely as possible.

John Challens recalls that Fuchs came to Fort Halstead to give lectures to the staff about the hydrodynamics of the weapon – its internal workings upon detonation. The tall German with the domed, balding head and the gold-rimmed spectacles was a 'star turn', says Challens. 'We all went along as a matter of course to indoctrinate ourselves.' Bill Moyce remembers hearing one lecture, in which the speed and craftsmanship of staff at Los Alamos were held up as an example: 'He spoke very well. I have an idea he had been primed by Penney, because he said that when he was in the US, if he wanted anything the engineers would get to work at once and by the next evening the result would be on his table.' Challens believes these lectures continued until very shortly before Fuchs was arrested.

At the same time as giving general lectures, Fuchs was providing HER with specific and detailed information on the design of the American weapon as he remembered it. In 1948 and 1949 he produced a number of written summaries of various aspects of the design, and these were studied by Penney and his mathematics team of John Corner and Herbert Pike. Corner and Pike met Fuchs to discuss design matters on three or four occasions. His material dealt not only with matters at hand, such as the nuclear physical considerations which would determine the specifications of the plutonium to be used in the core, but also with longer-term questions. Having attended seminars at Los Alamos on the hydrogen bomb, Fuchs was convinced that this was an important field and was anxious to see some research begun in Britain. Penney would not authorize it because he felt he could not spare the resources, but Fuchs discussed the American thinking with Corner and Pike. Both men found him impressive and helpful. 'Fuchs had a very organized mind', recalled Corner. 'He was able to pack a lot of detail into a few sentences.'[6] This did not mean that he was always right. The paper on plutonium specifications contained three errors, two of which were spotted by Corner as late as 1951.

One contribution which Fuchs made, whose value was only appreciated after his arrest, was a summary of the virtues and drawbacks of various possible layouts of the plutonium inside the weapon. This had been much discussed at Los Alamos in 1944. The Nagasaki weapon was solid all the way through, with each layer – explosive, uranium, plutonium – fitting snugly against the next. What if the plutonium core was a hollow sphere and not a solid one? Or what if a narrow gap was left between the uranium and the plutonium? Would the weapon be more, or less efficient? Answering these questions had been a job for theoretical physicists of the most mathematical bent, and Fuchs was one such. He had worked on the problem in America and remained interested, and he passed on his thoughts to HER. When Corner read his paper he thought it interesting, but a matter for another day. Penney was intent on copying the Nagasaki weapon, so alternative ideas were not being entertained. However in late 1950, with Fuchs already in jail, Corner had cause to look out the paper again. Penney, as we shall see, decided at that late stage that a re-design of the core of the weapon was needed. Corner and Pike produced a new proposal, which Penney eventually accepted. This was based on principles and ideas set out in Fuchs's report, as he had remembered them from the Los Alamos discussions.

Corner and Pike were both impressed by Fuchs's memory, which served them so well. 'Anything I asked him he answered straight away', says Pike. 'Various people had a lot in their heads to get us started, but Klaus Fuchs was the outstanding one.' That memory was supported by extensive notes. Pike recalls seeing notebooks full of mathematical calculations. 'I think that [at Los Alamos] every evening he wrote what he had done during the day, because he had the correct numbers for everything, and you don't carry that in your head for long.' This view is borne out by the experience of Derrik Littler, a Los Alamos and Harwell colleague of Fuchs, who went through his papers after his arrest. Littler found that Fuchs had accumulated an enormous amount of detail on both his and other people's work at Los Alamos. Everything found in Fuchs's safe at Harwell that was thought to be weapons-related was passed to Fort Halstead, where it was filed away for possible future reference by the meticulous John Corner.

For Fuchs to have carried notebooks out of Los Alamos would have been a breach of the rules laid down by the Americans governing the departure of the British scientists, but it would not have required any elaborate subterfuge. Rudolf Peierls recalls: 'Nobody examined the papers we were carrying, except for the normal customs checks, so it would have been physically possible to smuggle documents.'[7] We know in any case that Fuchs had succeeded in carrying documents out through the camp security barriers to deliver them to his Soviet contact at meetings in Santa Fe. And we know of at least one classified document which he smuggled out specifically for the British. This was a paper on hydrogen bomb theory which Egon Bretscher, a Swiss-born physicist in the British team, decided that Britain was entitled to have. As Fuchs was about to leave, Bretscher asked him to take the document to James Chadwick, and he agreed. Just before his departure, Bretscher's wife warned Fuchs that security had been tightened at the gates, and he told her: 'It's quite all right. I'm used to carrying secret papers.'[8]

The case of Klaus Fuchs is rich in irony. He has been called the man who stole the atom bomb. Whatever he could learn at Los Alamos he assiduously recorded, summarized and gave to the Soviet Union. After the war, thanks to the peculiar turn of Anglo-American relations, he found that this material was useful again, this time to his adopted country, Britain. The same notes he had used in drafting summaries for his secret Soviet contacts in the United States, and perhaps even the summaries themselves preserved in carbon copy, now provided vital early assistance to the British atomic bomb programme. Fuchs, the controlled schizophrenic, stole the secret, but he gave it away not just to one master, but to two. And the second master, Britain, later jailed him as a traitor.

Did Fuchs tell Moscow about his conversations with Penney, Corner and Pike, and his visits to Fort Halstead? We do not know. The principal source of information on Fuchs's post-war espionage activities is Fuchs himself, who made two confessions after his arrest and was subsequently questioned by FBI agents. By his own account, Fuchs had six meetings with a Soviet contact between 1947 and 1949. They met outside Kew Gardens underground station or at one of two London pubs, the Nag's Head in Wood Green and the Spotted Horse in Putney. The contact was always the same man, since named as Alexander Feklisov, and Fuchs normally handed over written material and answered a few questions. This was, again according to Fuchs, a period when his attachment to Britain was growing and his belief in the Communist and Soviet causes was waning. In one of his confessions he claimed that he deliberately did not pass on all the information he could have. He admitted giving details he had picked up at Harwell of the Windscale piles and the British gaseous diffusion plant, but there is not one mention of his work for Penney. It is possible, then, that he never betrayed the HER secret to Moscow. However it is also possible, indeed probable, that in his confessions Fuchs was not telling the whole story. Whatever the truth, anything Fuchs might have told the Soviet Union about HER would not have raised many scientific eyebrows in Moscow – as we have seen, HER had more to learn from Fuchs in those years than he from it. And if, in late 1947 or early 1948, he passed on the interesting political information that the British project had begun, he was at best only a short step ahead of Donald Maclean.

Two footnotes may be added on Klaus Fuchs and the British bomb. The first gives an indication of his high-security standing just a few months before he was exposed. At the end of 1948 Robert Cockburn, the scientific adviser to the Chief of Air Staff, conceived an extraordinary scheme for defence against atom bombs. This involved firing a gamma ray beam from a linear accelerator at a bomb as it fell, in order to prompt a neutron release in the core and cause the weapon to fizzle. The idea was taken very seriously by Tizard and by the Atomic Energy Council, which wanted it studied further. It was referred to an extremely exclusive group of scientists: Herbert Skinner, the head of general physics at Harwell and an accelerator expert; William Penney and Klaus Fuchs. The 'Cockburn Project' still existed in June 1949 but seems to have expired thereafter. Linear accelerators are heavy and require large amounts of energy, while identifying and targeting a falling bomb is problematic to say the least. The whole notion, if it was not a dalliance with science fiction, was at the very least several decades ahead of its time.

The other footnote is a sort of testimonial to Fuchs, written by Penney three weeks after his most valuable consultant had taken up residence in Wormwood Scrubs prison. In a memorandum about plans for senior appointments, Penney talks about the future of bomb research: 'We know that a given amount of plutonium can be made into more effective bombs than our prototype model, but we do not know any details. There is no doubt that the military value of our plutonium can be increased by fifty per cent, partly by some major improvements, and partly by a large number of minor improvements. Knowing the position as I do, I can say that there are only four people in this country who have the knowledge and ability to discover within three or four years what those major improvements are. One of the four is now in prison, two of the others are university professors who are unwilling to do more than give advice [presumably Taylor and Chadwick]. The fourth is myself.'[9]

IN THE SAME week that he learned of the finger of suspicion pointing at Fuchs, Michael Perrin made another shocking discovery, again thanks to the Americans. It was Saturday, 10 September 1949, and he was woken at his London home by a call from the British

107

embassy in Washington. Would he make his way to the US embassy in London to take part in a secure telex conference? At about 11 a.m. – 6 a.m. Washington time – Perrin and an MI6 officer were present at the embassy to begin an exchange with the Pentagon. For the past week, they learned, the US air force had been tracking a radioactive cloud which had first been detected in the North Pacific, just off Kamchatka in the Soviet far east. The cloud had since crossed the United States and was now drifting over the North Atlantic towards Europe. American planes had taken hundreds of samples from it and these showed that the radioactivity was the result of nuclear fission and that the suspect air mass originated in the Soviet Union. Whether it came from an accident in a reactor or from a weapon test was still not certain, and the Americans wanted more data. Would the RAF collect further samples before the cloud passed back into Soviet air space? Perrin said it would, and soon afterwards a Halifax aircraft took off from Aldergrove air base near Belfast carrying filtering equipment. Within three days the American suspicions were confirmed: late in August, somewhere in its vast Asiatic wastes, the Soviet Union had successfully detonated a nuclear weapon which, like the American device dropped on Nagasaki, employed plutonium as its fissile material. Stalin had the bomb.

President Truman refused to believe it. He could not imagine that any other country, no matter how determined, could reproduce the extraordinary effort which the United States had put into developing the bomb. He had, perhaps, accepted as a logical concept the notion that the American nuclear monopoly would one day end, but he had not grasped it as an imminent reality. Here he was in good company, for there was scarcely a scientist or military man who had predicted that, four years after Hiroshima, the Soviet Union would have its own nuclear weapon. Even those who had made intelligent guesses in 1945 or 1946 had failed to tick off the passing months and were taken by surprise. When eventually the President was confronted with the vast weight of evidence gathered from the radioactive cloud, and informed that his best scientists were ninety-five per cent sure, he yielded. But his scepticism remained and years later he was still expressing doubts about the Soviet nuclear capability.

The announcement was finally made on 23 September, and it

followed hard on the heels of another development shocking to the West: the proclamation of the People's Republic of China in Peking, marking the final Communist victory in the long Chinese civil war. To many, particularly in the United States, this was the moment which brought home the advance of Communism and the threat of a new world war. To Brien McMahon, author of the McMahon Act, it seemed that the time might have come to blow the Soviets 'off the face of the earth, quick, before they do the same to us'.[10] Not only did the Soviet Union command vast armies in eastern Europe, it also now ranked as a technological superpower, while its militant ideology had conquered the most populous nation on earth. In Britain the news coincided with an even more shocking event: the devaluation of sterling against the dollar. With no bomb, a feeble currency and a dwindling empire, the country scarcely seemed to count any more. And yet the cloud thrown up by 'Joe One', as Stalin's first atomic test came to be known, had a silver lining. American thinking had been slowly moving towards closer co-operation with Britain in the nuclear field; here was a powerful catalyst to accelerate that movement.

The exchange of information on atomic energy between the United States and Britain had been cut off, it will be remembered, in the spring of 1946. In London, the hope had never died that this policy might be reversed and British diplomacy worked ceaselessly to that end. In January 1948 Britain played the two cards it still had: it allowed the United States to take more from the stockpile of uranium over which Britain, Canada and the US still exercised joint control, and it agreed to tear up a wartime agreement which required the US government to consult the British government before using the atomic bomb. In return, the Americans made concessions on the release of atomic energy information. In nine specific and circumscribed scientific areas, there could now be an exchange of data. None of these was directly pertinent to the weapon. This secret accord was called, with fitting modesty, the 'Modus Vivendi'. Donald Maclean helped to draft it.

The British were never completely happy with the deal, and indeed the Americans never really kept their side of it, but it was a start and the next eighteen months saw a slow improvement in the relationship. In general, the opposition to closer co-operation came not from the Truman administration itself but from certain members of the Joint Committee on Atomic Energy in Congress and of the Atomic Energy Commission, the body now responsible for all nuclear development in the US, both civil and military. In the armed forces, too, there were objections. The arguments remained the same as in 1946: Britain was too vulnerable to defeat and occupation by the Soviet Union to be allowed to make and stockpile bombs; secrets shared with the British might find their way to Moscow; the British were trying to steal a march on the US in the production of atomic power; and, bluntly, everything must be done to protect the American atomic monopoly. There were many Anglophiles, keen to do business with Britain, but the anti-co-operation lobby, armed with the McMahon Act, fought them at every turn. When word reached Congress that Britain was conducting research into atomic weapons, for example, it was judged a breach of the Modus Vivendi and Truman was asked to reconsider the whole agreement. He stonewalled.

In the summer of 1948, the conflict in Washington descended into farce when Cyril Smith, an American metallurgist born in Britain, decided to take a holiday in Europe. He offered to visit Harwell and applied to the Atomic Energy Commission for permission to discuss with his British friends the subject of plutonium. One of the clauses of the Modus Vivendi permitted exchanges of information on the fundamental properties of reactor materials, and plutonium was just such a material. Approval was given on condition that the use of plutonium in weapons would not figure in the Harwell discussions, and Smith sailed for Southampton with his family. Eight weeks later word of this visit reached Lewis Strauss, the member of the Atomic Energy Commission most opposed to exchanges with Britain. He drew it to the attention of Senator Bourke B. Hickenlooper, a senior member of the Joint Committee who shared his views. They were appalled to find that plutonium metallurgy secrets were to be shared with the British. With all the considerable authority that between them they could muster, they demanded that Smith be stopped. Their views prevailed but no one knew whether Smith had already visited Harwell, and contacting him proved no easy matter. As desperate messages from Washington poured into his sister's home in Birmingham, he was happily completing a tour of Scotland and the Lake District in a rented car. Eventually, however, the word got through. It was not too late, and the discussions of plutonium at Harwell were prevented.

Against this background of intransigence, progress in dealing with the Americans was inevitably slow, but the British continued to nudge it along. The very next month, the Minister of Defence, Albert Alexander, proposed in writing that information should be exchanged on atomic weapons, particularly in the fields of plutonium metallurgy, fuses and arming devices. Coming so soon after the Smith affair, the proposal was doomed from the outset, but it was delivered in a mood of defiance; a marker for future talks. In the Truman administration, meanwhile, co-operation with the British continued to gain favour, for reasons both internal and external. By early 1949 the Berlin blockade had been going on for six months, US bombers were again stationed in Britain and the Anglophile Dean Acheson had become Secretary of State. A secret conference of policy-makers at Princeton concluded that the most effective way to counter the Soviet threat was to link arms with the British and Canadians and ensure that all resources – scientists and raw materials – were used with the greatest possible efficiency. Britain might be persuaded to relocate some of its nuclear programme in North America, and in return a full exchange of information could begin. Truman, hesitant at first, accepted the idea of a new approach to the British but when he put this to the congressional sceptics during the summer they vetoed it. Determined to make some progress, the administration decided to tackle the problem from the other end, and invited the British to talks in September on long-term arrangements which might replace the Modus Vivendi. Perhaps something could be worked out which might in due course be put to the Joint Committee of Congress.

It was at this moment that the cloud cast up by Joe One made its appearance over the North Pacific, announcing the end of the American monopoly and the beginning of the nuclear arms race. The mood on Capitol Hill was suddenly anxious and gloomy, and it appeared at last that the Joint Committee would be prepared to consider some form of co-operation with Britain to meet the new threat. (The Fuchs affair, it should be remembered, had not yet reached the public domain; he was suspected by the FBI and MI5, but had not confessed or been charged. None of the principals in Congress was aware of the case.) In late September John Cockcroft

111

and the British ambassador, Oliver Franks, opened talks with the Truman administration in Washington on a new collaboration arrangement. Their proposal was that Britain would curtail slightly its nuclear programme, retaining two, rather than three, atomic piles at Windscale and a small diffusion plant at Capenhurst for enriching uranium in fissionable U-235. The British weapons programme would continue and there should be full exchange of information on all aspects of weapons design. An eventual British bomb would be tested at an American site. In exchange – and this was now Britain's only card – Britain would allow the United States a far greater share of the uranium stockpile, still controlled jointly by the two countries and Canada. This was not good enough for the Americans. They responded that the diffusion plant should also be cancelled, that the actual manufacture of British atomic bombs should take place in the United States, and that the leading British weapons scientists should be integrated into the US programme as they had been in the Manhattan Project. This the British could not accept. Cockcroft and Franks insisted that to remain a sovereign power Britain had to have both its own civil nuclear programme and its own weapons programme, however reduced in scale. They accepted, however, an American proposal that only a very small number of atomic bombs should be held on British soil. The talks resumed in late December with Penney present, and the British team tabled a proposal for an agreement of three years' duration under which weapons production would be fully integrated and a stockpile of about twenty bombs would be kept on British soil. Britain would keep a minimal civil and military programme of its own, capable of expansion at a later date. There matters stood for a month, while the Americans mulled it over.

In London, there was considerable enthusiasm for such an arrangement. It had three main virtues: the transatlantic partnership would be revived, giving British scientists access to the very latest ideas in nuclear weapons design; the independent programme would survive, protecting British interests against any future rupture with the Americans; and the economic burden of going it alone would be eased. For Penney the implications were far-reaching. For a start, he personally was undoubtedly at the top of the list of British weapon scientists who were likely to be transferred to Los Alamos for two or three years. The Americans knew him

1. Operation Epicure: Air Vice-Marshal 'Dizzy' Davis (*right*) inspecting the Monte Bello Islands off Australia during the reconnaissance survey in November 1950. As a result of his secret visit, they were chosen as the site for the first British nuclear test.

2. William Penney in 1932, on a holiday visit to Robert Oppenheimer's ranch in the New Mexico mountains. Penney was to return to the region in 1944 when he joined the Manhattan Project at Los Alamos to help design the atomic bombs that were dropped on Japan.

3. Penney in 1952, leaving his south London home on his way to work at Fort Halstead in Kent. His involvement in the British atomic bomb project was kept secret for more than five years.

4. Atomic summit in Washington. President Truman (*left*) greets Clement Attlee (*right*) on the White House steps in November 1945. US Secretary of State James Byrnes looks on. Attlee believed he won a promise of American nuclear co-operation at this meeting, but he was disappointed.

5. Lord Cherwell, Churchill's principal adviser on scientific matters. He said of Penney: 'He is our chief – indeed our only – real expert in the construction of the atomic bomb and I do not know what we should do without him.'

6. Sir Henry Tizard, one of the most influential figures in defence research. He resisted the growth of Penney's team on the grounds that it diverted effort from more urgent projects.

7. Viscount Portal of Hungerford, the wartime Chief of Air Staff who became head of the British atomic project. He is pictured here after Klaus Fuchs's court appearance on spying charges in February 1950.

8. Klaus Fuchs. After spying on the American wartime bomb project for the Soviet Union, he provided Penney and his team in post-war Britain with vital advice and information. Then he was jailed. He is pictured here on his way to Heathrow Airport in 1959, when he was released and expelled to East Germany.

9. The plutonium processing building at Aldermaston during construction in 1951. The new establishment was built in great haste, and was ready just in time to make the core for the Hurricane Test.

10. Senior scientific staff on Operation Hurricane, photographed on board the *Campania*. *Standing* (*left to right*): Ted Marshall, Stanbury, Bisby, Pat Cooper, Ieuan Maddock, Bill Moyce, Redmond, Carruthers, Frank Morgan, Prier, Charles Luxford, John McEnhill, D.H. Pierson, Hart, Herbert Pike, John Butterfield. *Sitting*: John Rowlands, N.F. Moody, Roy Pilgrim, Leonard Tyte, William Penney, Charles Adams, John Challens, Alex Walkling.

11. HMS *Campania* at the Monte Bello Islands, just after completing the turbulent eight-week voyage from Britain. The helicopters – a novelty – can be seen on the flight deck. The *Campania* proved a most unsuitable base for the operation.

12. The laboratory on board the *Campania*. It was cramped and hot, but intensively used during the voyage as scientists hurried to prepare their equipment.

13. Landing craft in service at the islands. There were never enough of these workhorses.

14. Waiting to set off in a landing craft: Adams standing, centre, in bush hat; Challens crouching to light his pipe; Maddock closest to camera and Marshall pointing.

15. Cocoa Beach camp on Trimouille, set up after it proved impracticable for the scientists to operate from the *Campania*. The conditions were spartan, the food was bad and there were plagues of flies, but they preferred it to life on board ship.

16. A cinema show at Cocoa Beach. Challens, second from left in the front row, is one of those wrapped up against the evening chill.

17. Lugging equipment uphill to establish the unauthorized Press observation post at Mount Potter on the mainland. From there they got the news of the test back to London before most government departments had heard it through official channels.

18. An RAAF plane flies over Mount Potter to snoop on the Press. The British government was concerned about the capabilities of the 'Long Tom' long-range cameras, seen on the left.

19. Ieuan Maddock (*centre*) at the control desk in H1 camp during the countdown. The windows were blacked out against the flash.

20. HMS *Plym*, with the bomb on board, at its final berth in Bunsen Channel. In the foreground are Anderson shelters built to test their ability to withstand the atomic blast.

21. Admiral Torlesse (*left*) and Penney watch as the cloud rises above the Monte Bellos on 3 October 1952. After the tensions and difficulties of the preceding days, both were delighted with the outcome.

22. 'You may look now.' Having stood with their backs to the islands during the initial flash, men on the *Campania* turn to witness the eruption. Within a minute, the blast wave struck.

3. Winston Churchill leaves 10 Downing Street on 23 October to make a statement on the test in the House of Commons. He revealed to MPs that the bomb had been detonated on a ship. 'HMS *Plym* was vaporized,' he said, 'except for some red hot fragments which were scattered over one of the islands.'

24, 25, 26 and 27. 'The vastness of the upheaval.' After the first violent moments of the erupti
a dirty, mud-laden cloud like a giant cauliflower is thrown upwards. Then the wind pushes i
sideways and downwards into the shape of a galleon. Finally, after thirty minutes, the vapour
radioactive trail is twisted and stretched over fifty miles of sky.

28. A model of the atomic bomb with the explosive sphere, dotted with detonators, visible inside the transparent section.

29. The first British nuclear weapon: the Mark I, codenamed Blue Danube. Five feet across and about twenty feet long, it was delivered to the RAF in November 1953.

well, and wanted him back. A number of the senior scientists at HER would also be expected to cross the Atlantic, including almost certainly John Corner, Roy Pilgrim and some of the phenomenology team which had been studying the effects of atomic explosions. Aldermaston would go ahead, but the pace of its development would now be slower than previously expected – a particularly enticing prospect for Tizard and Lockspeiser since it implied a reduction in the demand for research staff. It was also clear that the link between HER and the Armament Research Establishment must finally be broken. Even Penney, who had fought to keep the two together earlier in the year, could see that the Americans would not tolerate such an anomalous arrangement if they were to share their secrets; the risk to security would be too great. Before 1949 ended, Portal was already thinking about how this upheaval could be effected in an orderly fashion. In early December he put it to Penney that he must appoint a deputy to oversee in his absence the development of the new establishment and the divorce from ARE, and Penney agreed to suggest some names.

Throughout the period of the Washington negotiations, from September to December, the name of Klaus Fuchs must have dwelt constantly in the minds of the British negotiators. John Cockcroft had first heard that Fuchs was under suspicion on the eve of his departure for the first round of talks. His reaction was: 'Well, thank God I'm just off to Southampton. Don't tell me any more about this; I'm going away and can't be got at.'[11] Penney was probably informed at the same time. Both of them must ardently have hoped that Fuchs would be cleared, or that the indiscretion would prove a minor one which could be dealt with quietly. If it proved worse than that, the consequences for Anglo-American relations could be grave indeed. Already, the doubts about Fuchs were causing problems at home. While the security services searched for a way to prove the case against him, some means had to be found to keep him away from secret matters, and this was not easy with so valuable a scientist. When the samples were taken from the drifting Soviet nuclear test cloud, for example, Fuchs was the obvious man to to carry out the analysis. He had to be excluded. Such difficulties were bound to arise again and again. It was clear that while the doubts remained he could not be allowed to stay at Harwell, but it was less clear how he might be obliged to leave.

Fuchs himself provided the way out. He approached the Harwell security officer, Henry Arnold, to inform him that his father, who was still living in Germany, had been offered a post at the University of Leipzig, which lay in the Soviet zone. Fuchs suggested that this might expose him to possible Soviet pressure and asked whether he should resign his position at Harwell in consequence. It was a curious initiative and the motives behind it are still not clear, but a line of communication had opened which would not be allowed to close. Before long Arnold passed the case to MI5's leading interrogator, William James Skardon, the man who had questioned, among others, Lord Haw-Haw. On 21 December, after a long discussion with Fuchs about his background, Skardon made a direct challenge: 'I am in possession of precise information which shows that you have been guilty of espionage on behalf of the Soviet Union; for example, during the time when you were in New York you passed to them information concerning your work.'[12] Fuchs offered an unconvincing denial and the discussion went no further. Two more meetings produced no progress. In January, Cockcroft called Fuchs to his office to inform him that, in view of his father's imminent move to East Germany, he should make plans to leave Harwell. Soon afterwards, Fuchs sought an interview with Skardon. They met at Harwell, and again Fuchs spoke at length about his background. Skardon renewed the challenge: 'You have told me a long story providing the motives for actions, but nothing about the actions themselves.' Fuchs replied: 'I will never be persuaded by you to talk.'[13] They broke for lunch, the scientist and his interrogator, and over coffee at a pub in Abingdon, Fuchs made the decision to confess. It was 24 January.

What spilled out in the days that followed confirmed the very worst that Perrin could have imagined back in September when he first read that message from Washington. When Fuchs was arrested a few days later and the news reached Washington of the scope of his betrayal of American secrets, the plan to revive Anglo-American co-operation in nuclear weapons development was killed stone dead.

7

Annus Horrendus

ATTLEE'S Labour government endured in 1947 what has been called its '*Annus Horrendus*'. That was the year of the great freeze, the humiliating withdrawal from Greece, the run on the pound and the resignation of the Chancellor, Hugh Dalton. For the party swept to power so emphatically in 1945, this was a period of struggle, disillusionment and occasional despair. The British atomic weapons programme also had its *Annus Horrendus*; it was 1950. The year began in hope, with the secrets of Los Alamos almost within reach, but the Fuchs affair put paid to that. In the months that followed, the aftershocks of the spy scandal and of the Soviet nuclear test shook HER to its shallow foundations, pushed Portal to the point of resignation and left Penney wondering whether he should return to academic life.

When the unequivocal message came through from Washington that nuclear co-operation was no longer a possibility, decisions were swiftly taken in Portal's department. The bomb project would go ahead as originally planned, aiming for a test explosion in late 1951 at the earliest. The development of Aldermaston would proceed without delay, and the earliest possible start should be made on the plutonium buildings there. In due course, all of HER save the Foulness operation would transfer to the new site. As to the divorce of HER and ARE, which had been planned with the new American partnership in mind, it was decided that this should go ahead anyway. This meant that Penney would lose overall

115

control of ARE and all the overlaps between the conventional and atomic organizations would have to be unpicked, a painful and lengthy process. Despite the fences and the other security measures intended to compartmentalize atomic weapons development, many people and many machines were employed for both HER and conventional work, as demand dictated. There was a consolation for Penney: Portal's proposal that he should have a deputy still stood. Now he could have someone to share the administrative burden.

The search for a suitable candidate had begun at Christmas and the experience conformed to the familiar pattern of disappointment and frustration. Penney had three senior superintendents working for him: A. H. Davis, W. Blackman and Alfred Highfield. He had a high opinion of all of them as scientific administrators but he believed they lacked the authority and the diplomatic skills he had found necessary in dealing with Whitehall. Moreover, as he told Portal, this was a job that could make a man's career; the three senior superintendents were all in their late fifties and what was called for was someone younger who showed exceptional promise. Penney believed that there was an outstanding candidate: William Cook, then working in the Admiralty as Director of Physical Research.

Bill Cook was a mathematics graduate from Bristol University who had joined ARD in 1928 and distinguished himself in rocket research during the war. He had since set up a new rocket development establishment at Westcott before moving to the Admiralty. He had, Penney wrote, common sense, good judgement and drive, and he was held in high regard by defence scientists. He was forty-four years old. Portal wrote to the First Sea Lord to ask for Cook to be released, emphasizing the importance of the job for the atomic weapons project and offering A. H. Davis in exchange (Davis had not been consulted). Almost by return of post, Lord Fraser said no. Cook was the best scientist he had and was pushing forward the Navy's most important research project: submarine detection. Moreover, the Admiralty was expecting to promote him in the near future. He could not be spared.

Penney next produced the name of Richard Beeching, another veteran of Fort Halstead and Woolwich during the war, and another engineer. Now at ICI, Beeching was well regarded both as

116

a scientist and an administrator, and he was forty-two. But when Penney interviewed him he asked for a salary of £2,750. This was roughly what he could expect upon his next promotion at ICI, but fully £500 more than Cook would have been paid and £150 more than Penney earned himself at the time. Terms could not be agreed and Beeching decided to stay where he was. Both Cook and Beeching, it so happened, went on to justify Penney's high opinions in distinguished careers rewarded by public honours. Cook worked on the development of the British hydrogen bomb and later at Rolls-Royce, while Beeching won notoriety in the 1960s for his rationalization of the rail network (on that occasion he was given the salary he wanted, £24,000, condemned in the Press as outrageous).

After these rebuffs, and when it became clear that Penney would not be going to America, the approach changed. A candidate was wanted who could be an assistant and a complement to Penney, rather than a substitute. Still there were difficulties. Three more names were considered and rejected over the next three months and each in turn had to be ruled out. Then, at the end of March, the First Sea Lord made a proposal which found favour. Vice-Admiral Patrick Brooking, DSO and bar, was about to retire as commanding officer in Gibraltar at the age of fifty-three. He was a proven commander with scientific experience in the development of naval radar and some familiarity with nuclear diplomacy, having served in the Admiralty delegation in Washington. Cockcroft rated him 'first-class', and Penney thought him an 'excellent fellow . . . He is shrewd, cautious and has a first-class technical brain. I know him fairly well and I am sure that we would work together harmoniously.'[1] The job was offered and accepted, but there was a final delay. Brooking was keen to defer taking up the appointment until August so that he could take a motoring holiday through Spain and France on his way back from Gibraltar. If he did not return to Britain until August, he explained, his car would not be subject to British purchase tax. This imperative was accepted and Brooking took up his post on 15 August 1950. He proved effective, reliable and discreet, and he lifted from Penney's shoulders much of the burden of the work associated with the development of Aldermaston. He had the brisk manner of the career officer, and a disconcerting habit of disregarding the usual formalities – on the telephone he would ask a question, and if he got the the answer he wanted, hang up without another word. Few were tempted to cross him.

At about the time that Penney offered Brooking his job, in the spring of 1950, he was drifting into his most bruising political battle. He was eager to begin the job of detatching HER from ARE, a step which would allow him to establish an independent management structure for the atomic weapons project. The divorce could not be completed and the new appointments made, however, until a new chief was named to head the reduced Armament Research Establishment. By April, Penney was becoming anxious and he urged both Portal and the senior officials on the conventional weapons side of the Ministry of Supply to see if the appointment could be expedited. Portal took the matter up with the Permanent Secretary, observing that as a result of the delay many aspects of the bomb work 'are now proceeding in an unco-ordinated manner'.[2] The result was promising: although no new CSAR was named, a proposal was put to Penney as to the division of staff. The new ARE would take on all the scientists who were not primarily involved in atomic weapons work, plus two relatively senior men employed as mathematicians with HER, Ken Thornhill and Ernest Hicks. Penney suggested that Thornhill and Hicks should stay with him and offered instead to part with four younger mathematicians. This formula, it seemed at first, was acceptable to all and Penney believed the matter closed.

It was not. Those in the ministry responsible for ARE refused to approve the scheme and Penney remained in limbo. By June Portal was reporting: 'Penney tells me today that his continued inability to make the necessary appointments to the new posts in HER is having a catastrophic effect on the work.'[3] The reason for the stalling soon became apparent. In mid-July, the Ministry's Chief Scientist, Harry Garner, who had replaced Lockspeiser, tabled a new bid, suggesting that the cake be cut far more generously in ARE's favour. There was, he argued, a case for assigning to ARE no fewer than eight senior scientists, as well as several junior men, who were involved in atomic bomb work. Those listed included Challens in electronics, Pike in mathematics, McEnhill in physics and an engineer, A. J. Marriott – precisely the kind of people upon whom Penney was relying most to get the job done. Having stated a case that he must have known would cause horror and dismay, Garner in the same letter offered to compromise: he would settle for four senior men.

Penney, in response, struck a note more of sorrow than of anger. 'We have had many disappointments and delays in getting staff, building equipment and houses,' he wrote, 'and if I now lost any of the men for whom you now ask, the effect on HER would be extremely serious.'[4] Worse was to come. A few days later, the Ministry finally appointed a new CSAR, H. J. Poole, a distinguished explosives chemist. Poole quickly submitted an even more ambitious claim, adding another twenty names to the list, including an entire team of men engaged on full-time lens trials at Foulness. Penney turned to Portal. It was, he said, time to put his foot down. The date of the trial was at stake, and 'we appear to be going backwards rather than forwards on the split'.[5] Portal for his part railed at what he called 'this extraordinary muddle'.[6] More than a month later the tug-of-war was still going on, and the Chief Scientist clearly had his eye on Challens, whose promotion was held up by the struggle. Penney's tone became plaintive: 'With regard to Challens, I can only say that he is one of the key men in HER. He is in charge, and he is the brains of the group which is designing and making the firing circuit . . . If he be moved now, I feel that we are running a grave risk in trying to run the trial at the date given . . . Delay is one thing, but what we shall risk is that the firing circuit actually produced at the delayed date will be unreliable.' He added: 'My staff demands have always been at the minimum level for safety.'[7]

If matters had come to a crisis, it was no accident. The dispute between Penney and Portal on one side and Garner and Poole on the other mirrored another controversy raging in the uppermost reaches of the defence establishment over the priority that should be accorded to atomic weapons development. Garner and Poole felt able to adopt their aggressive stance because of the successes marked up in this second and more fateful contest by Sir Henry Tizard. The fuse lit by Tizard the previous spring, when he persuaded the Prime Minister to order a review of defence research priorities by the Chiefs of Staff, had reached its charge.

Tizard had come to the view that the atomic project was damaging Britain's interests. The Americans could already make

119

bombs and the job should be left to them, he thought; British scientists would be much better employed on conventional programmes, and particularly on guided anti-aircraft weapons, which offered the only practical hope of preventing an atomic attack. This approach, he pointed out, had the virtue of economy, both in cash and in industrial resources. His views evolved slowly between 1948 and 1950, and were undoubtedly shaped by his experiences on the cake-cutting committee. At first they were greeted, as he put it, 'with the kind of horror one would expect if one made a disrespectful remark about the King',[8] but as time passed they received a more sympathetic hearing, particularly from those with interests to defend against the depredations of atomic energy.

The first advance came in the late summer of 1949, when the Chiefs of Staff ruled that, although atomic production – Hinton's work – should continue to enjoy the highest priority, the needs of research and development of the bomb and the means of delivering it – Penney's project and the bomber programme – should be considered alongside the needs of other vital defence research. Unless the demands of atomic weapons imperilled the survival of another project, however, they should still be met. This rather fuzzy judgement did not in practice represent a substantial departure from Attlee's priority ruling of the previous February, but there had been an ominous change of tone. Penney's atomic work appeared for the first time to have lower priority than Hinton's and to be on an equal footing with bomber development, while it was now set in stone that other defence research projects would not be closed down to free staff for HER. At the very least, this would restrict Portal's ability to bully the cake-cutters.

After the Soviet bomb test and the Fuchs case, opinion shifted further in Tizard's favour. At a meeting of the Chiefs of Staff on 10 February 1950, the First Sea Lord, Lord Fraser, proposed a thorough examination of the implications of the new circumstances for the British atomic effort. One of the questions which required an answer, he said, was: 'How does it come about that, knowing all that we did in 1945, we are still without an atom bomb, by contrast with the Russians who, starting from scratch, have apparently already passed us . . .?'[9] This was a new note of hostility. Opening their review a few days later, the Chiefs of Staff stated that they saw strong arguments for maintaining the existing course, but they could also see a counter-argument. This was summarized as follows: 'If it was true that the Russians had the bomb, was it not possible that the serious risk of war would develop earlier than 1957, and at the present rate of progress was there any chance of our being able, in the time and on our own, to make a contribution to the Anglo-American pool of bombs such as would enable us to exercise any influence on the war or on its conduct? If in the time available our contribution was going to be relatively insignificant, might it not be better for us to concentrate the resources we had on vital projects to which we were more suited and in which we were already behind-hand (e.g. guided weapons)?'[10]

Both Tizard and Portal took part in the ensuing debates. Portal put the view very strongly that any reduction of the priority accorded to atomic weapons would endanger the survival of the project; scientists would leave and many would be snapped up by the Americans. Any hope of securing a collaborative arrangement with the US in the future, moreover, would evaporate, since the Americans would have no interest in working alongside a second-rate venture. Tizard put forward his arguments, stressing the probable size of the existing US stockpile of bombs compared with what Britain could produce in the short term, and making the case for guided weapon defence. The Chiefs of Staff leant towards Tizard, reaching the conclusion that some delay could be countenanced in atomic weapons development in order to free resources to push forward other important projects as rapidly as possible. A list of no fewer than seven such projects, including guided weapons, was drawn up.

Portal exploded, declaring that if this policy were to be adopted, 'the effect on the atomic weapons programme would be disastrous'. Moreover, the official minutes record, 'Lord Portal felt that there would be no reason for him to continue in his appointment'.[11] The matter went from there to the Cabinet Defence Committee, where the debate raged through several sessions spread over several months. The threat by now was explicit: if the Tizard view were accepted by the Committee, the construction of Aldermaston, and consequently the completion and testing of the first bomb, would be delayed. Ernest Bevin, the Foreign Secretary, proved the stoutest advocate of a strong atomic weapons project, but the new Minister of Defence, Emanuel Shinwell, stood by his guided weapons. The result was a compromise, with the two projects being accorded, for the first time, an equal priority.

The worst had been avoided, but a danger remained. Guided weapons were one of the principal conventional projects being pursued by the Armament Research Establishment, so the new priority directive gave the conventional armaments side – Poole and Garner – every encouragement to take an even more aggressive approach to the separation of HER and ARE. In September, they tabled their final, and their biggest, demand, for thirty men from Penney's staff, one in ten of the total. Employing the same technique of proposing that his adversary meet half-way the most extreme position put forward by his own side, Garner wrote: 'With the recent ruling that guided weapons are to have equal priority with atomic energy there are strong reasons for distributing the good-quality staff equally between the two projects . . . I suggest that approximately half the staff in question should be allocated to HER and half to ARE.'[12] Penney was never averse to raising the alarm over dangers to his timetable, but when he did so in this case he was scarcely crying wolf. The implications of losing fifteen senior scientists, including Challens, more than half-way through his project would be grave indeed. The HER staff was at that time about forty scientists under strength, but fortunately the vacancies were almost all in junior posts. Senior positions, as the search for a deputy to Penney had demonstrated, were the hardest to fill – it was no accident that all of Penney's senior staff, with the sole exception of Brooking, were ARE men who had been with him from the start. The disruption and sheer effort involved in finding fifteen people who were willing, qualified and available to replace those whom Garner wanted did not bear contemplation. Penney fought the matter to the highest level in the Ministry of Supply. In the end the Permanent Secretary had to sit in judgement, and he gave the verdict to Penney. Only five men were transferred from HER, Thornhill and four more junior figures. Challens, Pike, McEnhill, Marriott and the others remained to complete their task.

AFTER A FIVE-MONTH delay, Penney was at last able to create a new structure for the freestanding HER which would eventually have its own home at Aldermaston. The changes began at the top. His own title was now Chief Superintendent, High Explosive Research (CSHER), with Brooking as his Assistant Chief Superintendent. At Armament Research the next level down had been made up of eight or nine men, mostly in their fifties, who had been in place when Penney took over in 1946. They included Blackman, Highfield and the mathematician J. W. Maccoll. As HER grew in Woolwich and Fort Halstead, it had spread through their departments, but all of them continued to administer conventional armaments research as well. As Penney told Portal, these men 'worked to the limits of their ability to get HER going', but he now left all but a few behind at ARE.[13]

With him he took A. H. Davis, who oversaw such varied activities as mathematics and field trials and was to become the number three in HER. Davis was a popular administrator, if not a very dynamic one, who had come to ARE only in 1946. During the war he had done military work at the Road Research Laboratory, helping with, among other projects, the development of the bouncing bomb. He had a curious sideline: having devised his own mathematical form guide to horse-racing, he was said to earn an impressive £400 a year as a gambler. Another senior figure whom Penney chose was Leonard Tyte, a veteran of wartime rocketry who had been supervising, among other work, the development of electronic intruments to observe test explosions. After some hesitation Penney decided to take A. W. Hothersall with him to run the metallurgy division; he had tried and failed to persuade W. P. Grove, the director of the radio-isotope factory at Amersham, to take the job. Hothersall became seriously ill soon afterwards, so his contribution was curtailed and a trio of Percy Greatbatch, David Lewis and Graham Hopkin saw the work through. On the conventional explosive side, Penney considered placing the irascible Ernie Mott on a level with Tyte and Davis, but thought better of it. Explosives were for a time under Tyte's wing, but later Wilfred Smith was brought in from the Royal Aircraft Establishment to handle Mott and his teams. There were promotions as well for John Corner, John Challens and Roy Pilgrim. Engineering remained a problem, and for some time the division operated without a leader.

The arrangements remained fluid and a couple of names would be added, but this, broadly, was the team which led HER in the final drive to produce and test the weapon. For the first time, it was a team personally appointed and shaped by William Penney, and although there were others whom he had wanted but failed to capture, it was a team in which he had confidence and of which he was proud. Below these levels, the eternal problem of staff shortages remained, and in fact worsened. The split with ARE had claimed only a handful of direct casualties, but in the months that followed several more scientists were persuaded to join Poole's guided weapons work, usually by the promise of promotion. The prospect of moving to Aldermaston also prompted a few people to look elsewhere. HER's appetite for new staff was at last showing signs of diminishing, but these new factors helped to ensure that there were never fewer than thirty vacancies waiting to be filled. And finding the people for the jobs was, if anything, becoming more difficult. The change of mood in Whitehall during the year, which underlay the debate about priorities, seems to have affected Penney's ability to compete for scientists and engineers with other parts of the civil service. The figures certainly point to a falling-off of recruitment. In the period from early 1948, by which time his core staff was established, to mid-1950, when the priorities were altered, numbers in HER were growing, net of departures, by a rough average of seven scientists a month. Thereafter, the average was about three a month.

Penney was particularly irritated by his failure to attract staff from Harwell. In the space of a few weeks in the autumn, five AERE staff turned down job offers from HER, most of them carrying promotion and higher pay. In November Penney's patience snapped. He had hoped to hire a British scientist, N. F. Moody, who had been working at the Chalk River reactor in Canada, but at the last moment Moody opted to go to Harwell instead. Penney complained to Shell-Mex House: 'Harwell has I think been running with the hare and with the hounds, and have allowed Moody to see an opening which has far greater attraction than top secret weapon work.' He went on to explain: 'This incident sharply illustrates the serious position in which I find myself in staffing HER . . . When I try to fill these vacancies with high-class men I encounter every time the same reaction: that such men do not wish to work in the top secret atmosphere essential to HER . . . We are taking serious risks in our HER programme, and with our present staff we shall only succeed if we are exceptionally lucky.'[14] Moody eventually joined Penney's team, but the Harwell problem was never resolved. Only one scientist of standing, the radiochemist Frank Morgan, was to leave AERE for HER in this period. Such was Penney's desperation that at the end of 1950 he suggested to Cockcroft that half a dozen Canadian scientists might be invited to take up posts at Harwell, thus freeing some existing AERE staff to cross over to HER. To Portal he declared that his only options were 'inferior men or pressed men', and he preferred the latter.[15] But forced labour was never, as Cockcroft pointed out, a real possibility; men would resign rather than accept compulsory transfer to HER.

In more general terms, Penney became convinced that bureaucracy was almost as much of an obstacle to fuller staffing as the national labour shortage. The Civil Service Commission and other centralized bodies had complete control over the terms, methods and even the paperwork of recruitment, and HER operated merely as their client. Special efforts were made – HER took a quota of successful civil service examination candidates, and was allowed to head-hunt among final-year undergraduates – but with these long lines of communication, hiring could seem like a game of Chinese whispers. Some cases from Penney's files are illuminating. One A. Carter was interviewed and approved as suitable to fill an urgent vacancy in plutonium metallurgy. He worked in industry in the Midlands, earning a salary of £725. Despite representations from David Lewis, for whom Carter would have worked, he was offered £700, which he naturally refused. Another metallurgist, F. C. Gale, was interviewed on 9 May but the offer of appointment for some reason did not go out until 20 June, by which time he had taken another job. One schoolboy interviewed for a job as a lab assistant did not receive his offer until ten weeks later. In a time of labour shortage, such inefficiency was very often decisive in losing candidates who were able to pick and choose among employers.

When Penney looked back upon the year 1950, just as the Labour Party did on 1947, he undoubtedly saw a year of struggle, disillusionment and occasional despair, a true *Annus Horrendus*. Besides the agonies of the divorce from ARE, the battle to preserve the priority of the project and the uphill work of finding staff, he had other headaches. It was in the spring of 1950 that HER took over the site at Aldermaston and started the huge and intricate building works there. It was in the summer of 1950 that the search began for a place to test the weapon, if and when it was eventually completed. And it was in the autumn of 1950 that he undertook a complete redesign of the heart of the bomb. It is little wonder that when, at the turn of the year, he received the offer of a university chair, he could not bring himself to reject it out of hand.

8

Aldermaston

THE airfield at Aldermaston formally became a part of Penney's domain on 1 April 1950 (a date which caused some amusement), but such was the hurry to start the building work that the actual transfer took place a few days early. The site was not at its most alluring for the occasion, as one of those present has described: 'The bleak March wind, laden with rain, swept across Baughurst Common and hunted hungrily among the low, dispersed buildings of the airmen's quarters, ruffling the surfaces of the puddles, chasing the sodden leaves of long-discarded newspapers between the lines of huts; it whistled between warped jambs and around the edges of ill-fitting casements, plucking the damp, bedraggled pin-ups from the walls. Then it swooped across the road, swirled angrily among a clutter of sprawling spider-huts, howled under the eaves of four gigantic hangars, and at last broke free to drive clear over a triangular complication of wet runways and away to the far reaches of the site – and beyond – it scudded the ground with only a lone flying-control post to obstruct it.

'In a cold, bare office in one of the spiders, two men were checking lists, occasionally consulting maps taken from a single plan-chest, sometimes glancing out of the windows at the bulk of Hangar Three and the vast emptiness beyond it. Then one of them picked up a swollen canvas bag, they both left the office, climbed into a van standing in the mud outside, and together toured the site, visiting each despondent building, opening the creaking doors with keys from the canvas bag.

'When they returned to the office, the ceremony was over and the first permanently resident official of the Ministry of Works had taken over from the last official of the Ministry of Transport (Civil Aviation). The date was March 21st, 1950.[1]

The Ministry of Works had good reason to jump the gun, for there was already some doubt as to whether the construction task that lay ahead could be completed to schedule. Most of the work would be done by the construction firm W.E. Chivers, which was soon ready to move in a workforce previously employed at Harwell. In the interval before their arrival, the Ministry of Works Mobile Labour Force – a body originally formed in the London Blitz – got the job under way, converting existing buildings to house the labourers and in the process turning large areas into 'swamps reminiscent of Passchendaele'.[2] So tight was the schedule that Penney's chief engineer at the site, Colonel N. Wilson, bet the Ministry of Works a champagne party that the plutonium fabrication building, known as A1.1, would not be ready in time.

Three primary buildings were required urgently: A1.1; A6 to accommodate a health physics team, and A3, where work would be done on the initiator. If these were to function, a vast array of support facilities would also be needed. A1.1 could be no simple laboratory or production line, since plutonium is so highly toxic. Although it is radioactive, the alpha particles it emits are fairly easily contained; the main danger comes when the metal oxidizes, or rusts. This occurs rapidly in air and causes a fine powder to form which quickly becomes detached and spreads easily in air currents. Breathed in or swallowed, these particles lodge in the bones or soft organs and can cause serious injury or death. Working with such a substance is no easy matter.

The basic rule adopted was that the metal and all the equipment needed to work with it must be enclosed in a leak-proof environment. This was a 'glove box', a sealed miniature laboratory like a large fish tank with a perspex side pierced by two holes. Fixed into the holes were two gloves, each the length of an arm. The scientist slipped his hands into the gloves and worked on the materials inside the box without exposing himself to contamination. And the precautions could not end there. There must be means of moving equipment and materials in and out of the box; there must be measures to protect personnel in the event that a glove tears or a box breaks open; there must be ways of disposing of the contaminated materials; there must be facilities to examine or treat people who have been exposed to, or who have merely been exposed to the risk of being exposed to contamination. Besides these more exotic requirements, the usual services would also be needed: engineering workshops, drawing offices, chemical laboratories, storerooms, offices, canteens, lavatories and security arrangements. Aldermaston, it was calculated, would eventually have a staff of 1,300 who would need homes; negotiations were soon under way with local authorities to build 700 new houses in the area. The construction team had been given precisely two years to complete the first phase: A1.1, A3 and A6 and their attendant services. They were expected to hand over the keys by 1 April 1952, a date when, it was hoped, Windscale plutonium would be ready for use.

It was a job for an army, and an army is what arrived: 2,000 Poles, Scots and most of all Irishmen set up home on the site, creating a lively new community in the Berkshire countryside. 'On pay day the Tadley postmaster set up shop in the camp and men queued to send money to their families. However, there always seemed sufficient money left over to enliven the local pubs for a night or two each week. Somewhat to the dismay of the local population, their days were now disturbed by wild Irish poesy, their nights by gay Irish jollifications, and on every St. Patrick's night for years the whole camp was burnt down with solemn ritual. At least, that's what we are told.'[3]

It was not long before the locals got wind of the 'atomic devilries' planned in their midst. On 1 April the *Reading Mercury* told its readers the new establishment was to be concerned with atomic energy, and the news was quickly confirmed. That it was a weapons establishment, however, remained a secret. The *Berkshire Chronicle*, plainly repeating the official 'guidance', wrote on 7 April: 'It is understood that the Ministry of Supply intend to use the aerodrome mainly for stores for the increasing amount of equipment being assembled at the Harwell Atomic Energy Establishment.'[4] This may have been good enough elsewhere in the county, but it is hard to believe that Aldermaston folk, once they had seen the extraordinary intensity of the work, would have fallen for such a story.

By this time an Aldermaston Committee, with Penney in the chair, had been at work for six months. It was already clear that time was so short that many of the tasks which would be carried out at the new site when it was fully operational would have to be performed at Fort Halstead or Woolwich in the interim. Teams were quickly formed in 1949 and 1950 to study the challenges involved in producing the inner components of the weapon and to design the production facilities for Aldermaston. Disciplines were involved which were totally different from those required for the outer components. These included new branches of chemistry and chemical engineering, nuclear physics, radiology and medicine, and above all metallurgy.

Chief among the scientists now drawn into the HER project was Graham Hopkin, a genial, modest Welshman who took charge of the metallurgy team. Born in Swansea and a graduate of University College, Cardiff, Hopkin had joined ARD in 1930 at the age of twenty-one and had worked, with distinction, on a series of metallurgical problems relating to guns and armour. Although he had no experience of working with plutonium – no one in the country did – Penney gave him the job of overseeing the production of the inner components. On the chemistry side, Penney found a team leader in David Lewis, another Welshman in his early forties, this time a miner's son from Brynmawr and a graduate of Aberystwyth. Penney rated Lewis as the second-best scientist on his staff. Recommending him for a promotion in 1950, Penney wrote that he was indispensable. 'He works harder and faster than any other chemist in the establishment, and his staff are inspired by his example.'[5] A big, burly man and a natural rugby forward, he had been a teacher before the war brought him into armaments work. Now he was to tackle the chemical problems involved in dealing with the materials at the heart of the weapon.

If Lewis was the second-best scientist on Penney's staff, the best was John Corner, whom Penney had first encountered when he needed assistance in processing the data he had brought back from Hiroshima and Nagasaki. Educated at Newcastle Royal Grammar School and Cambridge, Corner had come to Fort Halstead in 1943 when Lennard-Jones, his Cambridge professor, was drafted in to shake the place up. He had attended the Woolwich library meeting, but until 1949 atomic weapons occupied only a portion of his time. From then on, he was drawn steadily in. As professionally rigorous as he was brilliant, he was held in awe by many in HER. Colleagues remember him sitting at meetings, apparently absorbed by his own papers but always ready, without looking up, to throw some trenchant observation into the discussion. Because of his initials he became known, even to Penney, as 'Christ'. But Penney was in no doubt about his value, writing in 1950, during the same round of appointments that involved Lewis: 'I regard it as most important that we lose no time in promoting Dr Corner . . . If we do this he will stay; but if we delay, he will almost certainly get a University Chair and we shall lose one of the half a dozen men on whom our whole Establishment depends.'[6]

The task before these men was to copy, as closely as possible, the bomb that had been dropped on Nagasaki. While Mott, Challens, Bean and the others concerned themselves with the outer parts, the new teams turned their minds to the components that occupied the pit at the centre of the high-explosive ball. As we have seen, there were three of these: the sphere of plutonium, about the size of a grapefruit and manufactured in two halves; the initiator, a device little bigger than a pea whose job was to release a spray of neutrons to ignite the chain reaction in the plutonium, and the tamper, a shell of natural uranium surrounding the core whose job was to reflect escaping neutrons back in, thus giving the chain reaction greater intensity and producing a bigger bang. Uranium had peculiar properties which made it effective in this role.

To take the last first, the tamper presented relatively few problems of fundamental science, or of handling, since natural uranium is not dangerously radioactive and may be machined in the open like more commonplace metals. The difficulties, it seemed at the outset, would be practical ones of fabrication, not unlike those encountered with the high-explosive components. The uranium, an exceptionally heavy metal with twice the density of steel, would have to be cast in very large pieces and then machined to the most demanding specifications. As with the high explosive, impurities and porosity must be kept to the absolute minimum. Vacuum furnaces were chosen for the casting, and again water-cooled moulds, while Woolwich had some German-made precision equipment capable of doing the machining. The metal itself would be available relatively early so there would be little time pressure; the challenge would be to produce castings of sufficiently high standard.

The initiator presented quite different difficulties. The device had to work as follows: a tiny quantity of polonium, a metal so radioactive that it glows blue in the dark, is wrapped in the stable element beryllium, and this 'Urchin', as it was known, sits at the very centre of the bomb assembly. At the moment of detonation, when the convergent wave crushes the core, the two metals in the Urchin mix. Polonium emits a constant spray of alpha particles, and when these strike beryllium they shatter the beryllium nuclei, releasing a further spray, this time of neutrons. When these neutrons burst into the plutonium they ignite the fission chain reaction. The trick of the initiator, then, is to provide a barrier between the two metals which separates them until the required moment, but when disrupted, unleashes the shower of neutrons.

Beryllium is a light metal, at that time little known in Britain, and dangerous to work with because its dust can cause a lung disease akin to pneumoconiosis. It had one virtue: since it had a variety of innocent uses it could be bought off the shelf in the United States without breaching those provisions of the McMahon Act which forbade the supply of nuclear materials to foreign countries. A Welsh metallurgist, Geoffrey Ellis, was assigned the task of developing the intricate techniques required to prepare and machine it to the desired shape, and he set to work at Woolwich. Polonium, which was discovered by the Curies and named after Marie Curie's native Poland, was not available off the shelf in the United States or anywhere else. What was more, little or nothing was known in Britain about polonium chemistry or about the techniques that had been employed at Los Alamos to fabricate it. It was thought at first that it had the ability to propel itself about the laboratory in fine particles independently of the movement of air, and this caused some alarm, but it transpired that this was true only of certain compounds. Harwell undertook the research needed to design a plant for polonium production at Windscale, but the fabrication would ultimately be done at Aldermaston.

Plutonium was the biggest worry. Hopkin and his team had only a sketchy notion of the techniques used to make the spheres at Los

Alamos, and what they knew suggested that it was not only highly toxic, but behaved in most peculiar ways – for example, in certain circumstances plutonium expands as it cools. Among those confronted with the job of mastering this material was Bill Lord, a Lancastrian who had been convinced he should join the scientific civil service after the war when, as a student at Cambridge, he heard C. P. Snow lecture on its attractions.

Lord started on the conventional side at Armament Research in 1949, working on projects concerned with the stress tolerances of certain metals. He wrote later: 'I became fairly well aware of the work going on in other parts of the Metallurgy Branch, partly by personal contact with the people involved, and also because of the lectures which were arranged from time to time when members of the staff were required to give an account of their current work. But I was also aware that there were some people on highly classified work, who came to the lectures but never gave any, and who did not chat about their work across the lunch table. I cannot now recall the processes whereby I got the information – certainly no one ever took me on one side and told me directly – but I came to realise that they were part of a team working towards a British atomic bomb.'[7] Before long Lord was invited to join that group and, attracted in part by the promise that he would ultimately have a low-rent house at Aldermaston, he accepted.

The metallurgists assumed that the plutonium hemispheres could be made by melting the metal in a crucible, casting it to roughly the right shape and then pressing it into the precise final form at temperature in a die. These were techniques with which they had experience, although with other metals. They soon learned, however, that none of these steps would be straightforward. Plutonium, it emerged, would react with all the materials they would normally expect to use in making the crucible. The search for a safe crucible was a case study in the inhibiting effects of the US McMahon Act: it was an area where the British Los Alamos team had had no experience, so now HER had to 'get it on their own hook', to use Truman's phrase. Luis Alvarez, an American friend and former colleague from the Manhattan Project, described an encounter with Penney in this period. They were having dinner and the Englishman, perhaps fishing for assistance, was airing his frustration: 'In particular, he had been unable to find out

133

what crucible material Los Alamos had used for the melting of plutonium, something he could have learned in five minutes in the Los Alamos library. Without this small piece of information, which until the end of the war had been legally his, he had been forced to squander half a dozen man-years of his best metallurgists' time, so far without result. Plutonium, a highly reactive metal when melted, dissolved or interacted with all the crucible ceramics the British had tried. My position was difficult, because I knew the answer but couldn't tell Bill . . . I had to play dumb. But I saw at first hand the advantage the Russians won by spying.'[8]

The plutonium itself was to be made in the reactors at Windscale and would not be available before the spring of 1952 at the earliest. For experimental purposes a small quantity, produced in the reactors at Chalk River in Canada, would be delivered late in 1951. Until then, however, all the metallurgists had to go on was Los Alamos hearsay, the predictions of the theoreticians and their own professional nous. The hearsay was useful, if limited. Lord wrote later: 'The information leaked from the American project was that plutonium melted at a fairly low temperature (which was good) but that the metal showed several different phases between its freezing point and room temperature, and these changes in structure were accompanied by large volume changes. Thus in practice it would be difficult to cast a piece of metal without getting internal flaws, and if hot-pressed there might be changes in size and shape as the piece cooled to room temperature.' They had one vital further piece of information: 'These problems could be avoided, however, by making a small addition of another metal to the melt to stabilize the high temperature phase right down to room temperature, thus avoiding large and discontinuous volume changes as the metal cooled.' This stabilizing element, they knew, must be gallium.

Leaks from America of the kind Lord describes were rare but had the potential to be extremely useful. They may have come from a variety of sources, such as diplomats and academics, and from industry, but one of the most important was the conversation at Penney's dinner-table at home in south London. He and his wife routinely entertained any of his American friends from Los Alamos who visited Britain and, as his conversation with Alvarez demonstrated, he was not above pumping them for information. He wrote in 1951 that 'on a purely personal basis' he had been doing this for five years 'and in spite of the McMahon Act, the benefit to our work has probably been worth five to ten percent of the total effort of my group'.[9]

The theoreticians at HER were required to determine the specifications for the core: the precise quantity and configuration of the plutonium which would give the best possible performance. Penney was anxious to avoid committing his team to a deep study of the nuclear physics of the core and of the mechanics of nuclear fission. He did not have the manpower for it, and he believed that just enough was known of the Los Alamos work in this field to get by, provided the design remained as close as possible to the Nagasaki model. He thus turned for a plutonium specification to Klaus Fuchs at Harwell, who obligingly supplied one as early as 1948, having doubtless extracted the data from his Los Alamos espionage notebooks.

From about the same date, John Corner and his colleague Herbert Pike set about recruiting bright young graduates at Fort Halstead who would develop techniques for predicting the performance of the bomb. At a time when desktop calculating machines were the standard equipment, reproducing the various aspects of the implosion process in mathematical form was an enormous undertaking. The first big calculation they did related to the convergent wave and excluded the nuclear aspects of implosion. Pike recalls: 'The calculations are not terribly difficult; you just have to do the same thing thousands of times . . . It took six months.' Not surprisingly, they showed a keen interest in the development of computers and Pike's team made some use of Britain's first, built by Ferranti at Manchester University. Corner ordered a similar machine for Fort Halstead, but it entered service too late to be of use with the prototype bomb design.

Safety was by now becoming an important consideration, both in the planning of Aldermaston and in the design of the bomb. With the high-explosive components it had been sufficient to rely on the tried and tested safety routines of ARE, but the radioactive components demanded something more. Happily there was a department at Woolwich with expertise: the radiological branch, whose principal work to date had been in X-rays. They had, for example, played a part in wartime bomb disposal, and for HER they had already done useful work X-raying the explosive lenses to search for flaws. The man in charge was David Barnes, yet another Welshman (it used to be said that HER could turn out a full cricket side of native Glamorganshire men). Tall, smartly dressed and mild of temperament, Barnes was given the job of establishing a health physics regime for Aldermaston. This would involve monitoring the atmosphere for contamination and protecting the staff against exposure to radiation. A whole range of equipment had to be designed and produced, and safety procedures laid down.

One aspect of this safety question was criticality. It was naturally of vital importance that the plutonium spheres, once made, should only begin to fission at the moment of detonation. There was a powerful fear that this mysterious metal might, in some circumstances, fission spontaneously. Penney had been particularly alarmed by two deaths that had occurred at Los Alamos in 1945 and 1946, in the course of criticality experiments. This was two too many, he told his staff, and there were going to be no such accidents in HER. Unfortunately the criticality data brought back from Los Alamos were too sparse to be reliable, so Penney asked Corner to do some work in this field, and placed Bill Moyce, hitherto a member of the phenomenology team, in charge of criticality experiments.

Moyce was informed of his new assignment by A. H. Davis, who explained to him that his task would be to design equipment to test whether the finished hemispheres of plutonium could be combined in the bomb assembly without spontaneous fission. 'There's nothing much in it', he recalls. 'You have to devise a counting system; you have to find a way of doing the assembly very slowly and monitoring the neutron output as it comes, and you have to have ways of quick release.' This last was needed to separate the hemispheres in case there were signs of incipient fission. 'It was something quite new, but it didn't worry me', says Moyce.

FOLLOWING ALL THESE developments with close attention was an RAF Wing Commander, John Rowlands, who had been assigned to HER in its earliest days to represent the interests of the service which would eventually be responsible for carrying and possibly using Britain's atomic bomb. Rowlands was no ordinary airman, having taken a degree in mathematical physics before the war and then served in a variety of technical posts with the RAF. Among these was a spell working on field trials of new bomb disposal equipment during which he won the George Cross for repeated acts of conspicuous courage, including on one occasion defusing bombs in the midst of a burning explosives dump. In the spring of 1947, when he was just beginning an assignment at the Royal Aircraft Establishment at Farnborough, Rowlands was called for an interview in Dizzy Davis's office in the Cage at Shell-Mex House. He was surprised when he learned what was on offer, but he had no hesitation in accepting. His brief was to advise Penney on the RAF's needs, to ensure that the weapon could be safely transported, stored and used, and to prepare the training procedures for the RAF personnel who would ultimately be handling the weapon. To do this effectively he was encouraged to play a full part in the design and development of the bomb, and this he did. Rowlands's RAF team, which grew to be a dozen strong, proved a very useful addition to HER's strength, so useful that Penney was prompted to inquire of Portal whether there was any chance of drafting in more teams of bright technical people from the other services. Perhaps, he suggested, the Navy might like to become involved, with a view to developing an atomic torpedo? He was told firmly that this was out of the question.

Rowlands naturally took a particular interest in the plans for weapon-loading. It was considered unsafe at this time for a bomber to take off with a complete, assembled weapon on board – the risk of an appalling accident was too great. All plans from the earliest days thus assumed that the plutonium core and the high-explosive sphere would be kept separate during take-off and that only when the plane was safely in the air would the core be inserted in the main assembly. The bomb dropped on Nagasaki had been assembled on the ground (there had been no time for more elaborate procedures) so there was no American experience to go on, but it seemed logical that loading could be done by a cartridge method. A cylindrical plug, rather like the plug made by an apple corer, would be created, running from the outer surface of the sphere to the centre, with the plutonium on the end. Once the bomber was airborne, the crew would, by remote control, slide this plug horizontally into a matching hole in the side of the weapon and then seal the casing.

In this way, the implosion bomb assembly would be completed, ready for dropping.

Rowlands and his team investigated this idea closely, and in the spring of 1950 they reported to Penney that they had identified a problem. As the plutonium slid into the assembly, there was a risk that it might become supercritical because of the physical effects of passing through a mass of high explosive. They could not calculate the risk precisely since the characteristics of plutonium were still a matter of speculation, but they argued strongly that the risk was too great to be acceptable. Penney, when he looked into it, was forced to agree. Various solutions suggested themselves but all required a substantial increase in weapon weight or loading space, neither of which was possible. Through the summer, the period when he was so heavily involved in the separation of ARE and HER and in the Whitehall wrangling over the priority of the bomb project, this problem hung over him. Eventually, he made a fateful decision. The only way around the loading difficulty was to change the design of the core of the weapon itself. They would have to depart from the American model.

This was something he had ardently hoped to avoid. The logic of adhering to the Nagasaki design as closely as possible was unanswerable. Penney's own practical experience, and that of the other Los Alamos veterans, had been with this design. It had been tested at Alamogordo, dropped on Nagasaki and tested again at Bikini; it was demonstrably a design which worked. Britain, Penney had thought, did not have the resources for experimentation and could not risk producing a faulty design; it must stick with what was tried and tested. John Corner has summarized this view, which had become something of a motto at Fort Halstead: 'The atomic weapon was such and such and no change could be risked lest the weapon were then to fail.' Now the RAF team had shown that this was not an option and that the Nagasaki model was simply not suitable for a service weapon. Doubtless the Americans themselves had confronted and conquered this problem since 1946, but there was no way of knowing how. Like it or not, the British would have to experiment.

It was not a complete leap in the dark, for they had one piece of theoretical work to go on. This was the paper written by Klaus Fuchs. In 1948 and 1949, as we have seen, Fuchs had supplied to

HER various summaries of theoretical discussions in which he had taken part at Los Alamos. Among these summaries ('written for ourselves, as we thought', as Corner puts it) was one which examined the virtues and drawbacks of different possible layouts of the plutonium inside the implosion bomb. Corner and his staff noted it and filed it away. 'A subject for another era, we thought, but in fact we were to need this very soon, and in a great hurry.'

In September 1950 Penney came up with a new design for the heart of the weapon which removed the risk of criticality that had been identified by Rowlands and his team. Corner and Pike, however, did not like it. Consulting the Fuchs paper, which gave estimates of the different explosive yields to be expected from different designs, they concluded that Penney's proposed arrangement would mean a considerably weaker bomb. Corner recalls: 'In this situation it seemed essential for us to predict to Dr Penney the yields to be expected from (a) the Alamogordo-Bikini bombs, (b) the new British design, and (c) a version preferred by Pike and me, resting on Fuchs having a good memory. As each complete calculation, done on desk machines, would take several months, it deserved our very best attention. For this reason we roped in even our Cambridge graduates, whose robust self-confidence would stand up to a grilling by any top brass. By July 1951 it became clear that we were producing essentially correct results for the Alamogordo-Bikini bombs. Version (b) cut the yield by a factor of five, while (c) gave a yield thirty per cent up on (a). Therefore Penney moved to design (c). From now on it was too late for changes.'

In other words, thanks to the Fuchs document and the hard work and intuition of the mathematics team, a design had been identified which would not only solve the loading problem but would probably produce a bigger explosion. It had one drawback: it was more sensitive to flaws in the convergent wave. This was unwelcome news for those who were working on detonation and the high explosives, since they now came under even greater pressure to meet the highest specifications.

Even forty years later the precise design chosen by the British team in 1951 has not been revealed. It may have involved a combination of several possible departures from the Nagasaki model, affecting among other things the size and isotopic composition of the plutonium sphere and the working of the initiator. One of the changes which we know occurred involved the tamper. The Nagasaki weapon, Fat Man, was solid all the way through. The plutonium rested snugly in the tamper like the stone of an avocado in the flesh, and the tamper in turn sat equally neatly in the supercharge. In the new British design the uranium tamper still rested in the supercharge, but it was no longer a heavy mass. Instead, it was a shell no more than three-quarters of an inch thick. Between the tamper and the plutonium was a gap of about two inches, which was left empty. The advantage of this was simple: it is like the difference between pushing a nail into a wall and knocking it in with a hammer. The latter is more effective. In the implosion weapon the objective is to compress the plutonium with as much force as possible, and thumping could clearly do this more effectively than pushing. By leaving a gap between the tamper and the plutonium, the former was allowed to hit the latter just as the swinging hammer does the nail.

This new arrangement had an obvious drawback. How was the plutonium to be suspended inside the tamper without perturbing the spherically convergent implosion wave, which so much care had been taken to create? The answer was a special metal fitting which became known as the 'gauntlet'. The plutonium core was to be placed in the gauntlet, which was screwed on to the end of the loading cartridge. This then slid into the heart of the assembly to complete the bomb.

BY THE TIME the core design had been settled, in mid-1951, the construction of Aldermaston was well advanced. Among the bigger projects involved was a pipeline to take effluent to the Thames from the treatment facilities associated with A1.1, a distance of twelve and a half miles. A special workforce 150 strong was recruited for the task, which meant cutting trenches, burying and setting in concrete two all-welded steel pipes. One of the frogmen who investigated the bed of the Thames at Pangbourne, where the pipe was to discharge, was Lionel 'Buster' Crabb, who was to disappear in mysterious circumstances in Portsmouth harbour six years later. On the Aldermaston site itself, work proceeded rapidly. The account written twenty-one years later recalls: 'As the shells of the buildings went up, the plant came in: the lorries followed each other in so quickly that some gangs were employed solely on unloading them, while others moved the plant to the buildings and yet others installed it. And when the carcass of A1.1 was complete the lorries queued up all day and all night, while three hundred and fifty men were put on night shift and MoW [Ministry of Works] Clerks of Works took station on stands like traffic policemen or orchestra conductors, each responsible for the work within his immediate range of vision.'[10] From October 1951, the work simply never stopped.

James 'Jimmy' Hole, a member of David Barnes's health physics team, was one of the first scientists on the scene and recalls the buildings rising from a landscape of mud, with a throng of Irishmen and Poles milling around amongst them. Hole, a Londoner who had joined ARD in 1933 after taking an external degree through evening classes, had not at first wanted to move to the new location. 'I thought, "I'm not going down to Aldermaston. I'm going to watch Charlton Athletic on a Saturday, and maybe the odd Arsenal game. I've got my local pub and my mates, and my girlfriend."' In the end he was sent down at a week's notice and lodged in a hostel near the site. 'After about ten days Miss Anderson contacted me and said they had a house for me, close to the site because it was felt I should be close by for safety reasons. Doris [his girlfriend was by now his wife] was still up in London in a flat, so a house seemed heaven-sent. There were arguments galore, but we came down.'

Hole was among a team of people working on the safety installations for A1.1. Among these was an elaborate ventilation and filtration system, since air-flows through much of the building were to be carefully controlled. Inside the glove boxes, where the plutonium would be worked on, was to be an atmosphere of the inert gas, argon. Outside it, the air pressure in the laboratory, relative to the pressure in the box, was carefully regulated so that, if a glove tore or a box broke open, the rush of air would carry the contamination away from any personnel who were present. Hole, who spent many hours establishing the air-flow rates in various parts of A1.1, recalls working one night with Colonel Wilson when their anemometer, used to measure speed of air movement, broke down. Wilson suggested that they give up but Hole wanted to press on. 'I've got an idea', he said at length. 'If you were to stand here with a lighted cigarette and I stand at the other end, we could measure the time it takes for the leading edge of the smoke to go through the tunnel.' After a little experimentation, they found that it gave pretty good results, so the work did not stop. 'And we were both able to have a cigarette at the same time.'

All of this did not proceed without involving Penney in some further Whitehall unpleasantness. His management methods at HER had been criticized by some in Portal's Cage before. 'There is no planned chart for the job as a whole nor any part of the job as far as is known', it was said in 1949, and the organization had an 'ostrich-like attitude' to some of its responsibilities.[11] Penney managed on that occasion to put Portal's mind at rest, but when Aldermaston came along the attacks were renewed. There were complaints about 'the conspicuous absence of planning on both the technical and administrative sides of building up a new establishment', while the chief architect of the Ministry of Works declared intemperately that the whole scheme 'was enveloped in a fog'.[12] Hinton, the master of the big engineering project, eventually visited the site and, *de haut en bas*, offered his opinion. He was full of praise for the 'magnificent' work of the HER team.[13] Appreciable savings might indeed have been made, but given the lack of experience in HER and the shortage of engineers, this level of waste was quite understandable, he said.

For Penney all this must have been vexing. Although Brooking had joined in 1950 and was working effectively, so great was the workload at HER that it is remarkable, indeed astonishing, what was achieved. Penney was a man accustomed to making light of his burdens, but at times the strain must have seemed almost intolerable. It was not as though he was well paid: from 1946 to 1949 he earned a steady £1,900 per annum, roughly twice the pay of a chief draughtsman and substantially less than either Cockcroft or Hinton. Only in 1950 did things improve, and by 1952 he was earning a more respectable £3,400 (Cockcroft and Hinton were by then on £4,500). Bearing in mind his reservations about taking the job in the first place, it would be little wonder if he permitted himself the odd moment of rage and despair.

In mid-1951 he received yet another offer of a university chair and he went so far as to advise the Ministry of Supply that he was considering the move. 'Dr Penney informed me a few days ago', wrote a concerned official, 'that he will have to make up his mind very soon about his future with this Ministry. If he accepts an offer on which he has been sounded unofficially the very latest date by which he would have to have left his present work would be the end of 1952.'[14] It must have been all the more tempting because by that date his primary assignment, the building of a prototype bomb, would probably be complete. The ministry's response to the threat included a confirmation that Penney would have a good-sized house on the site at Aldermaston – up to £9,000 was set aside to pay for it. Penney ultimately decided against the move back to university life, but the Aldermaston house went on to become a *cause célèbre*, as the Ministry of Works tried to have the budget reduced to below £8,000. Ministers had to be consulted before the matter was settled, broadly in his favour.

AT THE END of 1951 the metallurgists were at last given the opportunity to test their plans for working with plutonium, when the first substantial sample of the metal arrived from Chalk River in Canada. Since the hot labs at Aldermaston were not ready, the work was done at Harwell, where Bill Lord and a few colleagues set up a glove box full of equipment. The team included two of the pillars of Woolwich metallurgy, Arthur Knight and Richard 'Guv' Willows. Both northerners and in their fifties, they presented in other respects a striking contrast. Knight was a non-smoking, teetotal, devout Methodist, mild in manner and speech and with a back straight as a ramrod. Willows was tough, scruffy and capable of bringing a meeting to a halt with a burst of expletives. 'You can't bring Guv Willows anywhere', one of his superiors once remarked, 'because he'll open his mouth and tell the truth. But he's the best non-ferrous metallurgist in the UK.'[15] Though highly regarded at HER, this pair of veterans did not fit in as lodgers at Harwell, where the younger scientists dismissed them as old-school 'heating and beating' men.

Some urgency attached to the experiments, for if the results showed up any faults in the fabrication methods there would not be much time to make adjustments at Aldermaston. The plutonium sample was in an aluminium container with a screw cap. Lord, anxious to start, pushed his arms into the gloves and opened it up. Inside was a greyish lump, the size and shape of a fried egg.

143

Lord recalls that he was anxious to 'get on', not only because of the demands of the HER programme, but also because he knew Harwell's metallurgists had their own sample and he wanted to produce results first. The plan was to melt, cast and press the sample just as the final cores would be, and at the same time to monitor the cooling of the metal and study the changes it underwent. Lord and an engineer, Frank Roberts, prepared the equipment and set everything up for Willows, the experienced man who was to do the actual casting. He was due to come down by train from London and be collected at Didcot by a Harwell car. Roberts and Lord switched on the furnace in advance so that it would be fully heated by the time he arrived. He was late, so they started to melt the plutonium. As they waited, Lord was alarmed to see a dull skin forming on the molten metal, probably the result of impurities in the argon atmosphere. This could not be allowed to go on too long, but Willows was still nowhere to be seen. 'I realised that there was only one thing to do', recalls Lord. 'I would have to make the cast. I had never ever cast metal before; my mind went back to an occasion in my childhood when I had tried to persuade my mother to buy me a kit for casting lead soldiers, and she refused.' He thrust his hands back in the gloves and started work. Before long, he and Roberts were able to switch off the furnace and sit back to watch two small castings cool. 'I reflected, I must be the only metallurgist in the whole world who has never cast any other metal but plutonium.' Just as they broke the samples out of the moulds, Willows thundered into view. 'Bloody train didn't stop at Didcot', he announced. 'Had to get a taxi from Swindon.'

This was the start of several weeks of tests and experiments, often running in shifts through the night, which allowed the team to become familiar with the ways of plutonium. Lord was able to study – before the Harwell metallurgists – the phases through which the metal passed as its temperature changed, and this allowed them to fix the amount of gallium that would be needed to produce a stable alloy. By the spring of 1952, when A1.1 building at Aldermaston was handed over and the Ministry of Works earned its champagne party, Hopkin's department was ready to make the core.

9
Trial

IF there was to be a bomb, there would have to be a bomb
test. This was a certainty from the day that High Explosive
Research came into being. The design of the weapon might at
the outset have been as close as possible to the Nagasaki model,
but even then the only way to be sure it would work was to blow
it up. As the design moved farther and farther away from that
model a full-scale trial explosion became ever more vital. There
were, in any case, other reasons for conducting a test than merely
to prove that the bomb would go off. The scientists wanted to
measure the performance of the individual components, to see
how efficiently the precious plutonium was used (at Nagasaki only
twenty-six per cent of the plutonium was consumed in the fission
process before the bomb blew itself asunder) and to establish the
explosive yield. Then there were the effects: for purposes of defence
as much as attack, planners needed to know about the results of
atomic explosions. How far would the shock waves travel? What
were the characteristics of the radiation that followed? What kinds
of buildings, or military vehicles, might survive an attack? What
difference did it make if a bomb was detonated on the ground, or
in the sea, rather than high in the air as in the attacks on Japan?
Only a test could provide reliable answers.

By 1948 the Americans had accumulated the experience of eight
atomic explosions: the wartime Trinity Test at Alamogordo, the
two in Japan, whose consequences they continued to measure; two

more tests at Bikini in 1946 and then a series of three in 1948 on the atoll of Eniwetok, also in the Marshall Islands. Penney had personally gathered and analysed huge amounts of data from the first five of these explosions and he knew better than anyone the value of such experience. Britain's first atomic test would not only be a trial of its bomb design; it would be a valuable lesson for British civil defence and a springboard to further weapon development.

In HER's first two years little thought was given to this matter, but during the summer of 1949, due probably to the influence of Dizzy Davis, a paper was submitted to the Chiefs of Staff asking for guidance on 'the nature of the trials, the information we should try to get from them and a suitable site for their conduct'.[1] The Chiefs of Staff referred the paper to their Sub-Committee on the Strategic Aspects of Atomic Energy, another body chaired by Sir Henry Tizard. The months that followed were the period of greatest optimism about co-operation with the United States and there seemed little point in worrying about test planning while a virtual merger of weapons research was on the cards. For the foreseeable future, it seemed, all bombs would be made in the US, and would be tested at American sites as well. After the Fuchs affair, and perhaps because Tizard was busy trying to push the atomic bomb programme down the priority ladder, the committee failed to tackle the question of a British trial. There was no real push for action until June 1950, when Davis wrote to the Chiefs of Staff saying: 'It is now necessary to initiate action in order to be ready in time for the test of our prototype model.'[2]

The questions remained the same as in 1949: what sort of test, and where? For the first, there were three options. The simplest was to explode the bomb on a tower, as in the Trinity test. It could also be detonated at sea, either on the surface or, as in the second Bikini test, beneath it. Or it could be dropped from a plane, as in the first Bikini test. This last option was not available to Britain since the device to be tested would be a prototype, without the ballistic case and the fusing needed for an 'air-burst'. As to a site for the trial, that would depend in part on which kind of test was chosen, but certain things were clear. The site had to be remote, either in a desert or at an island far removed from civilization. It was obvious that no location in Britain could possibly be used, so the test would have to be overseas. In 1949 Penney and Davis had listed the candidates: Australia, South Africa, Canada and the United States. Southern Rhodesia and Somaliland were also suggested, but were quickly ruled out. In South Africa, where the new National Party government was rather less friendly towards Britain than its United Party predecessor, the political situation seemed unfavourable. It looked like Australia, Canada or the United States.

In July 1950, almost by accident, the committee provided an answer to the first question: what kind of test? The members, who included Penney and senior representatives from the services and from interested government departments, discussed a report by the Joint Intelligence Committee on the possible clandestine use of atomic weapons. Robert Cockburn of the Air Ministry – the man who conceived the gamma-ray gun project in which Fuchs had been involved – observed that Britain was especially vulnerable to attack at its ports. Any merchant ship might sail into a British harbour with an atomic bomb concealed in its hold; the device could be detonated by time fuse or radio, and the result would be devastating. There was a short discussion and then Tizard moved the meeting on to the next item on the agenda, which was the British atomic test. Penney picked up Cockburn's remarks and pointed out that little technical information was available on the effects of an explosion in a harbour. He then suggested that the British test could be organized in such a way as to provide precisely that sort of data. He suggested two sites: the US trials base at Eniwetok and Fort Churchill in Canada, a military research station on the shore of Hudson Bay. In the discussion that followed the idea found favour, although the committee members thought a site in Australia would be preferable. The naval representative was duly asked to find an island off the Australian coast where a bomb could be detonated in a ship anchored in shallow water close to land, and the results observed and measured. The other options, in the meantime, would be investigated; Penney consulted the Canadian Defence Research Board about Fort Churchill while the Foreign Office approached the Americans about the possibility of using Eniwetok.

If the idea of simulating an attack of this kind on a harbour appears, after the passage of the years, to be nothing less than absurd, this may be only because such an attack never happened. In 1950 almost anything seemed possible and Britain's seaports, still so vital to the economy, to the Empire and to the Navy, appeared to be a genuine Achilles heel. Soviet shipping came and went occasionally in British ports, as did vessels from the growing number of countries friendly to Moscow. Any one of these, or even a chartered vessel from a Western country, might be used to carry a bomb. These were the thoughts that lay behind the committee's deliberations. No doubt Penney agreed, but when he embraced the idea so whole-heartedly, it was not the civil defence implications which excited him but the science, for in his eyes it represented an opportunity to explore a phenomenon he had observed at Bikini and worried about ever since: base surge.

Penney was convinced that this surge of air, laden with poisonous radioactive droplets and pushed out over the ground by the collapse of the mushroom cloud, would amplify considerably the ability of an atomic weapon to cause injury and death. 'Base surge is one of the most terrifying features of an explosion of an atomic bomb in water', he wrote.[3] Cockcroft agreed, writing in 1948: 'We have inadequate information on the degree of contamination by fission products resulting from the "base surge" from a water burst.'[4] Much of the experimental work done by Penney's phenomenology team at Fort Halstead was devoted to understanding this problem. John McEnhill, Bill Moyce and others spent many months setting off explosions in tanks of water and other fluids and developing techniques to observe what happened. Penney, who loved scale-model experiments of this type, took a lively interest and wrote an introduction to a series of papers by his team which was published subsequently by the Royal Society. It was with considerable reluctance that he had wound up the project to free the staff for more urgent work. Now he was presented with an opportunity to stage and observe at full scale exactly the kind of explosion in which the base surge was thought to be most deadly. If an atom bomb were detonated on a ship in the Port of London, or Liverpool, or New York, would the deadly fission products be sprayed over a vast area, condemning to death many thousands more than would be killed by an air burst? Here was a chance to discover the answer, and it might even be an answer that could be traded with the Americans, who had not yet carried out such an experiment.

The Navy, meanwhile, was sifting through its Australian charts looking for a site. The requirement was clear: an uninhabited island in water that was shallow but not too shallow to bring a ship fairly close to shore. The island had to be large enough to permit extensive measurements to be made within a ten-mile radius, and it had to offer vantage points for scientific observation. Finally, the prevailing winds had to take the cloud away from any populated areas without blowing it directly over important shipping lanes. Virtually every island or island group around the Australian coast was assessed, including Groote Eyland in the Gulf of Carpentaria and the Houtman Rocks off the west coast, but on 2 August the Admiralty produced a recommendation: the Monte Bello Islands. They were deserted and extremely remote from any large towns; the wind pattern at certain times of year was likely to be suitable and there was a channel close to shore of sufficient depth to accommodate a small ship.

Penney remained keen on Canada, which had clear diplomatic advantages over Australia. Since the days of the Manhattan Project the Canadians had been partners with Britain and the United States in the atomic field and they remained members of the tripartite committee regulating the use of the joint uranium stockpile (most of which came from the Belgian Congo). To conduct the test in Canada would be seen in Washington as keeping the atomic business within the 'club'; to conduct it in Australia might be construed as a departure from the three-cornered partnership and a security risk. Penney was also looking for a trial site with long-term possibilities where he might carry out a whole series of trial explosions, and it was not clear the Monte Bellos had that potential. In August he went to Canada to view four sites, telling Portal before he left: 'I am still afraid that the objections against Australia may prove insurmountable.'[5]

Whatever Penney's doubts, Davis and Portal wanted quick action to establish at the very least whether the Monte Bellos were truly suitable and whether the Australians would agree to a test there. In fact, Portal was already beginning to think that Australia was the only possibility. As he told the Chiefs of Staff, the bomb was now expected to be ready between July and October 1952, a season when Eniwetok, for climatic reasons, could not be used. An Australian site, moreover, had the advantage that a test there could be paid for in sterling, and not scarce dollars. 'Finally,' he wrote, 'the ability to carry out our trial independently of American facilities may strengthen our position *vis-à-vis* the U. S. and so enable our friends there to make a better case for collaboration.'[6] The matter was referred to Attlee, who agreed to approach the Australian prime minister, Robert Menzies, but who also insisted on a fresh approach to the United States. The Americans, who had accelerated their own programme following the Soviet Joe One test a year earlier, were by now planning their most intensive programme of trials – sixteen explosions in the year 1951 alone, some at Eniwetok and the rest at a new desert site in Nevada. It was October before they responded, and then the answer was no.

So it was that on 15 September 1950 a communication arrived at the British High Commission in Canberra. It was the first of a series over the next few weeks which bore the codename 'Epicure', and it had an ominous preface. 'This message', it said, 'deals with a matter of such secrecy that special security precautions should be taken in your office for dealing with it.'[7] It was a personal letter from Attlee which was to be passed to Menzies. In it, Attlee spelled out the British position over the test. An approach had been made to the Americans but the outlook was not good. If the position changed and a US firing range were offered, that would represent the best use of resources. However, time was now pressing and an alternative arrangement was required. British experts had identified a few possible sites around the world, one of which was the Monte Bello Islands. Would the Australian government agree in principle to a test taking place on its soil, and would it allow, and provide support for, a detailed study of the islands to confirm their suitability?

Of all Commonwealth leaders, none was more certain to agree to these requests than Robert Menzies. He was, he used to say, British to his bootstraps, passionately devoted to the old country and all it stood for. He was also a fervent anti-Communist and an enthusiast for the atomic bomb, which he described as 'an instrument of peace'.[8] Without hesitation, and apparently without consulting his Cabinet colleagues, he gave his blessing. From that moment, events moved with remarkable speed. No other option in the Commonwealth was pursued, as the Canadian sites were deemed unsuitable – at Fort Churchill, the most promising, it would have been impossible to bring a ship close enough to shore for the kind of test now envisaged, and the climate did not suit a test that might come as late in the year as October. So the peace of the Monte Bello Islands was now well and truly broken. In the ensuing months they were surveyed and re-surveyed, charted and re-charted before the engineers moved in to scatter jetties, roads and buildings across the landscape. Long before the bomb itself arrived, the Monte Bellos were desert islands no more.

REMOTE AND BARREN as they were before this invasion occurred, the islands were not entirely without history. Indeed, they had been a matter of concern in London and elsewhere on more than one occasion in the past, and Dizzy Davis's Epicure survey was not the first expedition from half-way round the world to have scrutinized them. The very charts that had brought the islands to the attention of the experts at the Admiralty were the fruit of a previous British mission of exploration in the year 1840. The strange names of the islands – Hermite, Trimouille and the incongruous Monte Bello – were the calling cards of other visitors, from France, in 1801. But before either of those, the islands provided the occasion for a remarkable lie, a lie told by a desperate man as long ago as 1622.

The man was John Brooke, who in that year was master of the *Trial*, an East Indiaman from Plymouth bound for Java with a full cargo and a crew of 142. After taking on provisions at the Cape of Good Hope, they headed east on 19 March. Brooke's account of the journey records that it was 1 May before they sighted land, a region 'formelie seen by the Flemings'.[9] This was close to North-West Cape, a corner of the Australian continent which had indeed been previously noted by Dutch mariners. This sighting has a place in history, for it is the first recorded occasion on which Englishmen laid eyes on Australia, but it is not for this that the *Trial*'s journey is primarily remembered. From North-West Cape they steered north-east, 'thinking to fall with the wester part of Java'.[10] This they were never to do, for on the night of 25 May, at 11 p.m., the ship struck rocks.

Brooke's account of the wreck makes much of the amazement of his crew that they should have hit rocks in such a place. There was, he says, 'faire weather and smoothe watter', and the men could see 'neither breach, land, rocks, chainge of watter nor signe of dainger'.[11] But rocks there were and for five hours in darkness, with the wind picking up, they struggled to save the *Trial*. It was not to be. A longboat and a skiff – the lifeboats – were put out and Brooke writes of trying to save as many lives as he could. At 5.30 a.m., after what can only have been a hellish night, the ship broke up and Brooke made for Java with nine men in the skiff. Thomas Bright had command of the longboat with thirty-six on board, and his description of their separate journey also survives. At dawn they sighted an island, five leagues at most to the south-east. There they put ashore and spent seven days preparing themselves for the journey to Java. Bright wrote of the place: 'Not any inhabitants thereon. We travelled over all the iland seeing nothing but ilands, some small, some greatt, breaches and shoules every way as farr as wee could see.'[12] This was almost certainly Hermite Island, and Bright and his companions were thus the first Europeans to walk on the Monte Bellos.

Both boats eventually reached civilization in Java, and from there Captain Brooke reported to his masters in England the existence of a hidden reef of rocks, for which he gave a longitude and latitude. These were noted and promptly given wide circulation, for nothing concerns a sailor so much as the possibility of a wreck of the kind suffered by the *Trial*, a disaster in 'faire weather and smoothe watter'. In the seventeenth and eighteenth centuries, before the southern seas were charted, it was customary for captains to carry with them – as Brooke had done – written accounts of earlier voyages to serve as guidance. The story of the *Trial* entered this cabin literature and the early maps of those seas conscientiously recorded the presence, off north-west Australia, of the 'Tryal Rocks'.

It was many years before it became clear that something about the *Trial* story was not quite right. Dozens of ships, including ships of the Royal Navy, lingered in the waters indicated by Brooke in the hope of establishing a definitive location for the perilous Tryal Rocks. Sightings were made, but were just as soon cast in doubt. Captains and geographers began to wonder whether the rocks existed at all. In the first years of the nineteenth century, with the mystery still unresolved, the Monte Bellos received their name. On a voyage to investigate the possibility of French involvement in opening up the new southern continent, the explorer Nicolas Baudin recorded the existence of the islands and their relation to the mainland. The historian of the venture wrote that three islands were seen, the largest being scarcely three leagues in length and all of them 'low-lying and barren'.[13] The names may well have been plucked from a current edition of the peerage list. Montebello, appropriately, was the most distinguished, for this was the name taken by Marshal Lannes, one of Napoleon's most heroic commanders, upon being made a duke – the Italian Alpine village of Montebello had been the site of one of his victories. Hermite Island has no connection with any hermit but is *l'Île l'Hermite*, apparently named for an admiral, Jean l'Hermite, who had been created a baron by Napoleon. Trimouille is an ancient if unremarkable French noble family owing its name to a small town in the department of Vienne. Why Baudin's third island received no French name we do not know.

Apart from supplying names, the French provided a valuable clue to the mystery of the Tryal Rocks, for the record of their voyage noted that to the north-west of the island group extended a long reef. 'The sea broke there with extreme fury', it said.[14] Could this have been the shipwreck site? Perhaps, but it did not match Brooke's longitude and latitude. In 1822 the Royal Navy went to have a look. Phillip Parker King visited the scene in HMS *Mermaid* and concluded that the Monte Bellos 'and the numerous reefs around them, are the identical Tryal Rocks'.[15] But the matter was still not closed, the opinionated King having sowed almost as much confusion as he thought he had cleared up, and the Admiralty in 1840 despatched HMS *Beagle* to chart the whole region. This was the same *Beagle* which a few years earlier had carried Charles Darwin on his historic voyage of biological discovery. Now, under Commander J. Lort Stokes, it was to visit, chart and describe the coasts of northern and western Australia. On the last day of August 1840 the *Beagle* duly dropped anchor off the eastern shore of Trimouille Island, 'a cliffy islet', and set down a surveying team under Mr L. R. Fitzmaurice in a small boat before proceeding southward to examine Barrow Island nearby.[16] A few days later the *Beagle* returned and, according to Stokes's memoir, 'Mr Fitzmaurice joined us, having completed the examination of the Monte Bello group, a large proportion of chart material in a very short space of time, considering the number of small islands . . .'[17]

That was not quite the end of the visit, for Stokes and some companions decided to go ashore to enjoy an evening of unusual sport. 'We found that Trimouille was as scantily supplied with vegetation as Barrow's Island; in one or two places was growing a stunted kind of wood, sufficient for fuel for a small sized ship; but .there was no sign of water. The wallaby, which were very numerous, must have got their supply of moisture from the copious dews. They were found lying very close in the wiry prickly grass, allowing us to kick them out, when they went off at speed, affording excellent sport quite equal to any rabbit shooting; among three guns we managed, in a couple of hours, to bag nearly twenty. It was quite a new class of wallaby and has been classed . . . as Lagorchester Conspicillata.' The wallabies were to have a small revenge, for when Stokes and company returned to the *Beagle* with their bag, they found that 'the flesh was by no means good to eat, tasting very strong; this was the only instance in which we found wallaby at all impalatable'.[18] It was Fitzmaurice's charts which were pulled out of the Admiralty files when the islands came under scrutiny in July 1950 and were then employed by Dizzy Davis's survey team. Fitzmaurice had, we know, been somewhat rushed in his work, but after 110 years his survey was found to be accurate, if sketchy.

The Tryal Rocks were by now firmly wedded to the Monte Bellos, but the location of the shipwreck remained a mystery. Two sites continued to crop up in maps: one to the south-west of Hermite and one to the north-west. It was only in 1969, when divers discovered the remains of a wreck off the reef in the north-west, that the answer came. No conclusive proof was found that it was the remains of John Brooke's ship, but the circumstantial evidence was compelling and it was at last possible to say what had been suspected for centuries. Brooke lied about the location of the rocks which claimed his ship. He lied in order to cover up his own incompetence, for he had been on the wrong course, in defiance of company orders. His deception, which caused such confusion for mariners and map-makers for so long, enabled him to escape the blame for ninety-seven terrible deaths and to resume his career as a sea captain. Three years later, however, disgrace caught up with him after he lost another ship, the *Moone*, in the Straits of Dover.

The British visitors of 1950 were probably unaware of this murky first chapter of the islands' history, but they could not have failed to know a little of the second chapter. By the end of the nineteenth century the Monte Bellos had an important role in a pearling industry which for a few decades turned the whole north-west coast of Australia into a playground for fortune-seekers and rogues. Shallow-water pearling began in northern Australia not long after Stokes's visit to the region in the *Beagle*, but it was not until Edward Chippendall, an adventurer with a colourful past and grand ambitions, turned up in 1884 that the Monte Bellos became important. Pearling, it should be said, was mainly a matter of gathering shells for mother-of-pearl, a highly-prized commodity in the days before plastics and modern ceramics, and if stones turned up in the shells it was viewed as a welcome bonus. Chippendall, with two large ships and four dozen divers, intended to become rich by raising shells on an industrial scale. He was the first to try the Monte Bellos, where the water was deeper and colder than had previously been dived, and he found there everything he had hoped for. The shells were big – just 380 of them made a ton – and to cap it all, in his first season a shell was opened and found to contain the biggest pearl discovered to date on the whole coast.

From then until the Second World War pearlers were busy around the Monte Bellos, and two settlements of sorts were established. Chippendall and his companion, Thomas Haynes, sank a well on Hermite and made a permanent base where Haynes experimented with oyster cultivation and in his spare time gathered samples of the flora and fauna, packaging them up and sending them off to the British Museum. Eventually he was driven out when a cyclone wrecked his house. In 1935 an Australian writer, Ernestine Hill, and a British naval captain, J. R. Grey, visited the islands by yacht and found the well and the remains of Haynes's dwelling. They too saw the possibilities of oyster cultivation. They cleared the trees from one of the mangrove bays, walled up the narrow entrance and installed a sluice gate to give them control of the water level. Here they produced pearl-shell of the very highest quality, so good it won a first prize at a Paris exhibition.

That settlement did not survive the outbreak of war and neither, for that matter, did the pearling industry, which had come to depend on Japanese divers who were no longer available. The advent of plastics, too, reduced international demand for pearl shell, so the north-western pearling fleet that resumed operations after the war was vastly reduced in numbers. Just as the gold rush had come and gone in these parts without bringing lasting wealth or substantial settlement, so it was with the pearl rush. 'The coast of hurricanes, the coast of pearls,' Ernestine Hill called it, and 'the coast of lost opportunities'.[19]

BY EARLY 1951 the shape of the test that would transform the Monte Bellos had been decided. The ship containing the bomb would be anchored inside the lagoon in the channel which ran along the south-west shore of Trimouille. The anchorage – 'ground zero' – would be about 400 yards off a long, curving bay. Arrayed along this shore, and in all possible directions outward from ground zero, would be land-based observation equipment to measure various aspects of the explosion. On the nearest islands across the lagoon, atop vantage points which afforded a good view, would be more observation equipment. These sites would be unmanned and remotely controlled. Situated at almost the most distant point in the islands from ground zero, just over six miles away on the southern tip of Hermite, would be the command post, to be called H1. From here the detonation signal would be sent and here all the data would be gathered from the remote observation sites. During the Epicure mission, Charles Adams had found a suitable patch of high ground which afforded a direct view of ground zero. Elsewhere, platforms, trenches, cables, jetties and about three miles of road would be required, while those carrying out the work would need accommodation, food and other support services. Penney calculated that this whole operation would require about two hundred scientists and technicians. The Royal Engineers could do much of the construction work and the Australian forces might assist, but without doubt this would be primarily a naval operation.

When the plan came before the Chiefs of Staff, the First Sea Lord resisted it, arguing that such a 'considerable expenditure of naval effort' would be 'wasteful and illogical'.[20] Far better, he said, to wait for the Americans to agree to test the British weapon. His colleagues disagreed. Delay, they thought, could prove highly disruptive. For climatic reasons it seemed that the only suitable period for holding a trial in the Monte Bellos was the month of

October. The weapon was likely to be ready in time for October 1952, but any hesitation might well mean a delay until October 1953, and this was unacceptable. Moreover, the view was expressed that the Americans might be more impressed by British resolution in this matter than by dithering. The recommendation was passed to ministers that an approach should be made to the Australians for permission to prepare the site for a trial in October 1952, and that the American authorities should be discreetly informed of the British intention.

On 27 March Attlee wrote again to Menzies asking for formal approval to proceed and requesting assistance in preparing the site. He explained that negotiations with the Americans were still under way and if these bore fruit the site would not be needed. If, however, the test did take place on the Monte Bellos, Attlee warned that parts of the islands would be contaminated with radioactivity to such a degree that even the customary short visits by pearl fishermen could no longer be permitted. 'The area', he wrote, 'is not likely to be free from contamination for about three years.'[21] Attlee conspicuously did not offer the Australians any access to the secrets of the weapon, but he said that Australian experts would be welcome to take part in the observation of the effects of the explosion. As to cost, he said he hoped this could be discussed at a later date. The British were optimistic that they could persuade Australia to shoulder a share of the costs on the grounds that the bomb would strengthen Commonwealth defence.

Menzies replied that he could not give formal approval since a general election was under way in Australia and this would properly be a matter for the incoming government. Ever eager to please, however, he acceded to an urgent request for a full survey of the islands and made available an Australian Navy survey ship, the *Warrego*, to do the job. In May, safely returned to office, he gave the formal go-ahead. This was a fateful decision, given that it opened the way not just for one British test, but ultimately for twelve, conducted at three different sites in Australia over the next six years. Menzies has been criticized for failing to put the matter before his Cabinet, for failing to seek scientific advice and for failing to demand some *quid pro quo* from Britain, perhaps in the form of civil nuclear co-operation. On all counts he is certainly guilty, but why he adopted this compliant approach is no secret:

his view was that the vital interests of Australia and those of Britain were all but identical, and that Australia should do everything in its power to assist Britain's defence effort. In the 1980s, following allegations that some Australians suffered health damage as a result of radioactive contamination from the tests, an Australian Royal Commission investigated the events of the 1950s and their legacy. In giving his permission, Menzies 'was merely acting according to his well-exposed Anglophilian sentiments', the Commission report concluded. 'It was consistent with his approach when, as Prime Minister in 1939, he announced that as Britain was at war with Germany, Australia was automatically at war with the same enemy.'[22]

In July the *Warrego* arrived at the islands to carry out its survey. With it, to do their own reconnaissance, came Major Pat Smith of the Royal Engineers and HER's Noah Pearce, who was number three to Roy Pilgrim at Foulness. Smith, who had been chosen to lead the team of sappers who would work on the islands the following year, busied himself taking measurements and samples at the main construction sites. By the time he left he had accumulated five large sacks of stones and five of sand for examination back in Britain. Pearce's job was to work out where the various gauges to be used for blast measurement should be placed. Clear runs were needed, in straight lines radiating out from the point of the explosion, and he had to pace the ground, measure heights and take photographs. While they were at work the *Warrego*, which had entered service only a few weeks earlier, developed a fault. There was no alternative but to return to Fremantle, and the decision was taken to leave the two Britons and six or eight Australians in a camp on Trimouille to carry on their work. The repairs to the ship, however, took longer than expected and the survey party was left high and dry. Pearce recalls: 'Our food got down to some biscuits and some not very nice water. Our radio didn't have the range to reach the mainland to send an SOS. The Australians were getting a bit edgy. I was sitting in my tent one day and suddenly there was a boom and two Australians said, "It's the *Warrego*!" and scrambled up the hill waving. We were rescued.'

The incident had a moral. If remoteness was vital for a test site, the Monte Bellos were perhaps too generously endowed. Even to the Australians, the place was barely accessible. In August, a thirty-

strong team from the Royal Australian Air Force airfield construction squadron reached Onslow with the first heavy equipment for
construction work on the islands. Their base was in New South
Wales, and they had hauled their bulldozers, generators, tip-trucks
and prefabricated accommodation two-thirds of the way around
the continent, first by rail to Geraldton on the west coast, where
the line ran out, and then by dirt road. In all, they covered 3,000
miles. From Onslow they were shuttled out to the islands to prepare
the ground for the more intensive construction work, to begin
early in 1952. With them came an Australian meteorological team
to make a detailed record of the wind patterns in September and
October. Similar records were being kept in weather stations all
along the north-west coast.

Back in Britain planning for the test, now named 'Operation
Hurricane', was proceeding apace. Penney's first task had been to
appoint a scientist as technical director for the trial. He approached
in turn Greg Marley and Ernest Titterton, both Los Alamos
veterans and both at Harwell, suggesting that they should join HER
on a temporary attachment. As so often before, Penney was
disappointed; neither wanted the job. So he fell back again on his
own resources and put Leonard Tyte in charge. Tyte was an East
Ender with a London University Ph.D. in physics who had joined
ARD in 1930. His background was in ballistics, developing gauges
to measure the pressure inside a gun at the moment of firing.
During the war he had been number two at the rocketry outstation
at Aberporth and in 1947 Penney had placed him in overall charge
of the electronics aspects of HER work, overseeing Challens's work
on firing circuits as well as the preparation of high-speed observation equipment by a team under Charles Adams. A square-built,
balding figure who looked older than his forty-four years, Tyte
was regarded by colleagues as an effective manager, if not a conspicuously able scientist. His style, it was said, was to refuse all his
staff's requests at first time of asking as a matter of course, obliging
them to justify themselves in full; then if he was satisfied, he gave
all the help he could. It was an approach that got results but won
few friends. Many thought him fussy and awkward, although by
other eyes the same traits were seen as conscientious attention
to detail. Penney valued Tyte for his experience, drive and planning
ability. 'Dr Tyte is a man of few words, but what he says is to

the point', he wrote in 1950 when recommending a promotion. 'Whenever I have asked him to do something, he has done it to time and in exemplary style.'[23]

The Navy, too, appointed a commander for Operation Hurricane, Captain David Torlesse, recently returned from distinguished service in command of the aircraft carrier *Triumph* in the opening phase of the Korean War. Torlesse joined the planning team in May, and he has summarized the assignment with which he was confronted: 'What had to be done was to transport 10,000 miles and set up on the site the equipment which would detect exactly what happened in the minute fraction – perhaps one-fiftieth – of a second after the initiation of the chain reaction, as well as the material which would measure the effect and strength of the explosion at various distances on land and water. Some 500 pieces of measuring equipment, ranging from electronic gear of great complexity to the simplest means of measuring a shock wave, had to be set up and serviced on a number of islands, separated by shallow lagoons and inlets, access to which was often limited by the state of the tide. The islands were without resources except stone for concrete construction. We had to take there every bit of wood, cement and steel we needed, either to bring or make our fresh water, and the provisions, tools and equipment of the men who would do the work.' He noted ruefully: 'If this had been an American project, a great armada would have been employed. I was given five ships and some 1,500 men and told that I must make do with them.'[24]

While Tyte concerned himself with who and what would be needed on the scientific side, Torlesse dealt with the ships and the servicemen. Of the five vessels he was assigned, the flagship was the *Campania*, a small aircraft-carrier. Originally laid down in Belfast during the war as a freighter for the New Zealand lamb trade, the *Campania* had been taken over while still a hull by the Navy for conversion into a warship. It saw action in that grimmest of naval theatres, the convoy route to Arctic Russia, but after the war it was mothballed. In 1951, however, it was a more famous ship than such an unglamorous record might suggest, for in that year it had been given the role of travelling show for the Festival of Britain, and had toured the country's ports bearing a compact version of the national exhibition in London. Now the *Campania* had been chosen to be home to most of the scientists on Operation Hurricane, as well as packhorse for the equipment and stores. As soon as its exhibition duties were complete it was sent to Birkenhead to have its festive trappings ripped out and replaced by cabins and offices, lavatories and washrooms, a laboratory and workshop, lifting and stowing gear, ventilation and a desalination plant for turning seawater into drinking water.

The other ships in Torlesse's little fleet were the tank-landing vessels *Narvik*, *Zeebrugge* and *Tracker* and a frigate, the *Plym*. The first two were to carry the advance parties out to the Monte Bellos early in the new year, so they were prepared in some haste. The *Tracker* was to be the Health Ship for the operation and was equipped with elaborate decontamination facilities. The *Plym*, last of the five, was a River class frigate, one of many lesser fighting ships built in great haste during the war. It had won battle honours in the invasion of Sicily and the Battle of the Atlantic but had been pensioned off in 1945 and handed over to the volunteer reserve as a training vessel. No longer needed even in that role, the *Plym* was now to be fitted out as the 'target ship' for Operation Hurricane, and would go up with the bomb.

These preparations were co-ordinated by the Hurricane Executive Committee, or Hurex, which met from May 1951 onwards under the chairmanship of the Deputy Chief of Naval Staff, Vice-Admiral Edward Evans-Lombe. Policy on such matters as safety and security was laid down, and liaison was maintained with a parallel committee in Australia, the Hurricane Panel. Torlesse, who was promoted to Rear Admiral in this period, was named overall commander of Task Force Four, as the expedition was known. In October he visited the Monte Bellos, sailing out from Onslow on an old pearling lugger. 'We lived on deck and ate well by trolling for fish; it was a good picnic and enjoyed by all. The islands, low, scrubby and treeless, were rather reminiscent of Scapa Flow without the hills. There was a small meteorological party in residence. We had a good look round over two days, and had some bathing, before returning to Port Samson, further north, where our Dakota was waiting.'[25]

By this time, however, the unexpected had occurred, and for a few weeks the whole question of a test in the Monte Bellos was again in doubt. The Americans, after what one British official called 'a complete reversal of policy', offered to allow the British weapon to be tested in Nevada.[26] This left the British government with a difficult choice. What had happened was that a renewed and by now routine British request for test facilities, made in August, had prompted the US government to think again about the issue. At first, an offer was made which the British could not accept: the US would carry out the test with just a few British scientists taking part. This implied complete British openness about the design of the weapon being tested with no promise of reciprocal American disclosure. The Chiefs of Staff decided that such an arrangement 'would mean not only that we should suffer tremendous loss of prestige, but that we should also be denied much valuable information'. The Monte Bello operation, they said, should proceed 'without further ado'.[27] Before this response reached Washington, however, the Americans changed their minds. A new proposal arrived, framed in more conciliatory terms which met a number of the British concerns. Penney was impressed and declared that 'from the technical point of view the proposals . . . gave us practically all we wanted'.[28] This view was based on a close reading of the text. The American Atomic Energy Commission, which would be responsible for the test, was now asking for 'complete details of this weapon to make its own estimate in assuring that United States public safety will be maintained'. Penney felt that this presented no obstacle, since 'enough information would be furnished to the Americans to satisfy them [about safety] without giving any details of the weapon which we would be reluctant to disclose'. Others saw that a substantial advance had been made, but were ready to accept the offer only as a basis for further discussion. Penney, meanwhile, was dispatched to Washington to look at the technical side in detail.

More was involved here than technicalities, however, and the revival of the American option stirred a wider debate. Nuclear co-operation with the US remained in the deep freeze to which the Fuchs affair had consigned it early in 1950. Two more security scandals had made a nonsense of British promises to tighten up their procedures: in September 1950 a Harwell physicist, Bruno Pontecorvo, defected to the Soviet Union leaving behind a fair amount of circumstantial evidence to suggest that he had been a low-level spy, and in June 1951 Donald Maclean, the diplomat who had been so intimately involved in US-British nuclear negotiations, fled with Guy Burgess to Moscow. There was outrage in Washington and in such an atmosphere Congress, which had the whip hand in these matters thanks to the McMahon Act, was unlikely to be impressed by any proposal from the Truman administration for exchanges of nuclear information with Britain. The British, for their part, had been bitten so often that they were now shy of American offers and initiatives. The Australian option had much to be said for it. At an estimated cost of £2 million, it was fairly cheap; it offered a chance to study the base surge, which Nevada did not; and it involved no compromise to British independence or prestige. This last consideration must have weighed heavily after four years of work developing the weapon without US assistance.

Penney returned from Washington pleased with his contacts with US officials and scientists, who had been 'most co-operative'.[29] In scientific and technical terms, he thought the test could be carried out satisfactorily in Nevada, although he stressed that Britain would acquire no information about American atomic weapons as a result of it. Even Penney, however, could not wholeheartedly endorse the American option. To cancel the Monte Bello test at this late stage would leave Britain entirely at the mercy of the US authorities. If the Truman administration seemed sympathetic at this stage, who knew whether it would stay that way, particularly with presidential elections due in 1952? As for Congress, its reactions to the present proposals could not be guessed with accuracy. Australia had become the safe choice, and that was what the Chiefs of Staff recommended. Final confirmation had to wait until after the British general election in October, which saw Churchill returned to office. He looked at the US terms and rejected them; he wanted a joint operation with the Americans, with full scientific collaboration, or nothing at all. On 27 December 1951 he informed Menzies that the test would definitely take place in the Monte Bello Islands.

10

Final Preparations

JUST as it was inevitable that there would be a test, it was inevitable that there would be an announcement. Ever since Albert Alexander's oblique statement in the Commons that Britain was conducting research into 'all types of weapons, including atomic weapons', ministers had not only avoided any substantive comment on the progress of the research, but had concealed the whole project beneath the blanket of D-Notice number twenty-five. A test, however, could not be kept secret, as the Soviet Union had found, and Britain's test would be all the more public since it was to take place in a foreign country. While the secret planning proceeded, it was the Australian authorities who first drew attention to the risk of a leak, and to the need to have reassuring answers ready on the subject of radioactive dangers if the story did break. Speculative reports had been cropping up in the Press since July 1951, when the *New York Herald Tribune* asserted that a British test was to take place in Australia within a year. When the *Daily Telegraph* published a similar story in August, a 'fairly severe' letter was dispatched from the chairman of the D-notice Committee, and the acting managing editor, Malcolm Muggeridge, replied that he was 'most distressed' at the lapse, which he promised would not be repeated.[1] No such gag existed in Australia; ministers were obliged to answer questions and the Press could report what they said. Hitherto, ministers in Canberra had been able to state honestly that no arrangement had been made for a British test, but now that there was an arrangement they were on exposed ground.

When the matter came up in the Hurex Committee in London, Penney observed simply that 'the longer it can be put off the less time there would be for fears regarding radioactivity to develop'.[2] This was not a realistic approach but then Penney, secure for so long behind the D-notice, may not have understood that the Press could not be prevented from reporting on preparations for an event of such international interest as the first British nuclear test. This would be covered by American and Australian newspapers and by the international news agencies; British papers simply could not ignore it. The Hurex Committee recognized the imperative and decided that a statement should be issued late in February 1952, when the first task force ships sailed. Work began on the wording.

In January there was an anxious moment when the Government learned that the *Daily Mail* had the story that two ships were being loaded in England with equipment for a British test on an island north of Australia. Evans-Lombe and Torlesse went to see Sir Anthony Eden, the Foreign Secretary, to discuss what should be done, and a cable was quickly sent to Australia warning that publication was imminent and promising a text for a joint statement 'shortly'.[3] In the end the scare subsided and the *Mail* did not publish. As Torlesse wrote: 'Probably the "D" notice was enough.'[4] It would not hold the line for long.

The *Mail*, if it really had the story in January, was a little ahead of events. It was not until early February that the *Zeebrugge* and the *Narvik* docked at Marchwood on Southampton Water to embark 200 men of the Royal Engineers who had spent the previous few months training and planning in great secrecy at Longmoor in Hampshire. With them were loaded more than 1,000 tons of equipment, from tractors to scaffolding, until, in the words of one naval officer, 'the main holds of both ships were crammed from bulkhead to bulkhead and from deck to deckhead'.[5] On 18 February the two ships were in Portsmouth, loaded and ready to sail. At last the prime ministers of the United Kingdom and Australia issued their statement: 'In the course of this year the United Kingdom Government intend to test an atomic weapon produced in the United Kingdom. In close co-operation with the Government of the Commonwealth of Australia, the test will take place at a site in Australia. It will be conducted in conditions which will ensure that there will be no danger whatever from radioactivity to the health of people or animals in the Commonwealth.'[6]

It was, in keeping with the spirit of Albert Alexander, the shortest, most grudging and most evasive announcement that could have been made. Neither the site, nor the approximate date, nor the naval preparations, nor the existence of an atomic weapons organization were mentioned. The next morning, after reading with satisfaction in *The Times* the assertion that the test would probably take place at Woomera, Rear Admiral Torlesse watched the two squat and heavily laden vessels that formed the vanguard of his expedition leave Portsmouth and make their way out to the open sea. 'Our enterprise', he wrote later, 'was really under way.'[7]

AT HIGH EXPLOSIVE Research the preparations were not going smoothly. Indeed, had Penney not been an invincible optimist the mood might well have been one of panic. The weapon was due to sail on the *Plym* in early June, but by March, after five years of work and with only weeks to go, only one of its seven principal components was ready and in satisfactory condition. Bean's detonators had been in full production for some time and although faint worries persisted about a dud finding its way through the selection process it was accepted that the specification had been met and that everything physically possible had been done to ensure that they were reliable. That aside, the checklist made depressing reading. Success with the plutonium core and the initiator lay by now in the lap of the gods. These parts would not sail on the *Plym*, but would be flown out to the Monte Bellos later to be inserted in the weapon just before the test. It was already clear, however, that even with the extra few weeks that this allowed, it would be a very close-run thing. If the deadline was to be met, Windscale would have to deliver the plutonium on time and the casting and fabrication process at Aldermaston would have to work like clockwork. As for the remaining four components – the firing system, the explosive lenses, the supercharge and the uranium tamper – every single one gave cause for anxiety.

The lenses had been the first problem tackled by HER back in 1947, and since then satisfactory moulds had been designed, prototypes had been tested and sample charges had been produced at Woolwich. For the weapon, thirty-two lenses were required, plus thirty-two more for the back-up assembly, and since the highest standards had to be met there was considerable wastage. This was clearly a case for large-scale production, and the job had been assigned to the Royal Ordnance Factories. Because of difficulties with the moulds, however, the production line did not start rolling until the beginning of 1952, and what came off it then was disappointing. Shrinkage was still occurring during cooling and there were many reject lenses; it was not at all clear whether enough shapes of a sufficiently high standard could be made in time.

Similar problems affected the supercharge, which was being produced at Woolwich. Here there were just six big pieces in each assembly, so volume production was not a factor, but quality was just as great a worry and Penney's visits to Mott's department became steadily more frequent as snags kept cropping up. Matters were not helped when a full set of high-quality charges, painstakingly X-rayed, tested and cleared as suitable for the Hurricane assembly, were all cut to the wrong measurements by mistake. 'You could spit', says Len Bunce. 'Penney didn't hear about that, but there was a great panic to get more bits made.' Only in March was the first complete and satisfactory supercharge casting produced.

The tamper was another headache. Since the re-design the previous summer, Penney and Pike had pushed the engineers to the limit in their quest for a thin uranium shell of perfect consistency. The first castings emerged from their moulds in a Woolwich metallurgy workshop in December. Deliberately, they had been made to twice the desired thickness. This was because the uranium metal always became contaminated on its outer surface by the mould material, and because it had been found that variations of density tended to occur in the upper part of the casting. Once these parts had been trimmed off by precision machine the end-products were objects of great beauty: two gleaming golden bowls about a foot in diameter which fitted together with a step-joint at the lip. They were well within the tolerance of error in terms of shape, but to the dismay of the metallurgists, particularly Guv Willows, who was in charge of the tamper, there were measurable imperfections both on the surface and in the porosity of the metal. As many as

167

half a dozen tampers were produced in short order, but the flaws were never eliminated. Only a complete revision of the production methods offered any hope of better results, and it was by now too late to contemplate that. As with the lenses, Penney would have to live with what he had, flaws and all, and hope that it was good enough to do its job.

As if these last-minute hitches and disappointments were not enough, the final stages of the development of the electronic firing system confronted Penney with some agonizing uncertainties. The trigatron – the switch which sent the current to the detonators – was giving Challens's team nightmares because, despite a year of effort, they had been unable to eliminate the 'Tuesday Effect' of occasional premature firing. One cause of the breakdowns was found to be a very slight change in the surface of the electrodes as a result of the high-energy charges being used. This change occurred every time the trigatron was test-fired using a high charge and it caused what was called a 'field emission' from the electrode, which in turn could provoke a premature breakdown at the next firing. The answer, which was to submit the trigatron to a special procedure between firings, emerged after consultation with a team at Swansea University which had been studying field emissions.

This was helpful but it was not the end of the problems and it was only early in 1952 that a design alteration was identified which would provide a trigatron of satisfactory standard. At first it was thought to be too late to make the necessary changes to the production process, and Penney and Challens reconciled themselves to the necessity of gambling on the earlier model. In March, however, they decided to improvise, and a hectic two-month dash began to develop, test and manufacture the new design at Fort Halstead in time for the Hurricane test.

It was an anxious time and at Shell-Mex House all the earlier doubts about Penney's flow charts and general management abilities must have come flooding back. He had been given generous resources, high priority, a substantial staff and five years to do the job, and still there was this stream of last-minute problems. Penney himself might have been forgiven some moments of despair, but he had been at Los Alamos and witnessed there even more desperate preparations. He never lost his faith and never allowed his staff to lose theirs.

THE ANXIETY IN Whitehall surrounding these final stages before Operation Hurricane was all the greater because the new prime minister was taking an extremely active interest in the progress. Churchill in opposition had been told little more than the man in the street about the British atomic project and for the first few years after the war he had been strangely quiet on the subject. On the wider issues of the atomic age he had of course been characteristically forthright. In his famous Fulton speech in 1946, for example, he attacked the notion of international control, declaring it to be 'criminal madness' to contemplate placing the secrets of the atomic bomb in the hands of the United Nations.[8] In 1949 he declared that, but for the American atomic bomb, 'Europe would have been "communized", like Czechoslovakia, and London under bombardment some time ago'.[9] On the British bomb, however, he said little until after the Soviet test in 1949, which he saw as a humiliation for Britain. During the general election in February 1950, which the Conservatives narrowly lost, he denounced the British failure to produce a bomb as 'one of the most extraordinary lapses that have ever taken place'.[10] More attacks in the same vein followed in the ensuing months. Churchill's view was that Britain should not be aiming for large-scale production, but that it should long ago have proved itself capable of making the bomb. It was, he said, 'a matter of complaint that after five-and-a-half years, with all the knowledge we had amassed in the course of our joint work with the Americans during the war, we have not succeeded in making a single specimen'.[11]

Attlee replied that this criticism was unfair, since Churchill was fully aware of the complexity of the weapon and the difficulty of producing it. This may have been so, but Churchill was certainly not aware of the scale of the effort being made. On his return to office, when he was briefed about it, he was surprised both by what had been achieved and by the manner in which the necessary expenditure had been kept secret from Parliament. Having complained so bitterly of Labour's failures, when he first spoke on the matter in the House of Commons as prime minister he found himself admitting that he could see no grounds for departing from the policies pursued by his predecessor.

In an important respect the project had already changed, for a few weeks before the election of 1951 Portal resigned. He had accepted the post with reluctance and had on several previous occasions contemplated giving it up. Now, he felt, the success of the project was assured and he could leave with a clear conscience to pursue a quieter and better-paid life in the City. It is a measure of his enduring stature at this time that Churchill asked him to be his minister of defence. He declined the honour. When they met again, and Churchill had learned of the progress made by the atomic project under Portal's management, the Prime Minister asked: 'Is this bomb going to go off?' The reply was characteristically succinct: 'Yes, sir, it is.'[12]

A successor to Portal had to be found, and the first thought was to appoint another former Chief of Staff. The possible candidates all refused, and the job went instead to General Sir Frederick Morgan. It was widely believed that this was the result of a mistake, that the intention had been to appoint Sir William Morgan but the names were somehow confused and the offer was made to 'the wrong Morgan'. On the evidence of their qualifications this is certainly plausible; both men were distinguished soldiers, but Sir William seems to have been much the better candidate. He was a science graduate, was highly regarded in Whitehall, had diplomatic experience as a member of the British military mission in Washington and was just coming to the end of his tour of duty there. Sir Frederick was no idiot – he drew up the first D-Day plans and then served as deputy chief of staff to Eisenhower – but he had been in retirement since 1946, having been withdrawn from an important UN assignment in occupied Berlin after making a series of undiplomatic public statements there. He himself was quite astonished when, as he put it in his memoirs, 'my name apparently came out of some unmilitary headgear' – so astonished that he failed to object to the rather paltry salary.[13]

Penney said later that however hard Sir Frederick tried, he was unable to acquire a basic command of the science of nuclear energy and thus found himself in an impossible position, being led by his subordinates. A senior civil servant took a less charitable view, describing the appointment as 'a bad joke'. 'He was quite hopeless – worked all day and had a stream of visitors, but no one could discover what he was actually doing.'[14] Morgan formed his own views about the organization he had taken over, dismissing as 'a pantomime of secrecy' the security arrangements at Shell-Mex

House. Steel bars might prevent access from the main staircases, he observed, but that was little use when 'cradleborne window cleaners made regular entrance from the "blind" side in the normal course of their business'. In any case, he wrote later, 'nothing was known of the lives of the civil servants once they had done their stint at their papers and left the premises'.[15] He was nonetheless the first to acknowledge the gulf of authority that divided him from his predecessor – Portal, he wrote, was *'persona grata* at all levels, I an unknown retired officer'.[16] This contrast doubtless caused dismay among the staff, but if it was a setback to the project it was not a grave one, for by late 1951 all the important policy decisions and all the Whitehall battles were in the past.

All, that is, except one. When Churchill informed Parliament that he would maintain the atomic energy policies of his predecessor he added one significant rider: that some improvement might be made to the organization of the work. This idea came from Churchill's long-time scientific adviser, now his Paymaster-General, Lord Cherwell. Unlike Churchill, Cherwell had remained in touch with atomic energy developments after the war as a member of a Ministry of Supply technical committee, and while he broadly supported the policy decisions that had been taken, he disliked the bureaucratic environment in which they were implemented. Like Churchill, he saw the early Soviet success with the bomb as a humiliating defeat, and he urged Attlee to take the whole project out of the hands of the Ministry of Supply and create a free-standing atomic energy corporation which would be capable of greater dynamism and flexibility. He wrote: 'The overwhelming majority of people who have really been concerned with the project, most of whom have considerable experience, take the view that such a change would reduce delays and increase efficiency.'[17] Raising the matter in the House of Lords, he argued further that the civil service was the wrong body to run such an enterprise: 'Only men used to tackling large industrial developments can successfully handle operations of this nature . . . You cannot expect to win a tennis championship if you insist on using a niblick instead of a tennis racket.'[18]

Portal supported Cherwell's proposals, and Penney, who had endured so many administrative frustrations in building up HER, also seems to have wanted to see change. But Attlee had no stomach for it and Cherwell had to wait. When the Conservatives took office in 1951 Cherwell expected to see the transfer swiftly effected, but again it was not to be. What he proposed was an enormous administrative upheaval that would affect thousands of people and require full-blown legislation. Many factors argued against it. With the Monte Bello test less than a year away the timing was not good. The Treasury and the civil service were opposed to the scheme, as were most of the staff who would be transferred to the new body. The Cabinet was divided and it did not help that responsibility for atomic energy was now shared by two men who disliked each other: Cherwell, who was the Prime Minister's adviser on atomic policy, and Duncan Sandys, the Minister of Supply. Sandys resisted the reforms, and early in 1952 Churchill, faced with so many contrary pressures, decided to defer action. 'Wait to see whether your bomb goes off or not', he told Cherwell.[19]

The Monte Bello test, by contrast, interested the Prime Minister directly, stirring in him an old enthusiasm for intrigue and military planning. Morgan wrote: 'As soon as he heard tell of the project to carry out a trial explosion of the first British atomic warhead, nothing would do but that a committee to control the affair must be formed under his personal chairmanship – to the irritation of his immediate entourage.'[20] In March this 'Apex Committee' came into being, a high-powered body including among its members Eden, Cherwell, Sandys and Earl Alexander, the Defence Minister. Penney was also present, with Morgan, Evans-Lombe, Torlesse and others. Cherwell was concerned about what impression Penney might make on Churchill, and wrote to the Prime Minister beforehand urging him to be gentle with the scientist. 'He is our chief – indeed our only – real expert in the construction of the bomb and I do not know what we should do without him', Cherwell wrote. 'The Americans admit frankly that they would give a great deal to get him back. But on an appeal to his patriotism he gave up the offer of a very attractive professorship and came into government service. He is not always very tactful, but his heart is in the right place.'[21]

In the event, Penney had no difficulty coping with the peculiar demands of the Apex Committee. Churchill opened the proceedings with a bizarre little speech. 'You may wonder why I have called this the Apex Committee', he said. 'The other day I saw a cartoon –

two ape-like creatures in a blasted landscape, the male approaching the female with an ingratiating look on his face, and she saying, "No! We are not going to start all that over again!"' The Prime Minister paused for laughter and then added: 'The X, of course, stands for the unknown quantity.'[22] He had one or two serious thoughts about Operation Hurricane, and these he aired. He was concerned that the Soviet Union would try to interfere with the test, a fear shared by Alexander, who declared that successful sabotage of the test would be 'a major political triumph for the Russians'.[23] Some thought was given to how this might be prevented and a series of operations were eventually mounted to give the impression that the test would take place some weeks later than was actually planned. One of these was Operation Spoofer, which involved booking airline tickets to Australia in Penney's name close to the decoy date. It was assumed that the Press would find out about these and that both the newspapers and the Russians would be thrown off the track, but in the event the bookings were never noticed and the effort was wasted.

Another matter that concerned Churchill was publicity. The committee minutes record the firmness of his views: 'The Prime Minister said that he would personally approve any communiqués or statements which it was desired to issue to the Press. Apart from these, nothing whatever should be said to the Press and nobody should be given any discretion at all to make any statement of any kind. In matters of this kind the less said the better, and all enquiries for further information should be met with a blank refusal.'[24] Here again, he was perfectly loyal to the practices adopted by Attlee.

In general, though, the Apex Committee was something of an embarrassment to those required to attend. It had no executive functions, since that job was in the hands of the Hurex Committee, so beyond briefing the Prime Minister, which was briskly done, and hearing his views, which were straightforward, there was little to be said. The exchanges could be banal, as when Penney explained that the bomb was expected to have a yield equivalent to about 20,000 tons of TNT. Churchill replied: 'Just fancy! I don't suppose I ever saw as much as one thousand tons go off at once.'[25] Torlesse was able to find amusement in the sparring between Sandys and Cherwell, 'who sat on either side of the PM and conducted their war across him until told to desist', but these were slim pickings.[26] The meetings, fortnightly at first, soon became monthly, and the ministerial attendance became steadily less impressive. Roger Makins, of the Foreign Office, recalls sitting through some long, awkward silences and says that the committee was eventually put out of its misery after Penney, asked for his thoughts, admitted frankly: 'Well, Prime Minister, I just don't think there is anything more to say.'[27]

ON 1 APRIL, atomic energy matters made one of their rare appearances in Cabinet discussion, in circumstances of some alarm. That morning the *Daily Express* and the *Daily Mirror* published on their front pages the story of a shocking new security lapse. '4 a.m. Latest, Atom Papers Found', declared one. 'Boys Find Atom Secrets in Street', said the other. On the previous evening, two north London schoolboys, Harry Sibley, aged fourteen, and Neville Thompson, a year younger, had presented themselves at Highgate police station with an envelope of papers found beside a bus stop. The papers plainly concerned atomic research and were quickly transferred to Scotland Yard where, the *Express* said, they were confirmed as missing from Harwell. Concern was quick to spread, and a Conservative backbench MP, Charles Orr-Ewing, placed a question on that day's House of Commons order paper asking for a Government statement. In Whitehall the affair looked even worse than either the Press or Orr-Ewing knew, for as Scotland Yard very rapidly informed the Ministry of Supply, on the top of one of the pages in the envelope were the words 'Atomic Weapon', and included with the papers was a technical blueprint. Ministry scientists were despatched to examine the package.

When the Cabinet met that morning, the Home Secretary, Sir David Maxwell-Fyfe, appraised his worried colleagues of the progress of inquiries. In the afternoon, Sir David rose in the Commons to answer Orr-Ewing's question. The chamber was full and the mood grave, but the Home Secretary permitted himself a smile. 'This incident', he said, 'has been reported on the appropriate day.'[28] It was an April Fool, perpetrated by a boy who had no idea that he might dupe the whole country. The House subsided into laughter while, as *The Times* reported, 'for a few minutes Mr Orr-Ewing had the thoughtful air of a practical joker's victim'. The joker was Victor Mehra, a fifteen-year-old apprentice draughtsman who had typed out a false chemical formula, added some imposing titles and foreign-looking signatures, attached a blueprint for a humble washer and a letterhead from a Scandinavian firm and topped it all with the words: 'Plan for Atomic Weapon C.D. ZZ29679'. For good measure, he marked the sheets: 'Important: This must be burnt when checked.' His intended victim was not the police or the House of Commons, but whoever he could fool at his local youth club. That proved to be Harry Sibley. The next morning the joke was on Mehra. 'I never thought anyone would take it seriously', he told a throng of journalists on his doorstep.[29] A police officer later called at the house to deliver a formal warning.

APRIL SAW THE start of rehearsals for the test in the Thames Estuary. They began in spectacular style with the detonation of an 8,000 lb. charge at the Shoeburyness ranges, leaving a thirty-foot crater in the clay. This was laid on to provide the various photographic and other observation teams which would be working on the Monte Bellos with a large explosion on which to practise their operations. In the ensuing weeks there followed an intensive series of tests of the communications and control systems. The *Plym* had completed its refit at Chatham Dockyard and was docked in Stangate Creek near Sheerness, Penney's old home town on the north Kent coast. On the Essex side of the estuary, at Shoeburyness, a control room was set up with Ieuan Maddock in charge. The distance between these two points, of just under six miles, was approximately the distance between H1, the control centre on Hermite, and the anchorage off Trimouille where *Plym* would lie. So for a month in the spring of 1952, while merchant ships ploughed along the Thames waterway to and from Europe's busiest port, the airwaves across the mouth of the river were filled with the chatter of electronic signalling between Shoeburyness and the *Plym*, punctuated by the occasional sonorous countdown to an atomic explosion that never came.

Good communications were vital to the test in a hundred different ways. Not only would H1 and the *Plym* have to be linked so that the bomb could be detonated at a distance, but two-way links would be needed with many of the unmanned observation sites: one way to send commands and the other way to receive the signals to show what was happening. This was called telemetry. The link to the *Plym*, it had been decided, would be by cable, but the rest of the traffic, including the telemetry, would be over the air, and state-of-the-art radio equipment to handle this vast volume of information had been specially designed by Maddock and his team. The countdown was an elaborate sequence lasting twenty-four hours, into which hundreds of different tasks were carefully meshed. It would begin with the phased priming of all equipment, including the bomb, and as it progressed technicians would be evacuated and periodic tests would be made on equipment by remote control. In the final moments, cameras or other devices would be activated to do their job, and after detonation, as the explosion unfolded millisecond by millisecond, the equipment would feed its readings back to the control centre. All this had to be rehearsed.

Again and again, Maddock practised sending the firing signal from Shoeburyness to the *Plym*, each time setting off, not a bomb, but a single detonator. 'It's quite a crack', recalls John Davies, who was working at the other end. 'We had a firing installation on deck, and it turned out that we had put it just above the captain's cabin, which didn't please him. Each time we fired, he made a fuss.' Bigger rehearsals were also conducted which linked these detonation procedures with the observation teams, who were at Foulness. In these trials, at the same instant that the detonator exploded on the *Plym*, a 64 lb. charge would be fired on the ranges at Foulness to simulate the full atomic explosion. In this way both groups were obliged to respond to the same sequence of commands at the same time, as they would in the real test. Two full-blown rehearsals were conducted, one involving a twenty-four-hour countdown sequence. The results were encouraging, and in the second half of May the communications and telemetry equipment – equivalent to a small telephone exchange – was packed up and transferred to Chatham, where it was loaded on to the *Campania*.

At about the same time another rehearsal was taking place at Shoeburyness. It had been decided that immediately after the Hurricane explosion, rockets should be fired through the cloud to take samples. By comparing the ratio of un-fissioned plutonium to fission products in these samples a measure could be had of how efficient the explosion had been. The task of analysis was assigned to Frank Morgan, the radiochemist whom Penney had lured across from Harwell, and Morgan was anxious to test-fire the rockets. This was organized with the assistance of a colleague, David Deverell, and an army battery commander. Deverell recalls setting up a smokescreen of zinc oxide through which the rockets, equipped with filters, were to pass. He and his group then retreated to an agreed point of safety some distance away. 'Unfortunately the battery commander got his co-ordinates wrong. Instead of firing the rockets at the zinc oxide cloud, he fired them at the location of our party. I think there were forty-eight rockets, and I remember the Wren radio operator shouting into the radio: "For God's sake stop them! Stop them!" A rocket landed three feet away from me. It was very lucky that nobody was hurt.'

THE *ZEEBRUGGE* AND the *Narvik* reached Fremantle in mid-April 1952, having made the journey via Suez and Ceylon, to find the Australian newspapers alive with speculation that their ultimate destination was the Monte Bellos. The cover story for the activities on the islands – that they were being prepared to house equipment to monitor rocket-firings from Woomera – was plainly fooling no one. When the two ships reached the Monte Bellos themselves, ten days later, a party of journalists in a small yacht was there to greet them. A lieutenant on the *Narvik*, Peter Bird, wrote later: 'We found them anchored in a secluded little bay, in none too good condition after their voyage and, despite our admiration for their courage and initiative, and the fact that the islands were not yet declared prohibited, we had to ask them to leave. They took the request with good grace (they had accomplished their objective in finding us there) and returned to the mainland.'[30] It was not until four days later that this eviction was given legal authority, when the Australian government declared a 5,000-square-mile exclusion zone for shipping; any unauthorized person landing on the islands or flying within forty miles risked six months in prison.

More preparatory work had already been done by a second RAAF construction team which arrived in the islands in March, after the worst of the summer heat had passed. Tracks had been bulldozed and graded, and 350 tons of steel planking had been laid to give the sappers a head start. Showing considerable ingenuity, they had also laid on a freshwater supply from the mainland. The islands, it will be remembered, had no streams or ponds, and although the naval ships would carry desalination equipment to turn seawater into drinking water, this would not be adequate to meet the demand. The nearest suitable source was found to be the Fortescue River, on the mainland eighty miles north-east of Onslow. The river is dry for much of the year and at the estuary the water is brackish, but upstream there are deep pools of fresh water. With remarkable speed, eight miles of four-inch pipeline were made, delivered and laid, to bring the water down to a jetty in the estuary. From there, a 400-ton motor lighter shuttled constantly back and forth the fifty miles to the islands for the rest of the year, providing a valuable supplement to the task force's own supplies.

Water shortages seemed unimaginable to the Royal Engineers in the days after their arrival, when they found themselves working in torrential rain, a 'dense, driving downpour' that must have accounted for the whole of the islands' average annual rainfall of eight inches in that year.[31] The unloading went ahead, however, and the work got under way. The main sites were at H1, the control centre at the southern tip of Hermite, and T2, the shore camp on Trimouille at the spot closest to the *Plym*'s anchorage. Smaller teams scattered to other points, and even to some of the small islands, where they were deposited with tents and food and left to work alone for up to a week at a time. Quarries were cut in the rock, and in the weeks that followed the various teams laid eighty concrete platforms for instruments, built nine jetties and five concrete blockhouses, put up four scaffolding towers and erected the steel structure that would house all of Maddock's instrumentation at H1. Specially equipped landing-craft laid the long cable from H1 that would carry the final signal, weaving it in and out of the jagged coral on the sea-bed, while the high-strength moorings that would hold the *Plym* in exactly the right place were set on the sea-bed. 'All over the islands', wrote Bird, 'odd little sites of all sorts were found: concrete beds of varying shapes and sizes, wooden and concrete posts embedded in the rock, areas of rock and sand levelled and pegged out to the specifications of the scientists. Explosions became a regular feature of the day's work as tons of rock were brought down by demolition charge in the two quarries established ashore by the sappers to supply aggregate for concrete making, and as paths were blasted through rocky outcrops to give access to some of the more remote sites.' Some thought and effort was also given to recreation. Bulldozers were used to create football fields, and a hockey pitch big enough for seven-a-side games was fashioned with hessian sheets. Two bays were fenced off at the mouth and the waters cleared of their more sinister denizens to provide, 'at worst, a cooling paddle and splash, and at best, good, safe swimming'.[32]

Working sixty- and seventy-hour weeks and responding to ever-changing specifications wired to them from the scientists, the Royal Engineers in this phase of Operation Hurricane did all that was asked of them and more, and earned general admiration. Torlesse wrote later of the 'great credit' due to all concerned, and praised the good training and high morale of the sappers. Leonard Tyte declared: 'Truly the REs are magnificent.'[33]

EFFORT ON THIS scale could not be concealed, not even in the Monte Bello Islands, and as the weeks passed the secrecy surrounding the preparations became a mockery. On 14 May, Downing Street at last issued a fuller statement. The test, it confirmed, would take place in the Monte Bello Islands. Details were given of the five Royal Navy ships that would be involved; Torlesse and Penney were identified by name – the first time Penney had been officially associated with the British bomb in a public statement – and mention was made of the co-operation of the Australian government and armed services. At 8 a.m. that same morning in Chatham, Torlesse hoisted his flag on the *Campania* as Flag Officer Special Squadron, and formally transferred his offices to the ship from the Admiralty in London. He wrote later: 'I was received with guard and band, was met by the heads of departments and the staff, and walked round the ship later in the forenoon. I had the staff to drinks in my cabin, and the captains of *Tracker* and *Plym* stayed to lunch.'[34] The following day Penney, Brooking and Tyte came to inspect the ship and they too were entertained to lunch.

The belated confirmation that the test would be in the Monte Bellos provoked controversy, but it was not of a kind that Churchill's staff could have expected, and the Prime Minister needlessly aggravated it. In the Commons the Labour MP Emrys Hughes, one of the few members brave enough to raise questions

179

about atomic matters, asked about the danger to wildlife on the islands from the planned explosion. Churchill made light of it: 'An expedition which went to the islands fifty years ago reported that giant rats, wild cats and wallabies were seen, and these may have given the honourable member some anxiety. However, the officer who explored the islands recently said that he found only some lizards, two sea eagles and what looked like a canary on a perch.'[35] These remarks were greeted with laughter in the Commons, but annoyance elsewhere. A letter in *The Times* soon pointed out that the islands were home to twenty sub-species of birds, including a pipit and the black-and-white fairy wren, which did not exist elsewhere. 'It will be very regrettable if these notable birds are blasted out of existence', observed the correspondent tartly.[36] Hughes asked about the birds in the Commons, and was told by Churchill that 'every effort will be made to inconvenience them as little as possible'.[37] But the matter refused to be joked away. Publicly and privately, experts of all kinds emerged to express concern about the flora and fauna of the Monte Bellos and to identify an exotic menagerie of rare creatures thought to be under threat. Could animals and birds not be trapped and moved before the test? Was there time at least for an authoritative survey? Was anybody doing anything, they asked? Somebody was, although Churchill seemed to know nothing about it.

Frank Hill had joined HER under unusual circumstances. A Londoner from a family of modest means, he had held various jobs in industry working on radios and early televisions, and had taken an external degree from Birkbeck College, London. When war came he had transferred to military work and afterwards he and a friend set up Rapid Radio Repairs in south London, with a Morris Minor for their delivery van. In 1950 Hill was approaching forty, and he began to feel he should be in pensionable work. His eye fell upon an advertisement in *Wireless World* for a Ministry of Supply job at Farnborough. He didn't want to move to Farnborough, but he had the idea of writing to the Ministry to ask if there were any similar vacancies elsewhere. What he would really like, he wrote, was a job in electronics at Fort Halstead.

This inquiry caused a flutter of alarm in HER's security department, where it was viewed with the gravest suspicion. In no time at all, Hill found himself sitting in an office at Shell-Mex House being grilled by a rather fierce man who expressed no interest what-soever in his qualifications or references. The man was Dr Tyte, and all he wanted to know was what Hill knew about Fort Halstead, how he knew it and what had prompted him to ask for work there. The explanation was surprising: Hill had since child-hood been an amateur naturalist, and during the war he had visited Fort Halstead on defence work. 'I found', he recalled later, 'that the labs were situated on a site on top of the North Downs, over-looking the Weald of Kent, with beech woods and hazel coppice, full of wild flowers, especially orchids. I thought this would be an ideal place to work.'[38] Hill eventually managed to convince Tyte that his ulterior motives were limited to studying wild flowers in his lunch hour, and after passing through the usual civil service hoops he was given a most important job at HER, designing the control system which would send the signal to fire the weapon.

When he learned that the test would take place in the Monte Bello Islands, Hill's curiosity as a naturalist was aroused and he obtained permission to visit the Natural History Museum and the Botanic Gardens at Kew to discuss making a study of the islands' flora and fauna. He was given some instruction in the proper techniques and when he sailed for the islands he had in his personal luggage all the equipment he needed. And he was not the only natural historian making the journey. A naval officer, Commander G. Wedd, had laid plans for a similar study of the marine life. Had Churchill known, he might have spared himself some criticism.

AT THE END of May, HER was ready to bring together the principal components of the weapon, with the exception of the plutonium core and the initiator. A bare sufficiency of satisfactory lenses had been produced; a complete supercharge was ready and the tamper, imperfect as it was, was cast. One last job had to be done: Len Bunce had to cut the loading cartridge from the high-explosive sections. This was the plug that, with the core fitted to its tip, would be slid into the sphere at the last moment to complete the Hurricane assembly. Creating it was a difficult job, partly because no special-ist machine had been developed to do it. Boring the four-inch hole into the supercharge was straightforward because it went through the middle, but with the lenses it went half in one lens and half in another. Great care had to be taken.

The weapon was assembled at Foulness over several days at the beginning of June, amid exceptionally tight security. Ernie Mott and George Gallie from Woolwich were in charge, and they brought with them their very best technicians. Most of the parts came from Woolwich as well, but others arrived from the Royal Ordnance Factory at Chorley in Lancashire, from Fort Halstead and from Chatham Dockyard. They were brought together in Building 23, a large hall in the Magazine area in which a special gantry had been erected to support the bomb. Screens were drawn across the front of the building to prevent anyone seeing in when the doors were opened.

A team had been at work in Woolwich for some months designing a structure to hold the weapon together. It was an interesting challenge: no screw or rod could be allowed to penetrate the sphere itself, and yet the whole assembly was five feet across, comprised more than forty separate pieces and weighed several tons. Moreover, once all the pieces were in place no settling of any kind could be tolerated, since this would create gaps which would be likely to disrupt the implosion wave. The solution chosen was to wrap the sphere in a rigid coat and exert a constant inward pressure from all directions. Aluminium alloy plates were made to match the hexagons and pentagons of the lenses; these were then locked together by piano hinges – fine hinges which run the whole length of a joint, so called because they are used on the keyboard lids of pianos. When all the plates were connected together and the hinges secured, the result was a rigid ball. Inside this, the weapon itself was covered with thick felt, and between the felt and each aluminium plate was a rubber bag. When everything was in place all the rubber bags were pumped full of air, placing the sphere inside under steady inward pressure. This ingenious arrangement was the work of many hands, including a team from Percival Engineering, the aircraft firm in Luton.

To lift the heavy high-explosive sections into place, they used Bunce's system of vacuum pads. A pad was placed against a block and suction applied until it could be lifted. Then the block was hoist into position, manoeuvred to ensure it sat comfortably with its neighbours, and released. There were constant inspections, measurements and discussions. Occasionally, work stopped while a piece of equipment was sent to the workshop for repair or adjustment. Once or twice, PVC tape was used to give a tighter fit between segments. The job took Mott's team several days to complete, working very long hours. Penney visited to watch the progress and give encouragement. When the sphere was complete it was draped with a dust cover, lifted on to an open lorry and covered with a heavy tarpaulin. It was ready to begin its journey to Australia.

On Saturday 5 June, at 8.30 a.m., the lorry was driven out of Building 23 and across the Essex marshes, with Mott, Gallie and the others following in cars 'like mourners at a funeral'.[39] Leaving the ranges, the convoy made its way through Shoeburyness town, passing the occasional plainclothes security officer reading his newspaper with studied nonchalance. Down the High Street to the waterfront it went, and on to the pier, where the large, dustbin-shaped load was transferred to a barge. From there it crossed the estuary to Sheerness, to be hoist aboard HMS *Plym* and manoeuvred into place in the weapon room deep in the hold. Three days later, the little frigate set out on its final journey.

11

The Voyage Out

JUST after 2 p.m. on 10 June 1952, delayed a few hours by an unseasonably foggy morning, HMS *Campania* left its berth in Portsmouth to begin the 10,000-mile voyage to the Monte Bello Islands. Steaming out past the Isle of Wight and into the Channel, it bore little outward resemblance to a fighting ship. On the flight deck were three Dragonfly helicopters and two Sea Otter light aircraft, but they could scarcely be seen for crates, Land Rovers, cranes and above all boats – eighteen of them in all, ranging from dinghies to thirty-five-foot pinnaces. Below decks, crates and boxes were everywhere, some stacked together in cages, some loose. And besides the freight, there were the passengers: eighty-five scientists, about half of them from High Explosive Research and the rest trawled from other branches of the civil service. They had boarded the previous afternoon and spent an animated evening registering their arrival and finding their way around the ship. They were particularly struck by the bar arrangements. 'It was a pleasant surprise', wrote Noah Pearce in his diary, 'to learn that a third of a tot of gin costs 2d and one is allowed nine such thirds per day. A comparable amount of whisky costs 3d. It was at once obvious that, even without the intention of becoming intoxicated at frequent intervals, at least one aspect of life in *Campania* looked attractive.'[1] They were to be away from home for up to five months and they had been allowed to tell only their immediate relatives the purpose and destination of their voyage. A

184

number of those relatives waited on the quay through the damp morning to wave goodbye as the ship departed.

The notion that the bulk of the scientific team should sail to the test site, rather than fly, had been accepted only with reluctance. As early as January 1951, when he read the Epicure report on the islands, Penney had suggested that his staff should go by air. 'A substantial proportion of the scientific effort of HER's main project' would be involved, he wrote, and 'it would therefore be most uneconomical to take them to and from this distant site by sea'.[2] He also observed that the domestic life of the scientists, who were after all civilians, would suffer less disruption if they did not have to spend long weeks sailing to Australia. These views were not accepted; most of the scientists were to sail, not fly, and they would make use of the time preparing their equipment and planning the detail of the test. There were good reasons for this: hundreds of tons of scientific equipment were required for the test and this was far too much for the RAF to handle. It would have to go by sea and to be at the site in time it would have to leave in June. Rather than be separated from their apparatus at such a crucial period, the scientists would have to go with it. Dizzy Davis thought they should count themselves lucky; it would be 'a prolonged rest-cure', he said, and 'any right-minded man would regard these trials as a grand experience combined with the fun of a picnic'.[3]

The voyage would be made in six stages, punctuated by calls at Gibraltar, Sierra Leone, South Africa, Mauritius and Fremantle. The Cape route had been chosen for security reasons; anti-British unrest was rife in Egypt and the thought of any difficulty with HMS *Plym* in the Suez Canal was not to be contemplated. Not only was it to be a long trip, it would also be a slow one, for the *Plym*, which had sailed directly from Sheerness and joined the *Campania* in the Bay of Biscay, could manage a modest pace at best, and struggled with an ocean swell. Throughout the voyage the frigate was described merely as the *Campania*'s escort and the Press attention which met the two ships at every port was concentrated on the aircraft-carrier, on which it was assumed that the weapon was being carried.

On the second day out from Portsmouth, everybody on the *Campania* was assembled to hear an address by the task force commander, Rear Admiral Torlesse. It was a dramatic speech, referring to Churchill and the importance of the task ahead. The Admiral took his theme from the ship's motto, 'All of one Company'. This was, he said, a joint endeavour of the armed services and civilian scientists, and each man on the operation (not a single woman was on board) should strive to create unity. These were noble sentiments, but in fact precious little thought had been given to what appears to have been an unprecedented circumstance aboard a Royal Navy ship: the presence on a long voyage of a large number of civilians who were not merely passengers but partners in a mission of the highest importance. Each of the scientists, before leaving England, had received a circular from Brooking giving a brief description of life on a naval vessel. The Navy for its part did not feel the need to brief its men on how civilians might behave, but it took the exceptional step of declaring all the scientists honorary officers. This resolved several pressing questions of naval etiquette and gave all the scientists full membership of the officers' mess – in naval terms the wardroom. The *Campania* also carried a liaison officer, Pat Cooper. A naval captain who had spent some time at Fort Halstead, Cooper might have been well placed to iron out little difficulties between scientists and sailors, but he was to find himself fully absorbed with organizational work. In short, the ship was unprepared for a clash of cultures, and that is what occurred.

There had been signs of it even before Admiral Torlesse delivered his sermon on team spirit. Officers had been affronted by the conduct of the civilians as the ship left the quayside at Portsmouth. While all naval hands had stood to attention on deck in accordance with tradition, a crowd of scientists lolled over the side, as one of them put it, 'waving to mum'.[4] Then, on the first morning of the voyage, it was the turn of the scientists to be irritated, as they were turned out of their cabins, barred from the wardrooms and chased around the decks by sailors armed with buckets and mops. This was the daily ritual of 'scrubbing over'. For an hour or more from 9 a.m., just as the scientists were expecting to get down to work, they could do nothing. When they protested they were told that this would happen every morning of the voyage and, to make matters worse, nobody on the naval side seemed to regard this as a problem. In the weeks to come, trivial matters of this kind came to assume some importance.

Scientists and sailors could hardly be more different. Scientists are expected to think independently and to doubt received wisdom. Even in the British civil service of 1952, how they dressed, behaved or spoke mattered less than the quality of their work. Hierarchies existed but it was accepted, indeed expected, that some of the best work would be done by the youngest, sharpest minds. By contrast the Royal Navy of 1952, largely for good reasons, lived by discipline, rank and tradition; everybody on board ship was required to know exactly how he related to everybody else at all times and in any given circumstance. Officers did not fraternize with other ranks and among themselves observed a precise protocol. In the very best of conditions these two cultures might have coexisted peacefully, but the conditions on board the *Campania* were far from the very best. Among the scientists, the isolation and reduced activity aboard ship in these final, tense weeks before their work reached its climax bred frustration. More than half of them, moreover, were junior and young, some of them in their early twenties. These men were quick to balk at naval ways and give offence to officers, who soon grew to doubt whether they deserved their place in the wardroom. On the naval side, Admiral Torlesse and his senior staff were formal even by naval standards, to a degree that had not been anticipated either by Cooper, the liaison officer, or Brooking. A pattern soon developed in which the scientists felt aggrieved at the Navy for not being more flexible, and the Navy felt aggrieved at the scientists for not making more effort to conform.

Our chief witness is the physicist J. J. McEnhill, who had been in Penney's blast effects team but was now assigned to Operation Hurricane as official historian. A Scot, and a perfectionist in his scientific work (he it was who built the best of the home-made televisions), McEnhill found much in what he saw to offend his tidy nature. His account of the expedition, written some time after his return to Britain, bears some resemblance to a school report written by a disappointed teacher. Its early pages are dominated by descriptions of the tensions on board the *Campania* and though he struggles to be even-handed, a thread of irritation with the Navy is woven through the text. Of the scrubbing over problem, for example, he records that, after considerable delay, the Navy agreed to leave the lower wardroom free for the scientists while the ship was cleaned. This arrangement 'should have been possible from the beginning, but for some reason it was ignored. Thus staff were made to feel that during certain hours they were an encumbrance in the ship and certainly not "of the ship". This was not very good either for morale or efficiency.'[5] The voyage had hardly begun.

Portsmouth to Gibraltar took four days and, once scrubbing over was out of the way, the scientists were able to get down to work. They knew before they boarded that they would be divided into teams relating to their tasks at the test and the first step was for the team members to get to know each other and establish what each person's functions were. Another early job was to get the laboratory and the workshop up and running, which was swiftly done, and both were to be used intensively throughout the voyage. The principal task, however, was to arrange the stores. The crates of scientific equipment had been packed and loaded in a great hurry; some which contained delicate equipment had been broken; others were stowed with their 'This way up' arrows pointing stubbornly down, and a fair number carried no markings at all. It was to prove a monumental task to get them in order, with proper inventories, ready for rapid unloading at the correct sites in the Monte Bellos. There were thousands of boxes and in the end every one was opened, examined and re-stowed; the job took the whole journey to complete.

In the approach to Gibraltar, on the Saturday morning, another ship of the task force, HMS *Tracker*, was seen moving out on its way to Australia via the Suez Canal. They would meet again at Fremantle. For those on board the *Campania* and the *Plym*, Gibraltar afforded a weekend of leisure. Pearce enjoyed 'a day of touring, swimming, shopping, dinner and eventually a night club with various acts including a striptease . . . We left about 2 a.m. and made our unsteady way back to the ship and bed.' The next day, the garrison laid on three-ton lorries to provide tours of the Rock which were, McEnhill records, 'enjoyable if rather breath-taking', and then on the Monday morning, in perfect weather, the two ships embarked on the second and longest leg of the voyage; the length of Africa with just one brief pause at Freetown.[6] Their speed was kept to a stately twelve knots so that the *Plym* could keep up. Soon, however, the temperature rose, the waters became bluer and flying fish and Portuguese men-of-war could be seen – intimations of the tropical waters ahead.

The *Campania* now began to demonstrate some of its shortcomings as a passenger ship. The whole interior was stuffy at best, even in cabins and other rooms which had portholes or 'scuttles' that could be opened. Windscoops, designed to pull fresh air in through the scuttles, were issued but it was found that they were the wrong size and were virtually useless. The ventilation machinery was scarcely any better. In the conference room, for example, where Admiral Torlesse held daily staff meetings, 'the roar of the ventilation system made it almost impossible to follow a discussion, and if it was switched off, as usually happened, the atmosphere rapidly became unpleasant'.[7] In some of the cabins things were even worse. It turned out that ventilator intakes on the starboard side had been placed just behind the engine exhausts, so that they pumped diesel fumes directly into the sleeping quarters. Three single cabins and four four-berth cabins were rendered uninhabitable, if not actually dangerous. Tyte, the senior scientist on board, laid the blame squarely on the Navy. He noted indignantly in his diary: 'The trouble seems quite fundamental and appears to have arisen from the Admiralty failing to carry out an adequate conversion of the ship to meet in full the tasks required from it. It seems that no easy remedy can be effected, at least a month's work in harbour being required.'[8] At first, camp beds were issued, and some of the displaced scientists slept in the fresh air on the flight deck, but they soon gave up when they found that the Navy's tropical routine involved noisy activity on deck from 5.30 a.m. – 'rather disturbing to their beauty sleep', chuckled Tyte.[9] In the end a number of scientists were condemned to a gypsy existence for the rest of the voyage, moving around among the spare cabins as and when they were habitable.

The hot weather also brought to a head another problem: dress. The letter circulated to the scientists before they left England had indicated that they should not expect strict standards of formality, but McEnhill writes that it was apparent very soon that 'service officers were preserving a fairly high degree of formal evening dress wear and . . . the civilian staff were expected to conform as far as possible'.[10] A few stubbornly attended dinner in shirt-sleeves, to the annoyance of their hosts, but most tried their best, even if this involved some stoicism. Their predicament was demonstrated most clearly on the second Saturday night of the voyage, with the ship well into the tropics. McEnhill wrote: 'It was rather a festive occasion at which the wardroom mess were dining Admiral Torlesse and Dr Tyte [these two were normally served their meals in their cabins]. Consequently the complete mess were assembled in the lower wardroom which was brim full. The dinner was excellent but the heat was overpowering and the men were sweating profusely. Most civilians had adopted, as suitable wardroom wear, light trousers, shirt and tie and a lightweight coat [jacket].'[11] While naval officers sat serene in their purpose-made tropical 'whites', the scientists suffered. Noah Pearce was among the victims: 'How hot and sticky it was! Everybody perspired and mopped and perspired again. I could see McPherson's back from where I sat. His jacket looked as if he had been out in a severe thunderstorm. My own shirt was quite soaked.'

It was not only at meal times that the naval dress code set demanding standards. The scientists had been issued with army khaki outfits suitable for the tropics but these were frowned on by some of the naval staff. They certainly lacked elegance, particularly after they had been shrunk in the laundry, which had a rough way with much non-naval attire. Amongst their own in the laboratory or the workshop, or in their cabins, the scientists would often strip down to just shorts, but this would not do in the wardroom. Most of the men followed the rules, McEnhill writes. 'A few people, however, often used the wardroom much as they would a youth hostel, with shorts rolled up to their buttocks and even an occasional body was seen on view without a shirt. These are small matters but they create friction when naval staff realize that, should they desire to do these things, they would be prohibited.'[12] The dress code was to cause the worst incident of service-civilian hostility of the voyage, when a naval order was issued reminding civilians that ties should be worn to the evening cinema show and a number of scientists responded by turning up in ties, but without shirts.

Another point of friction was fraternization. Naval officers were annoyed to see some of the civilians striking up friendships with stewards in the wardroom, and indulging in what McEnhill calls 'comradely banter and argument' with them.[13] They were also irritated to learn that some of the junior scientists routinely spent their evenings below decks with the crew. These were serious breaches of the rules. In a general way, the naval side felt that what they perceived as a stubborn refusal to conform was poor return for their efforts to be good hosts, and these efforts are well documented. In the first fortnight of the journey they laid on a programme of lectures about the ship and its organization, intended to help their guests adapt to naval life. There were tours of the engine room, the command centre and the bridge, where all who wished to were allowed take the wheel for a short spell. Courses in navigation were offered, and taken up by no fewer than twenty-eight civilians, and, after the ship reached the Equator on 25 June, the scientists were included in the ceremony of Crossing the Line. This last was judged a great success by all. A tarpaulin was rigged up on the flight deck and filled with water, and all first-timers across the line, irrespective of rank, were thoroughly dunked. 'In the robust frolic which ensued', wrote McEnhill, 'a sense of good fellowship was engendered.'[14]

This was not enough, however, to overcome the resentments of some of the scientists. Here there was a problem of discipline which did not pass unnoticed by the naval officers. No formal arrangements for discipline among the civilians had been made before departure and Tyte, living as he did quite separately from the rest of the scientists, was not disposed to establish any. Where work was concerned, junior scientists were responsible to their team leaders, the team leaders to the Assistant Directors and the Assistant Directors to Tyte. In matters of general conduct, however, while senior men might take it upon themselves to speak to errant juniors, their authority was not clear-cut. Thus when scientists defied naval instructions and wandered on to gun platforms or other restricted areas, it was by no means obvious what should be done about it, or by whom. This problem of discipline was not only a factor in relations between Navy and scientists, it also caused concern on the security side when it emerged that some scientists, in their correspondence with home, were making a mockery of what little secrecy still pertained to the task force's movements. In letters not just to family, but to friends and even to banks, solicitors and building societies, they were giving dates and addresses of future ports of call so that they might receive replies. Here again, Tyte was reluctant to act and it was only after an incident at Mauritius, when one scientist returned from shore leave so drunk he needed medical attention, that a meeting of senior scientists was called to discuss staff conduct. The response was to send a memorandum to all members of staff. McEnhill's verdict was caustic: 'This caused a certain amount of resentment to the majority of staff who required no reminders of this nature to conduct themselves as reasonable civil servants, and to the small minority to whom it was presumably directed it is somewhat doubtful whether such a procedure was really effective.'[15]

McEnhill insists again and again that relations between Navy and scientists were broadly correct, and that friction was the exception and not the rule, but just as insistently he returns to these tensions in almost every page. Even when he writes about the happy mingling of different groups at social events on board ship, he adds: 'There was a natural tendency, of course, for intermingling of civilian and naval staff not to occur completely and naval officers and civilian staff tended to keep in roughly separate groups.'[16] He also remarks that 'the civilian staff and the naval staff were naturally critical of their respective functions'.[17] There is an assumption that the two, like oil and water, cannot mix, and he develops this notion by wondering aloud whether separate messes for the two groups would have been a better arrangement. Although McEnhill tries to be fair to the Navy, his heart is clearly with the scientists and there is no mistaking his underlying satisfaction when he reports, for example, that 'occasionally in the evenings people tended to congregate and have a loudish chat or a frolic immediately under the open scuttle of the Admiral's cabin'.[18]

McEnhill's view receives broad support in another report on the expedition, written by Captain Cooper, the overworked liaison officer. While the civilians mixed well among themselves, Cooper wrote, 'friendships and close contacts with the naval personnel were slower and only partial at the best, but in spite of natural criticisms of their respective points of view, a great benefit was obtained from the intermingling; on the other hand there were points of friction and trouble. Most of them were small, taken independently, but in their aggregate they fostered the feeling which unfortunately existed . . . that the Navy thought the civilians rather a nuisance and the civilians thought the Navy were not being sufficiently helpful.'[19] Cooper, himself a naval man by background, provides us with another instructive insight into navy-scientist relations. Most mornings of the voyage, after breakfast, Admiral Torlesse held a rather formal staff meeting in the infamous Conference Room. Tyte usually attended, and so during the latter part of the journey did Cooper. He was dismayed by what he saw. 'Although these meetings should have been a means of constant and intimate touch between scientific and naval staff, they seldom achieved this desirable state and covered normally only service affairs. There was unfortunately a continual difficulty in getting closely together at any stage of the operation.'[20] This points to the nub of the matter: the awkward relationship between Tyte and Torlesse.

Before the task force had sailed, Admiral Torlesse, at meetings in London of the Hurricane Executive, had shown himself to be uneasy about the matter of command and authority. Hurricane was explicitly a naval operation, and the Rear Admiral was formally its commanding officer, but he could foresee the difficulties that might be caused by the existence within the task force of a chain of command quite separate from and quite alien to the naval one. Worse, this other structure, which was the scientific side of Hurricane, was in practical control of the bomb and all its paraphernalia and had a fairly exclusive understanding of it. Would the naval commander really call the shots? The Hurex records show Torlesse more than once stepping in, during the drafting of orders, to ensure that he would, and that his authority was made explicit. But the value of these written orders proved limited. Tyte had from the outset taken the opposite view to Torlesse's, expressing to his colleagues grave reservations about the wisdom of placing the operation under service control. 'The great majority of service people just can't play fair in such an arrangement', he felt.[21] Whether by oversight or because of this mutual suspicion, the preparation of the expedition had been hampered by the failure of the two men to work together. They had maintained separate offices, Torlesse at the Admiralty and Tyte at Fort Halstead, and met only in formal circumstances. To make matters worse, Tyte was never made a member of the Hurex Committee.

All this would have mattered less had the two men got along personally once the ships sailed, but they did not. Torlesse, whose naval career had started at the age of sixteen in the Grand Fleet at Scapa Flow, was an officer of the old school. Among fellow-officers he could be relaxed and charming and he undoubtedly enjoyed to the full the privileges of rank, but he was also formal and strict where he thought necessary. If the Admiral decided to attend the ship's cinema show, for example, everybody was required to stand up as he walked in. Torlesse tried to draw Tyte into the clubbish circle of his senior naval staff, but failed, and thereafter they communicated purely on formal terms. These were not the best conditions in which to tackle the misunderstandings and frictions that arose on board. Tyte, for his part, took offence easily and had a short fuse. Like McEnhill, he was not above taking pleasure in naval irritation: at the very end of the journey he was still joking mischievously about 'the right hand side' and 'the sharp end' of the ship, and he remarked in his diary: 'Personally, I don't think I shall ever become the complete sailor; I still slip from grace from time to time and refer to Captain Cole's command [the *Campania*] as a boat; I don't think he likes it very much.'[22] Tyte also preferred to keep the Navy at arm's length so far as scientific business was concerned. He did not bring his senior staff to Torlesse's daily meetings, although this might have made possible a closer collaboration; instead, he alone represented the scientific side.

Just as Cooper viewed this with dismay, so too did some of the scientists. In particular they had reason to wish they knew more about what went on at the staff meetings. 'Even in these early days', writes McEnhill, 'there was a growing feeling among senior civilian officers that they were not being kept fully briefed on matters relevant to their interest. This sense of divorcement tended to grow as time went on.'[23] This was partly a practical matter of distribution lists and the availability of copies of documents (then so cumbersome to produce), and McEnhill indicates that a share of the blame lay in Tyte's office. But the 'sense of divorcement' also reflected a lack of liaison with the Navy. Towards the end of the voyage, Tyte and Cooper complained to Torlesse at a staff meeting that they were not receiving copies of certain naval signals relevant to their work. Two communications had come in which had not been passed on, one relating to stores and the other to biological observations that might be required at the test site. The Admiral agreed that this should not happen again, but it did.

And what about work? Did the scientists at least put this captive period to good use? They tried, but on the whole the results were disappointing. McEnhill noted: 'In an expedition of the present type it would be unwise to assume that because there is, say, seven or eight weeks available during transit, this could be used to do an amount of work or planning by men unaccustomed to naval life, comparable with what they could achieve in their normal surroundings.'[24] What he meant by this can be deduced from a look at the routine that became established on board. The day began with breakfast, from 7.30 to 8.45 a.m. Then in the first half of the morning, as we have seen, scrubbing over took place and it was hard to get down to work. The period that followed, between 10 a.m. and lunch, was the most productive of the day. For some there were team meetings and lectures, usually in the officers' study (a room so noisy that the one function it could definitely not accommodate was study). Those with calculations or other paperwork to do tended to gather in the upper wardroom, which 'at these hours, had the untidy appearance of a students' reading room'.[25] The laboratory and workshop were in constant use, indeed work benches were in such demand they had to be reserved in advance. Meanwhile, down in the holds, often the hottest part of the ship, the arrangement and re-arrangement of stores continued day after day. After lunch, which was at 12.30 p.m., productivity tended to slip. The laboratory remained busy, but many scientists not involved in practical work simply put their feet up. They had been impressed from the beginning by the art sailors displayed in 'getting their heads down', and it was not long before they learned to follow suit.[26] The interval between lunch and tea at 3.30 p.m. thus became an unofficial siesta. The later afternoon was the time for most of the organized sports on board. These ranged from volley ball and tennis on the flight deck, with the occasional 'fierce bout' of hockey, to badminton and table tennis in the recreation area on the hangar deck.[27] Those with a lesser appetite for exercise walked up and down what clear deck they could find, while those with none at all took advantage of the deck-chairs at the aft end. At 7.30 p.m. there was dinner, followed by coffee, drinks and evening entertainments. On two nights a week there were officers' film shows on the hangar deck, while on other nights the fiction library was busy; duplicate bridge was popular and darts were played in the lower wardroom.

On the face of it, it seems a very pleasant, undemanding life, like a cruise with homework thrown in, but McEnhill takes care to clear his colleagues of any suspicion of having enjoyed themselves. 'It requires great force of personal discipline', he found, 'to complete in a day as a passenger an amount of work which might be regarded as normal in a shore establishment. There are many distractions of noise, loudspeakers, buzz of activity and the novelty of surroundings to which it takes some time to adjust and enable one to carve a working day out without allowing distractions to enter. Life in a ship appeared, moreover, to have a soporific effect which was engendered partly by the fact that often the ventilation was not too good, and, although it appears paradoxical, it is true to say that fresh clean air is often not available for long stretches of the day in the ship.'[28]

Heat was not the only obstacle to work. Although Cooper, the sailor, put on record his view that the sea was relatively calm for the whole of the voyage, that was not how the landlubbers saw it. True, in the first three weeks the worst they had to contend with was a slight roll, but on 28 June, three days south of the Equator, the ship encountered its first strong headwind. By the following morning it was blowing a chilly force six, the *Campania* was rolling uncomfortably and a number of the scientists had taken to their cabins. Laboratory work became difficult and study was hampered by the struggle to prevent books sliding to the floor. This rough spell, which lasted three days, was the first of four encountered on the voyage, each of which disrupted work and sleep, and depressed morale.

The time-and-motion mathematics of the journey are unimpressive. It took fifty-nine days to sail to the Monte Bellos. If shore leave, Sundays and other rest days are excluded, there were thirty-seven working days at sea. Subtract the days when the weather was either oppressively hot or disturbingly rough and only twenty-one remain. In other words, only slightly more than one day in three was a proper working day. Small wonder that Cooper concluded: 'Measured on a works' value basis, there is no doubt that a sea voyage is wasteful.'[29]

On 3 July, the day before arrival in South Africa, a naval commander gave a talk on the points of interest and beauty in the Cape Town area. The halt was keenly anticipated, for the scientists had been at sea for eighteen days and had received no mail since Gibraltar. A number were expecting the results of promotion interviews which had taken place just before departure – they cannot have welcomed the attentions of an albatross which stubbornly followed the ships in the few days before arrival. Before dawn on 4 July, McEnhill writes, 'the twinkling ribbon of lights of Simonstown lay ahead. Most of the staff were up early to see the approach and were well rewarded by the beauty of the sunrise and the splendid colours in the skies.'[30] They watched as, with some difficulty, the *Campania* was manoeuvred into a narrow dock, and then they 'melted off to study "apartheid" at first hand', many of them remaining ashore in hotels until early the following Tuesday.[31]

The next leg of the voyage began in wintry weather, with an icy wind and a heavy swell as soon as the Cape was passed. For two days the *Campania* rolled badly, rendering both work and sleep difficult. Then there was a pause of a couple of days, and then worse weather arrived, with winds reaching force six, persisting until the following Wednesday, the eve of arrival (a day late) in Mauritius. 'A pronounced feature of these days', writes McEnhill, 'was the lethargy and mood of frustration and boredom which was prevalent among the staff.'[32] This proved more than a mere passing phase, and McEnhill was not short of explanations: the movement of the ship in the swell, poor ventilation, lack of exercise, the rich naval diet, not enough positive work, homesickness and, finally, a sense of hiatus. 'The journey was obviously taking a long time, and a long time yet remained before the site was reached and a real live active job of work could be tackled.'[33] Efforts were made to raise spirits. Shipboard sports were revived, albeit with some difficulty on a tilting deck, while in the wardroom special events were organized. There was a tombola and, on another night, a quiz contest between Ministry of Supply staff and a team picked by the chaplain from the ship's writers, or clerks. Whether these improved morale is not recorded, but it is certain that the sight of the jagged peaks of Mauritius at first light on 17 July was greeted with considerable relief. A thirteen-gun salute welcomed the ships into Port Louis bay, and even an accompanying rainstorm did not impair the pleasure of returning to terra firma.

In Mauritius this visit by the task force was serving as a substitute for the usual call at the island by the Indian Ocean fleet, and the welcome was correspondingly formal and full-hearted, with parties, outings and sporting events. The highlight of the stay for many was a day at the races in Port Louis which, in McEnhill's words, was 'colourful, if perhaps not too remunerative'.[34] The visit was not without incident. On the second night one of the ship's cooks fell from a boat and drowned, and it was at Mauritius that one of the scientists returned so drunk he had to be taken to the ship's doctor. This event drew from McEnhill his primmest sermon: 'The blame for this cannot be wholly attributed to the man who, in fact, was little more than a boy and one of the youngest on board. Those colleagues of his who were with him, as older men, should have had a sufficiently developed sense of responsibility to have prevented this occurrence, or at least have sobered him before returning to the ship.'[35]

They set out on the eleven-day leg to Fremantle on the morning of 20 July. At first, the weather seemed much improved, but on the fifth day it broke again, this time worse than before. For the first time, 'fiddles' were fitted on wardroom dining tables to prevent plates and cups sliding about, and the ventilation system played a final trick on its captive victims, sluicing seawater through its ducts into the upper wardroom. The rolling of the ship caused the first serious accident to a civilian on board when a junior scientist, Percy Pridgeon, returning to his cabin after breakfast, was thrown against a lorry on the gallery deck and broke bones in both arms. The event caused some alarm, for an expedition so thinly staffed could ill afford to have men out of action. Pridgeon, a member of Challens's weapons room team, spent several weeks with his arms in plaster but in the event was able to play his part in the final days before the test.

When it came to bad weather, those on board the *Campania* had it easy by comparison with the few scientists on the *Plym*. A passage from McEnhill's record gives some measure of the small frigate's difficulties in an ocean storm: 'After dark it was quite impressive to stand on the quarter deck of *Campania* and look aft towards *Plym*. All that could be seen were her lights, and the sense of motion was highly accentuated because in the blackness the sea could not be seen and the motion could only be judged relative to *Campania*. The rise and fall of the lights seemed out of all proportion and their apparent extinction as the frigate slid into the trough of the swell was uncanny.'[36] It is no surprise that the unfortunates on the smaller vessel suffered acute seasickness. Since practical work on the *Plym* was almost impossible even in calm conditions, they were achieving little by being there, but a skeleton staff was needed to keep an eye on the weapon.

By this time, the scientists were at last beginning to see an end to the voyage. On 28 July, three days out from Fremantle, the last storm abated to allow a final burst of activity. Tyte was holding daily planning meetings with his Assistant Directors to go over the minutiae of the preparations. Stores destined for unloading at Fremantle were made ready and space was cleared to take on eight tons of food, some of which would be used in contamination experiments at the test. To prepare the ship's company for some of the hazards of working on the islands there was a series of first aid lectures. Attendance was compulsory but apparently worthwhile, if only as entertainment. Tyte records of Surgeon Lieutenant Etherington's exposition on bleeding: 'He was really excellent, grimly amusing and realistic, so much so that he nearly had one or two sinking cases on his hands.' Tyte adds a sceptical note: 'He kept quoting from the Admiralty's manual of first aid, "Keep the patient cheerful", but offered no views on how to do it. In fact he did it very effectively by saying that a doctor would arrive by helicopter in ten minutes to the scene of any accident on the islands, which certainly did not tie up with my enquiries.'[37] The last day saw a final lecture on the dangers of sunstroke, scorpions, coral snakes, fish-hooks and foreign bodies in the eye, followed in the evening by one of the highlights of the entire expedition – a screening of *A Streetcar named Desire*. On the Thursday morning, in beautiful weather, the *Campania* and the *Plym* slipped up the Swan River to Fremantle, where the *Tracker*, the Health Ship, was already docked.

In security terms, this four-day interlude on the Australian mainland represented one of the most vulnerable moments of the expedition. Once in the Monte Bellos, the scientists and the ships' crews would be isolated from outsiders; here, they were exposed to a local Press and population which were intensely interested in the goings-on to the north. The Perth papers had been energetic in their pursuit of information relating to what was, after all, the biggest story on their patch in many years, and the scientists were put on their guard. Tyte commended to them a naval formula for fending off enquiries: 'I can neither confirm, nor deny or comment upon your information, aspersion or allegation, as the case may be.'[38] A battery of photographers with long lenses watched the ships dock while a light plane flew over to get an alternative view, and the papers next day drew attention to a hut at the end of the *Campania*'s flight deck, speculating that this might be the accommodation for the bomb. It belonged, in fact, to the meteorologists, who would use it when filling their balloons. The *Plym*, meanwhile, received little attention. Although most of the civilians took advantage of the opportunity to swap their cabins for hotel rooms for a few nights, and spent their time as tourists and racegoers in Fremantle and Perth, there seem to have been no lapses of security.

For the senior officers and scientists, it was a busy time. Not only were the *Tracker*'s officers to hand for consultations, so were the commanders of the naval and Royal Engineers contingents which had already been at work in the Monte Bellos for three months. They brought with them fresh, first-hand information on the islands, the state of preparations and the problems to be overcome. In addition, a number of British and Australian officials closely interested in the test had come across from Melbourne and Canberra. A series of conferences took place to discuss progress at the site, Australian collaboration and other matters. An Australian expert provided a further briefing on health hazards on the islands, adding to the known dangers the threat of stonefish poisoning and salmonella infection, to which Tyte's response was: 'It seems the only thing to do when we empty our packing cases is to curl up in them and patiently await burial.'[39] At another meeting, Tyte was dismayed to find himself being teased by an Australian official about a slip-up in deliveries of equipment to Melbourne University, where some radiological work was to be done. Shaking his head at 'the Australian idea of ribbing', he wrote in his diary that he found the incident disconcerting because, although it was a minor matter, 'I am convinced I shall be shot over something in this job sooner or later'.[40] Admiral Torlesse, meanwhile, was heavily involved in formal functions, meeting the Lieutenant-Governor and Premier of Western Australia and attending a civic reception given by the Mayor of Fremantle. He scored a hit by agreeing to a demonstration flight by one of the helicopters on the *Campania*, the first seen in the area.

The last leg of the voyage, north to the islands, took three days and was graced by calm, sunny weather. With everyone absorbed in practical matters such as preparing equipment for unloading, the time passed quickly. On 8 August, eight weeks and three days after they waved goodbye to their families in Portsmouth, most of the scientists were on deck to catch their first sight of the Monte Bello Islands. In accordance with naval tradition, a signal of greeting was received from the vessels already there which referred simply to a biblical text, Luke: 13: 24: 'Strive to enter in at the straight gate . . .'[41] The *Tracker* and the *Plym* did just that, weaving their way by the narrow channel through the rocks and shallows into the lagoon, where the *Narvik* and the *Zeebrugge* were waiting to welcome them. Once inside, the *Plym* moored at the spot in Bunsen Channel chosen for its obliteration. The *Campania*, too big for the lagoon, took up position just to the east of the islands in the Parting Pool (so called because that was where HMAS *Karangi*'s cable 'parted', or broke, in a storm during the Epicure expedition). At long last, Admiral Torlesse saw his task force assembled for the final phase of Operation Hurricane.

12
The Core

WHILE the scientists who sailed out on the *Campania* began to find their way around the Monte Bellos, some of those who remained behind had still to make their contribution. Their chance came one morning in late August when the Aldermaston security barrier was raised to admit a lorry which had travelled down overnight from Windscale. It was a standard three-tonner, without military escort, and once inside the fence it made its way to building A1.1, where a knot of people was waiting on the step to greet it. One of them was Jimmy Hole, of the health physics team, who waited for the lorry to stop and then jumped up into the back. He found it empty save for 'an innocuous-looking dustbin' tightly secured at the back. 'It was yellow, with a lid which was padlocked', he recalled later. 'There were two drivers with a couple of guards and, to their surprise, I asked them to stand back while I did the external radiation check. I detected a certain amount of gamma-radiation coming through the containment. It was carried into A1 and placed in the middle of the floor in lab number one, one of the three laboratories opposite the main production line. I called Barnes to tell him it was here. I went in to monitor it every hour on the hour and the readings were steady. A couple of days later we opened it up. Inside was a cylinder, and a container inside the cylinder. We took out three small pots, each about the size of a two-pound jam-jar, made of stainless steel, with a handle. That was the first consignment of plutonium.'

All was now ready for the manufacture of the core. Graham Hopkin called a meeting in the conference room in A1.2, where many of his staff had been sleeping on camp beds during the previous hectic weeks. He went over the whole process step by step, discussing possible snags and identifying each of the people who would be performing the necessary tasks. There were no surprises, for the process had been rehearsed several times using lead instead of plutonium and everyone knew what they had to do. One job, however, had not been rehearsed, and that was the retrieval of the finished core at the end of the line. This would have to be done via the 'frog corridor', the contamination zone behind the glove boxes. Hopkin asked Bill Lord to do it. Then it was time to start.

The steel jam-jars were placed inside the first glove box of the line, Guv Willows pushed his hands firmly into the latex gloves, lifted one and twisted open the lid. At this moment, the plutonium was exposed inside the box and all the specialist equipment created to contain the contamination over the previous year and a half began to do its job. David Lewis announced over the Tannoy: 'Aldermaston is now active.'[1] What Willows produced from the box was a 'slug', a disc resembling a metallic muffin, covered in lacquer but gritty and generally unimpressive in appearance. Willows passed it from Box One, through a little passage with a hatch at each end, to Box Two, where it was weighed, broken into pieces small enough to fit into the crucible, and passed on to Box Three. This procedure was repeated until sufficient discs were ready. Then the required quantity of gallium was weighed and passed through. When the ingredients were assembled in Box Three, the casting began.

The box was small, like an enclosed laboratory desk-top with a double-thickness perspex screen on the working side. The gloves, too, were double-thickness and reached right to the shoulder, but they were flexible enough to do delicate work, having been made for Aldermaston by a London firm of contraceptive manufacturers. Inside the box, in an argon atmosphere, was a small furnace, some crucibles (the material eventually chosen for these was cerium sulphide), some moulds and the pouring and monitoring equipment, some of it on rotating trays to ensure it was in easy reach. The scientist, with his hands in the gloves and his forehead resting against the perspex, had to perform complex tasks which would have been difficult even in an open laboratory. It was hot work, slow work and anxious work. Bill Lord recalls: 'Despite the assurances of the theoreticians, there was a persistent and lurking fear that as the plutonium slugs were melted and the molten metal took up a compact shape in the bottom of the crucible, a criticality incident could occur, giving an intense neutron flux.' A sudden release of neutrons was one form of radiation against which the glove box gave no protection; if it happened, the man working at the box would almost certainly be killed and others standing beside or behind him would also be at risk of radiation poisoning. Lord notes: 'The neutron monitors in the building would indicate that such an event had occurred, but not in time to give any warning.'[2]

Soon after the furnace was switched on, as the temperature steadily rose, something unexpected happened. A blue flame appeared around the melt. Hearts stopped. What was it? Had something gone wrong? Could this be a sign of imminent criticality? Lewis announced flatly: 'Well, boys, it's too late to run', so they just waited.[3] The clicking of the neutron counters remained steady, the flame died away and no disaster came; the moment had passed. It was a chemical reaction, apparently from some impurity in the argon supply catching light. The melting went ahead. Once molten, the metal – now a plutonium-gallium alloy – was poured into the mould and set aside to cool. After this, it was broken out of its mould, tidied up and examined. The result was not so much unimpressive as distressing, given the high standard of cast required for the bomb. The hemisphere was 'honeycombed, and depressingly like a mouldy cheese'.[4] It was now passed through to Box Four, the press box, in the hope that when compressed in the die it would look better.

This was the first moment in the procedure when the plutonium, cool, clean and freshly cast, could be seen. It was a dull grey in colour, but it was without doubt the most expensive, dangerous and exotic piece of metal ever cast in Britain. Beside it, a dome of pure platinum would have been commonplace. Lord wrote later: 'Everybody who had access to A1.1 came to have a look. At that time, with the building only just completed, there were many people still on the access list who may have needed access during the building stage but who certainly did not need it once the building work was completed, but as their names were still on the board they could walk into the building, and they did. I have a picture in my mind of Knight with his hands in the gloves of the press box working on one of the half-cores, the sweat running down his face, his body pressed hard against the box front by the mass of people behind him, all trying to get a view of what was happening. Hopkin was very put out by this situation, and after that first day's experience he had the entry limited to those of us who were actually involved.'[5]

Plutonium is a very hard metal, but one of the advantages of alloying it with gallium is that it becomes easily workable and can be pressed cold. This was Knight's job and once he had finished there was universal relief: the holes had gone and on first evidence it seemed the specification would be met. From Box Four the hemisphere was passed to Box Five, which contained a small lathe. There, the little fringe left by the pressing process was carefully trimmed off and the plane face of the hemisphere was machined flat so that the two halves would mate without any gap.

Box Six was the last of the line and here the plutonium was clad in a skin of gold, just a few thousandths of an inch thick but sufficient to prevent oxidization and make the hemisphere safe to handle. The cladding was done by placing a gold cap on top and a gold plate beneath and pressing them together until they sealed in a cold weld. Here now was the finished product, a gleaming, golden dome the size and shape of half a grapefruit, with a small dimple set into the centre of the flat face to accommodate the initiator. Its weight has never been revealed, but was probably four or five pounds. Another was needed, so the metallurgists went back to work and the production line ran through the night. It ran smoothly, with one exception. After the machining in Box Five, a small groove was found, a few thousandths of an inch deep, running all the way round the surface of the hemisphere just a half an inch from the pole. There had been a slip-up in trimming but no one knew whether such a tiny scratch was serious enough to require the whole hemisphere to be melted down and cast again. Penney was called in to inspect the damage, but since he had almost certainly not seen an unclad core before that day, he had little more to go on than his staff. He had a look, shook his head and confidently declared that it was nothing to worry about.

The final procedure was measurement, and the hemispheres were kept on the production line to be measured and re-measured over several hours to ensure that this peculiar metal did not play any unexpected tricks. At the second examination, there was disastrous news. One hemisphere was found to be very slightly altered in size. If confirmed, this meant that the gallium in the alloy had failed to stabilize the plutonium as it had been expected to do. This in turn would mean that both hemispheres should start to alter, and with the Hurricane test still weeks away they would certainly be unusable when the time came to insert them in a weapon. Lord had by now gone home, but Hopkin called him back, and painstakingly they set about repeating the measurements. As the new readings came up, it seemed that the hemisphere was within the specified limits. It could not have changed dimensions twice, so what had happened? An answer suggested itself. The measuring equipment had a dial-gauge like a clock face. Readings depended not only on what the needle was pointing to, but on the direction in which it had moved to reach that position. It was being used for the first time so perhaps someone had misread the directions and put pluses where there should have been minuses. The calculations were done again, this time using the incorrect procedures, and the result which had so distressed Hopkin duly emerged. It was a false alarm.

Hopkin was to receive more shocks as these tense days passed at Aldermaston. The next involved Bill Lord's mission to retrieve the half-cores from the last box. The line of glove boxes in which the cores were made formed the barrier between two rooms: the 'operating corridor', in which Willows, Knight and the rest had stood to do the work, and the 'frog corridor' behind the boxes. The former was a clean area which could be entered without protective suits; the latter, offering access to the back of the boxes, was designed and built in the knowledge that it would become contaminated. Anyone entering it, to service equipment in the boxes or deliver or remove materials, wore a heavy protective 'frogsuit' with a helmet and air supply lines. It was through the frog corridor that Bill Lord was to gain access to the end of the production line so that he could clean, pack and then bring out the first complete hemispheres. He had been surprised to be asked to do the job at such a late hour but agreed willingly and practised some of the procedures.

At the signal from Hopkin, he and a technician entered the

changing rooms, dressed in their frogsuits and walked down a 'throat' tunnel, one of the points at which air pressure was controlled. A metal door was opened by remote control and then closed behind them. Then a second metal door was opened. Lord wrote later: 'We went into the frog corridor with the transit containers (each the size and shape of a two-pint casserole) and other kit in polythene bags. We got each half-core on to the table in turn, decontaminated it using the agreed procedure and then transferred it to its transit container, which had a hermetic seal. Though out of sight, we had intercom contact with the frog supervisor and with the people standing in the operating corridor, so I was able to give a running account of our progress. The job was easily done and, each carrying one half-core, we made our way back down the frog corridor to come out.'

While they had been at work, of course, the two metal doors, known as Door A and Door B, had been closed. They were of an ingenious design, to seal off the corridor from the outside while still permitting the air lines connected to the two men's helmets to move freely. They were steel, about six feet wide, and they opened by sliding upwards. When they were closed, the bottom of the doors sat below floor level in a shallow trough of water. The water completed the seal, and at the same time the air lines passed safely through it beneath the doors. Lord and his companion now presented themselves at Door B, the first to confront them on the way out, and reported their position. On the intercom they heard the order: 'Open Door B.' Nothing happened. The instruction was repeated. Again nothing happened. Lord thought at first there had been a muddle, but before long it was clear that the door was jammed, and he and his companion were trapped inside the contaminated area with the core of the first British nuclear weapon.

This was a crisis. Hopkin was summoned, as was Alan Grange, the engineer in charge of A1.1. Soon David Deverell, who was in overall charge of frogging, was at the scene too. Called at home, he dashed back to Aldermaston down the quiet, twilit country roads to help. Door A was eventually opened but the machinery to lift door B could not be brought to life. Deverell, in desperation, tried to heave it upwards with his bare hands but it was hopeless; the thing weighed several tons. Then someone had a bright idea. The water-trough at the bottom of the door was drained, leaving a narrow clearance. Lord, still communicating by intercom, passed the two canisters carefully out through the gap to Deverell. The fear at this stage was that the door mechanism would suddenly give way and the canister would be crushed and broken open. It didn't happen. Next, Lord decided to try to squeeze through. The widest part of the suit was the helmet, and luckily this just fitted through the gap. By lying on the bottom of the trough and wriggling sideways it was just possible to get under the door, and both men were soon safely out. Once they had passed through the decontamination procedures and dressed, they were able to join a very relieved party celebrating in the local pub, the Pineapple.

The half-cores, meanwhile, were passed to another team, with another job to do. Bill Moyce's staff seized on the canisters with enthusiasm. The first thing they did was to take one hemisphere and rotate it very slowly, measuring the neutron output. The results were satisfactory, but then a hitch developed. When the test apparatus was taken apart the hemisphere would not budge. It had been resting on rubber and the natural heat of the plutonium had made the surface sticky. Half of the bomb core was stuck to their rig. Frank Morgan was watching. 'What the hell do we do, Frank?' they asked. 'I don't know', came the reply.[6] A long, worried silence ensued before a suggestion emerged. A vacuum pump was fetched from another lab and switched to blow. The cold air cooled the plutonium and it came unstuck.

By now, after a typical last-minute rush, the initiator was also ready. A Harwell team had prepared the highly radioactive polonium, shuttling backwards and forwards to Windscale to get the extraction plant running. This was only achieved as late as June 1952 and the metal was soon found to be every bit as dangerous as had been feared; several staff having to be withdrawn from work temporarily because of polonium ingestion. The fruit of their efforts, when the extraction process was successfully completed, weighed less than a milligram. It was quickly dispatched to Aldermaston to be united with the beryllium parts machined under Geoff Ellis's supervision at Woolwich. The final process was to coat the completed 'Urchin' with nickel, and then it was ready: a shiny ball-bearing no bigger than the top of a thumb.

The principal job of Moyce's team was to test whether these radioactive parts could be loaded into the bomb without risk of a criticality incident. They had prepared specialist machinery for this task and the idea was that, to give the scientists protection in the event of a sudden neutron release, it should be run from outside the room, by remote control. The necessary hydraulics and electrics, however, were not yet working well enough to allow that, so the operation was controlled from a corner of the room in which the machines stood. First, the plutonium hemispheres, which had hitherto been kept well apart, were tested on the smaller 'distance meter', which came to be known as Eric (as in 'little by little'). With counters running constantly to detect whether there was any movement towards criticality, the two parts were edged closer and closer together, in steps of one-thousandth of an inch over several hours, until they met. There was no fission. In this configuration, the core was safe. Then it had to be tested again, this time with an initiator and a uranium tamper. The little golden sphere was set in one half of the tamper and then, painfully slowly, cranked up into the other half. Safe again. The final test was to place the core in a simulated version of the full weapon assembly to ensure that no unpredicted effect from the surrounding materials could cause a movement towards criticality. For this the big machine, later to be dubbed Atlas, was used.

The big sphere had been simulated using graphite wax blocks in place of the high explosive. The core was attached to the end of a loading cartridge and the experiment began. Aubrey Thomas, a young member of Moyce's team, describes the scene: 'We had the cartridge hanging up and we had a little hydraulic hoist that lowered it gently. Getting it absolutely vertical was nearly impossible – we are talking about a few thousandths of an inch of clearance. We couldn't get the cartridge in; it would jam. In the end, we had some aircraft steps and I sat on them, with a lever and a wheel to move the machine this way and that.' While Thomas manoeuvred the cartridge into the tube from atop the steps above the assembly, a colleague sat near by with a curtain ring round his finger, watching the counters and ready to take drastic action. Everybody present was conscious that during criticality experiments at Los Alamos there had twice been accidents, and each time a man had died of radiation poisoning. So, at the first sign of trouble, the man with the curtain ring would give a tug, the string would flip back a knuckle joint and the big assembly would instantly drop down to the floor, leaving the cartridge hanging in the air at a safe distance. There were occasional false alarms: a flicker on the meter, a pull on the string and, with an almighty crash, the great five-foot sphere hit the ground. Then they started again. Thomas recalls: 'We started at 9 a.m. and finished at 5.30 a.m. next morning. Bill was flat out in a chair. He rang Penney, or the Admiral [Brooking], or both. It was safe to assemble.' They tidied up, put the plutonium in a safe and went home to bed. That night, the landlord of the Pineapple found himself host to another mysterious celebration.

Before being flown out to Australia the core had to undergo one more examination. An X-ray would provide the final reassurance that the plutonium casting contained no bubbles or impurities. As yet there was no X-ray set powerful enough for the job at Aldermaston so the cores had to be taken to Woolwich. Again, the job was given to Bill Lord, and again through no fault of his, things did not go exactly to plan. He set off early in the morning in an official car with a driver, the two canisters sitting in the back seat and an escort car following behind. The route chosen was through the Hampshire lanes and villages rather than the main A4. Before they reached the fringes of London, however, the HER car broke down. Lord, determined to stay with the plutonium, remained at the roadside and sent the escort driver to find a telephone and call Aldermaston for instructions. A pub was found, the landlord roused, and the call made. Hopkin was consulted, and his view was that Lord and his precious cargo should continue in the escort car without back-up. The journey was completed without further incident and the subsequent X-rays were satisfactory.

It was Bill Moyce who was given the job of flying with the core to the Monte Bellos. As the criticality expert, he would be required on the *Plym* to supervize the final fitting of the cartridge and core into the real weapon, although the loading itself would be done by Wing Commander Rowlands's RAF team. The flight out was organized by Rowlands, who had the core and a spare delivered to RAF Lyneham in Ministry of Supply furniture vans. They flew in a Hastings aircraft, the RAF's new four-engined transport plane, and the route included stopovers at British bases in Cyprus, Sharjah in the Gulf, Ceylon and finally Singapore, where Moyce, the cores and their RAF escort transferred to a Sunderland flying boat for the final leg direct to the islands.

Moyce had never flown before, and his instructions for the flight were hair-raising. If the aircraft looked likely to crash into the sea, the core was to be placed in a cork container and floated down by parachute. Attached to the container was a bag of dye, which would be released into the water on impact. There would then be some possibility of finding and recovering the core. (The passengers, recalls John Rowlands, were supposed to 'cling on and ignore the sharks'.) If, on the other hand, the plane was going to crash on land, Moyce was supposed to bail out, taking the container with him, and descend by parachute. He had his doubts about whether this would be possible. 'I used to wonder how I was supposed to hold it. We never went through any rehearsal', he recalls. 'I was given the offer of going through a parachute course but I declined. I thought the chances of the Hastings coming down were very small, and I might not get through the course; I might cripple myself.' He might not have been so trusting had he known the fate of an earlier flight to the islands. An HER contingent including Roy Pilgrim, David Barnes and Jimmy Hole flew out a week before Moyce and were lucky to survive. Half-way between Ceylon and Singapore two of the four engines gave out. The plane dropped down to a lower altitude and continued slowly on its way, only to encounter a typhoon a hundred miles out from its destination. When it finally limped in to Changi airbase in Singapore the runway was lined with fire engines and ambulances, confidently expecting a crash-landing. Happily, Moyce's journey was completed without drama, and he arrived at the Monte Bello Islands on the morning of 18 September, replete after a hearty fried breakfast cooked for him in the galley of the Sunderland.

13

Rehearsals

B Y the time Bill Moyce arrived at the islands, the main scientific party had been there for six weeks. They had been eventful weeks, and some things had not gone to plan.

Throughout the *Campania's* voyage from Britain, one of the chief worries had been the unloading of stores. In the event this passed off smoothly. Every available hand was turned to the task and a job which had been expected to take seven days was almost finished within two. Preparations on the ground were ahead of schedule, too. Team leaders who went ashore to view the work of the sappers and the RAAF team were most impressed. But there were hints of troubles to come. Cooper had drawn up a boat timetable to enable scientists and others to move between the *Campania*, the main sites ashore and the four ships in the lagoon, but it was quickly found that the journey times had been under-estimated by as much as a hundred per cent. When Noah Pearce and John Tomblin, leaders of blast effect teams, returned from Trimouille on the second day they had to wait an hour and a half for the boat to the *Campania* and it was 10 p.m. by the time they were able to convene their team meeting on board. The next day they decided to take an earlier boat back, but it was an hour late. The experience was typical. Matters worsened when it was discovered that the *Campania's* pinnaces, eight boats which were expected to do about a third of the water-transport work, could not moor close to the ship at night because the waters in the Parting

Pool were too choppy. The only suitably sheltered anchorage was in Stephenson Channel, five miles away at the southern end of Hermite. Getting the pinnaces back to the moorings in the evening in time for the crews to return to their quarters on the *Campania*, and getting the crews out to the pinnaces first thing in the morning to start work, lopped several hours off the working day for the scientists who were expected to use them. The effects could obviously be mitigated by stationing the crews in tents on Hermite close to Stephenson Channel, but this the naval command was reluctant to do. Cooper wrote angrily that 'it was only after much pressure and long delay' that the arrangement was approved.[1]

All such worries were rendered irrelevant on the morning of the fourth day, Monday, by rough weather which marooned almost the entire scientific party on board the *Campania*. Two attempts were made to get a landing-craft alongside, and in the second attempt four of the nimbler scientists managed to jump on board, but the ship's ladder was smashed and the operation had to be abandoned. Noah Pearce wrote in his diary: 'It was decided to write off today, so after lunch I had a nap.'[2] The next day too was written off, and the next. As the advantage gained by speedy unloading and the sappers' hard work drained away, a drastic decision was taken: the scientists would have to live ashore. The helicopters, at least, were able to operate, and they proved their usefulness by fetching senior officers from the ships in the lagoon to consult and by taking senior scientists out to the islands to inspect the sites. About a hundred scientists had to be accommodated and two camps were planned, one at H1 on Hermite for Maddock and his team, and the other at T2, or Cocoa Beach, on the shore of Trimouille close to the *Plym's* anchorage. The weather improved in the second half of the week and the preparations went ahead. By Sunday, Pearce was able to write: 'Our camp at Cocoa beach was started today. An LCM [landing-craft] came alongside *Campania* at 0800hrs and loading of stores and personal belongings began. We eventually ran up on Cocoa Beach landing ramp and many willing hands formed two "chains" and all was safely landed. The camp had been enlarged and now consisted of sixteen tents, each about twelve foot square and intended to take four camp beds. There was also a Nissen hut for a mess, a marquee for an anteroom (lounge), another for the seamen and one or two odd tents for POs, stewards, etc. There was a generator supplying light to all tents, buildings, etc, and a galley in which two oil ovens were installed. Lengths of PBS, a sort of roofing felt, had been laid in and around the tents to keep down the ubiquitous fine sand. Altogether it looked a pretty good camp.'[3]

The scientists found much about the camps that they liked. They were spared the frustrations of hanging around on the *Campania* waiting for the weather to improve or for the boats to arrive, and they no longer had to endure the sailors' mockery as they struggled to cope in small boats. Planning became easier as team leaders could count on continuity of work, and the work itself was more readily to hand. In some respects, there were improvements to the conditions of life itself: for example, the *Campania* tended to be stuffy and sticky at night whereas the camps were cool, so people found that they slept better. The escape from naval routine and formality was also welcome, and the camps had no dress code. For their part the officers on the *Campania* were no less grateful for the change since, with the exception of a dozen of the more senior scientists who remained on board, they had their ship and their wardroom to themselves again.

Cocoa Beach became a busy little town, hub of all the activities on Trimouille. The day there began with a wash in a bucket of salt water by the sea, or, for those brave enough, a swim (this was not one of the bays fenced off against sharks). After breakfast, the area around the jetty became crowded with scientists and servicemen waiting to embark for the ships in the lagoon or for work on the other islands, while every incoming boat brought visitors from elsewhere, on their way to sites on Trimouille. There was a queue for the 'bus' service – in reality a three-ton lorry – which ran all day up and down the island's steel-mesh-and-sand roads, starting from Cocoa Beach at 8.30 a.m. 'The ride to sites, along extremely bumpy roads, was exhilarating if perhaps a trifle hazardous', wrote McEnhill.[4] And at the same hour of the morning there was the daily ritual of haggling over Land Rovers, of which there were never enough. Officially they were allocated to teams the evening before by an officer at the army base at Gladstone Bay to the north, but since co-ordination was poor the decision as to who got what tended to be made in heated discussions first thing in the morning.

One good reason to have a Land Rover was that you might be able to get back to the camp for a midday meal. The fare was basic, lacking in variety and often cold by the time it reached the table, but it was generally preferred to a packed lunch. The scientists accepted that the naval cooks, with little fresh water and no cold-storage facilities, were doing their best. In the evenings there were film shows, and there was the duty-free bar. This stood in a corner of a marquee, loftily referred to as the Common Room, which contained a few comfortable chairs and a supply of magazines. Sunday papers arrived weekly from London. Frank Hill, who spent most of his evenings in his tent cataloguing his natural history collection, recalls that the bar did brisk business: 'Those people who had come out with nothing to do but the work, when it came to having a bit of spare time they had nothing to do but drink themselves silly in the bar. There was a darts board and they had a cinema rigged up. They used to hold sing-songs which tended to go on into the small hours and keep other people awake.'

It is a conspicuous fact that one commodity of which there was no shortage was beer. The servicemen in particular took full advantage. Eddie Howse travelled to the *Campania* one evening with a boatload of sailors returning from a break ashore. 'They had been playing darts and one of them had a dart thrown into his shoulder. There was blood pouring down him. They staggered up and stood to attention on deck to salute – perfectly still, but quite drunk – and the officer took no notice at all.' In the camps, 'Time' was called by turning the lights on and off a little before 11 p.m., and soon afterwards the generator was turned off for the night. Camp life certainly had its privations and discomforts. At Cocoa Beach there was soon a plague of flies, and persistent spraying in the mess seemed to have little effect. McEnhill remarked: 'It became increasingly obvious that these insects also knew a thing or two about multiplication rates.'[5] On Hermite the problem was termites. Maddock had to call the *Campania* one morning to ask for three large tins of DDT to repel an invasion. His last words were: 'Help! They're all marching towards me!'[6]

There were breaks from the rigours of life under canvas. Very early on it was decided that the working week should run from Monday morning to Saturday lunchtime, and that scientists could return to the *Campania* at the weekends to wash, do their laundry and attend meetings. Tyte, seeing his staff clambering back aboard the *Campania* on the Saturday after the camps were set up, noticed that more and more of them were growing beards to save themselves from shaving in salt water. 'The betting is heavily against any individual having the temerity to face his wife in such a condition', he noted.[7]

As to the preparations for the test, with the foundations so well laid the scientists were able to make rapid progress. Their work divided into three distinct functions. One group of teams was concerned with the weapon; maintaining it, arming it, firing it and carrying out all the attendant equipment tests. Challens, arriving by plane with Adams and a handful of other senior men three days after the task force ships, took charge on the *Plym* while Maddock and Hill worked on the communications related to the firing from H1. Eddie Howse had the job of maintaining liaison between them. A second group of teams was concerned with those kinds of observation of the explosion which required telemetry. These were effectively remote-controlled experiments. Some, such as the elaborate photographic systems, would be activated at the appropriate time in the countdown. Others would not only need to be tested and activated during the countdown, but would communicate their results instantly over the airwaves. Again, the redoubtable Maddock was at the hub. Finally, there was the group whose apparatus had to be sited and primed, but who required no complicated electronics. Pearce and Tomblin were in this category, laying out gauges up and down Trimouille to measure the blast wave. They would learn the results by examining the apparatus *in situ* after the explosion.

There were dozens of different experiments. One team, led by N. F. Moody, set up equipment on the *Plym* which employed crystals to turn gamma radiation into tiny flashes of light. The light was then made to generate current, and the level of the current could be related to specific numbers of nuclear fissions. This was a means of measuring the multiplication rate of the fissions – how quickly the chain reaction occurred, and thus how much of the plutonium was used up in the nuclear explosion before the bomb blew itself asunder. The events being measured would happen in milli-microseconds, so equipment was attached which would lengthen, or slow down, the signals originating from the crystals.

These would then be fed by underwater cable to a hardened bunker at Cocoa Beach, where another battery of equipment slowed the signals down further. From there a ground cable carried the signals to T1, at the southern tip of Trimouille, whence they were transmitted by radio to Maddock's base at H1. Someone there would record them on magnetic tape for subsequent analysis. This was difficult, delicate and complex. If any of the ten or more links in the chain failed, the whole experiment failed. So, for safety's sake, the whole experiment was duplicated. And to be absolutely sure of getting a result, other experiments were set up to measure the multiplication rate using different techniques.

On the simpler end of the scale, there was a descendant of the famous 'tin can' measurement system used by Penney at Bikini. Pilgrim's team had refined the idea and used unfilled toothpaste tubes instead of jerry-cans. These were set in wooden frames, each holding five tubes, and placed at fifty sites over Trimouille. The principle remained the same: the extent of crushing of the tubes would indicate the strength of the blast pressure wave at that point. The crushing was measured by the simple means of pouring water into the tube to determine its capacity and comparing that with the capacity before the blast. Pilgrim's team was also responsible for an experiment to measure the ground movement caused by the explosion. This involved sinking posts into the ground at selected points, fixing their location precisely by careful surveying, and then re-surveying after the blast to see whether, and how much, they had moved. It was thought that the results would help to show the stresses that would be placed on buildings by an atomic attack. Other items scattered around Trimouille belonged to experiments run by the services, the Home Office and other interested parties. There were Anderson shelters, concrete blockhouses, parts of a Lancaster bomber, dummies wearing different kinds of uniforms and protective clothing, scale models of ship parts and, courtesy of the Medical Research Council, a variety of foods, from Sunny West butter packs and Rubor tea to sacks of flour and whole tomato plants. Besides these, a huge effort was devoted to photographing the explosion, and cameras were mounted on vantage points all around the lagoon. They ranged from conventional cine- and stills cameras to the Kerr-cell cameras, which were the pride and joy of HER. Designed and built by a team under Charles

Adams, these were capable of taking photographs at the rate of 100,000 frames per second, the exposure time for each picture being one ten-millionth of a second.

There were, in all, several thousand individual pieces of experimental apparatus to be set in place, more than three hundred of them involving electronics. Most were on Trimouille, but there were also big installations on North-West Island, Alpha Island and on Hermite, and smaller ones on a dozen or more of the lesser islands. Setting up the equipment and checking it could be a strenuous and even a heartbreaking business. The outpost on Alpha Island, for example, stood on top of a hill called A4, which offered a commanding view of the lagoon. At the foot of the hill, in a cove called A3, there was a jetty which could only be used at high tide. McEnhill tells the story of one man who set out armed with an oscillator, a device which generated pulses and could be used in calibration, to perform some tests at A4. 'The tide was lowish and the coxswain came as close as he dared and told the scientist that he would have to wade ashore. Carrying the instrument and papers he started, stubbed his toe on a rock and fell headlong into the sea. All was soaked, oscillator, papers and man. Eventually at A4 he dried the instrument out, tried it and to his joy it worked. His joy was premature, however, because it worked on three ranges, while on the fourth and last, which of course was the one he required for the tests, the sea had done its worst. There was no transport to take him back to his main base at H1 and he spent a complete day without even having the small satisfaction of completing the task for which he came.' McEnhill could see the funny side, but he noted that 'the man concerned found it stretching his sense of humour too much to view it as other than irritating.'[8]

Waiting for the boat to come back became a feature of life. The scheduled services rarely kept to their times and the practice developed of referring to 'the nominal five o'clock boat' because whatever time it appeared it would not be five o'clock. Even when a boat was on call, it would usually take three-quarters of an hour to answer a summons. And when it arrived, the journey was often painfully long. From the *Campania* to H2, the landing point for H1, took an hour and a half, while a return journey from the *Campania* to the *Plym*, which might involve changing boats in mid-lagoon, could take three hours. And that was if everything went to plan. Choppy waters often disrupted services, particularly in the Parting Pool, and navigation held its hazards. Inside the lagoon, the waters were treacherous at low tide and boats would often run on to a sandbank, or worse. Herbert Pike found himself ship-wrecked on one occasion after the junior naval officer in command of his boat ignored navigational advice and hit a rock. 'Water poured into the boat and we all started to bail, one farsighted man with a teacup and the rest with our bare hands', Pike wrote. They limped to the nearest land, from where the naval officer reported the mishap by radio. Pike recalls that the reply, heard by all present, caused the officer to turn pink all over – 'at least I think he did; his knees certainly did.'[9]

The boat problem, everybody soon recognized, had been eased but was certainly not resolved by the opening of the shore camps. In all, there were thirty-three boats of sufficient size to be useful; five were LCMs (landing-craft mechanical), twelve were the smaller LCAs (landing-craft attack) and the remainder were the pinnaces and other boats attached to the ships. Between them they had not only to ferry the scientists from site to site, but move equipment and provisions, lay cables and buoys and conduct surveys. The landing-craft, having been in service at the islands since April, had taken a battering and by August four of them were likely to be out of action for maintenance or repair at any one time. Even then there were not enough crews; the Royal Marines who operated the landing-craft were among the hardest-worked men in the task force. Tyte, contemplating these difficulties and thinking of the prospects for the weeks to come, noted in his diary: 'It seems incredible that the whole of this important, expensive operation should hang on the thin red line of three or four LCMs, but that is, I fear, the grim truth. So much for planning. I trust with luck we should make it, but we sure need luck.'[10]

This was a matter that caused some friction with the Navy. One incident, in which a landing-craft was holed while running up to shore, left bad feeling on both sides. The scientists put it down to careless navigation while the crew were annoyed by the way in which they were left to beach the craft alone while their passengers rushed off to get on with their work. Cooper raised it with the naval command, although Tyte had been inclined to let the matter lie. The scientific director was more concerned by complaints about the procedures involved in leaving and boarding the *Campania*, which many scientists found frightening and humiliating. They had been surprised in the first place to find themselves clambering up and down ladders on the ship's side, rather than the more sedate companion-ways, and some of the less fit scientists had encountered difficulties. They were further surprised to find that they were often required to do this on the weather side, rather than the sheltered lee side of the ship. 'The reason for this was sometimes unknown,' McEnhill observed, 'but often it was because of the possibilities of spoiling the companion-way for the use of the Admiral's barge or Naval launches. The return of a liberty cutter from a fishing trip with a handful of Wardroom Officers on board usually occasioned more attention and assistance from the watch on duty on the embarkation space than the return of an LCM loaded with disreputable looking civilians back from a day's work on the islands.'[11] Tyte, at his most diplomatic, raised this with Torlesse's staff, who complained that the scientists tended to be overcritical. On the general question of boat availability, the Navy side accepted that there was a shortage, but they felt that the civilians were being less than helpful. For example, because some of the scientists had chosen to remain aboard the *Campania* the need to transport them placed an additional burden on the boats. Furthermore, every weekend there were a few scientists who insisted on staying on site to work rather than returning to the *Campania*, and they required a disproportionate amount of boat support. As to the companion-ways, only once was there an accident, and the Navy responded in exemplary fashion. The luckless Percy Pridgeon, now recovered after breaking both arms on the voyage out, returned one evening from his work on the *Plym*. Mistiming his jump from the tossing landing-craft to the *Campania* companion-way, he fell into the sea between the two. A senior naval officer, Commander Bromley, who happened to be watching from the top of the companion-way, immediately ripped his jacket off, dived into the water and fished him out. 'I assume you wanted that man back', he is said to have remarked.[12]

Another cause of frustration, and friction, was radios. Good voice communication between the various shore sites and ships was obviously vital for the scientists, and the Navy supplied its standard equipment for this purpose. This proved to be well-worn and far from state-of-the-art, and though it might have suited the Navy's crisp and formal signals procedures, it could not cope with the long interchanges required by the scientists. The sets tended to overheat and the signal faded and became unintelligible. Maddock spotted this during the Thames Estuary rehearsal and took the precaution of buying a number of commercially produced sets similar to those then in use in police cars. When these were unpacked at the Monte Bellos, the Navy took it as an affront. Frank Hill recalled: 'The naval signals officer suggested that we carry out comparative trials of the two systems. A ship carrying both types of equipment steamed away towards the horizon and the naval equipment was soon out of range, whereas our simpler equipment was still in communication and our representative on the distant ship quoted a ribald rhyme to prove it. Our leader, Mr Maddock, turned to the naval commander and said: "What do you think of that?" The reply was: "Performance very good; procedure terrible." '[13] The matter did not lie there, for there were not enough of the commercial sets for the scientists' needs and they were obliged, under noisy protest, to use the naval equipment as well. Torlesse for one found the complaints irritating and one day, while visiting a camp on Trimouille, he resolved to hear for himself what all the moaning was about, so he switched on a set to listen. 'Unfortunately', noted Tyte none too sincerely, 'our people were in the middle of a scientific test and he was told, pointedly and not too politely, to get off the air – which he did.'[14]

Tyte was harbouring dark thoughts about his hosts on the *Campania* and was reassured to find that Cooper shared his feelings. Cooper had been outraged at the reluctance of the naval command to quarter the pinnace crews ashore so that boat services could run for longer hours during the day. This, he wrote later, was evidence of 'the apparent complete lack of understanding and unsympathetic interest for the scientific conduct of the trial' shown by the naval command.[15] And Tyte and Cooper were not alone. The scientific team as a whole had been quick to contrast the helpfulness of the Royal Engineer detachment with the indifference to their needs displayed by the Navy. One instance was a difficulty that arose over servicing the many batteries needed for equipment at the various sites. The technician brought out to do the job proved unsuitable and the Navy was asked if it could spare someone for the work. The response was sympathetic but no action followed, so the scientists turned to Colonel Smith of the sappers, who speedily produced a solution. Tyte, in his Sunday meetings with the senior scientific staff, took care to calm tempers and show understanding for the naval point of view. In a reflective moment, he wrote: 'I have a personal feeling that it's just fear; neither side has full confidence in the other; we are afraid that they are a clumsy lot of so-&-so's who would ruthlessly, nay cheerfully, dump us in the drink and they have no confidence in us at all and are certain that they will all be sterilized.'[16]

Moved partly by a concern to improve relations, and partly by a suspicion that senior officers on ships in the lagoon had a limited understanding of what the scientists were up to, Tyte laid on what he called a 'lecturette' at H1 for a dozen naval and Royal Engineers officers on 4 September. H1 was by now an impressive installation, stretched out along the crest of a bluff and bristling with tall masts and camera gantries and Maddock and his staff were able to show off their batteries of oscilloscopes, their telemetry centre and their firing desk, with its dials, lights, buttons and keys. They talked their guests carefully through what would happen on D-Day and in the subsequent phase when records were recovered from the various sites, emphasizing the sound scientific reasons for all the effort that would be required from the service side. This was received politely, Tyte wrote, 'but one of the things I have learned is that naval officers are trained to be polite under the most trying social conditions so I do not regard that as evidence of having achieved our object.'[17] He need not have worried. Lt. Peter Bird of the *Narvik* was in the audience, and he found the tour a revelation. 'As far as I was concerned,' he wrote later, 'that afternoon shattered for me the myth of "absent-minded professors', for in a matter of an hour or two the scientists reduced the mass of intricate wiring and machinery to terms that any average layman could understand.'[18] A few days later, Tyte noted an improvement in relations with the Navy. Commander Bromley, he wrote, was making such an effort to be charming and helpful that 'you can almost hear him creaking.'[19]

At about this time, concern arose about the activities of the Press. Ever since the intrepid yachting party had been expelled from the islands in April, reporters had maintained a constant watch at

Onslow, faithfully noting all movements of personnel, equipment and ships bound for the test site. Scientists arriving at the airstrip were kept under guard so there were no interviews, but they could be counted: twenty-four arrived on 11 August, twenty-six on 11 September, and so on. When the RAAF construction team left the islands in early September the development was greeted with great excitement as evidence that the test was close. This attention, though unwelcome, was generally viewed with resignation on the *Campania*; it could hardly be prevented, and it was harmless and often inaccurate. It was another, more ambitious piece of journalistic enterprise farther up the coast which rang the alarm bells.

In late August a nine-strong party representing Perth's sister morning and evening papers, the *West Australian* and the *Daily News*, arrived at the foot of Mount Potter, a small promontory ninety miles along the coast from Onslow. Mount Potter was just 285 feet high, but they had calculated that it was the closest vantage point on the mainland to the Monte Bellos. With military efficiency – the expedition leader, Jack Nicoll, was ex-Navy – they set up a base camp by a creek a short distance from the hill, just at the point where the Perth to Port Hedland telegraph line ran overhead. With them they had a mobile telegraph station which, with the prior blessing of the Post Office, they hooked up to the line. Then they cut a track through the spinifex to the top of the hill and began to construct an observation post. Mount Potter may not have been high, but it was exposed, and a tent would quickly have blown away, so they collected stones and built shelters to live and sleep behind. They hauled up a small darkroom on their backs and fixed it by blowing postholes in the rock with gelignite. After that came their equipment, notably a variety of cameras including two, specially designed at their offices in Perth, which they believed to have the longest focal length of any cameras in the world. They called them the 'Long Toms', and they were derived from the cameras in use at that time to take cricketing action shots from the boundary line.

Once their camps were established, they began a routine of shifts to maintain a twenty-four-hour watch on the islands, or rather on the appropriate spot to the north-west, since the islands were sixty miles away over the horizon. They could not hope to see anything of the preparations, but when the test came, the Long Toms would enable them to photograph the cloud. Conditions on the hilltop were rather tougher than anything endured by the task force on the Monte Bellos. They slept by turns behind their dry-stone walls, covered with army groundsheets which filled with pools of dew in the night. 'It was intensely uncomfortable,' recalls Dan O'Sullivan, one of the reporters, 'but it was also a lot of fun in many ways; we were all young.' Before long they had the satisfaction of witnessing the growing curiosity of the authorities about their operation. Planes flew low overhead almost every day; people from the local sheep-stations began to spy on them, reporting their movements to Onslow, and eventually they received official visits. On the *Campania*, Max Phillips, the representative of the Australian security service, sought advice on whether he should have them removed. Tyte's view was that he should, and he informed Torlesse that photography from Mount Potter was 'completely unacceptable from our point of view since it could reveal the nature of the burst.'[20] Naval staff, however, said that since the horizon would obscure the bottom six hundred feet of the cloud, this was hardly a risk. The matter was referred to the Hurex Committee in London. Meanwhile, further investigations were conducted to establish how good the equipment on Mount Potter was, and a few days later Tyte received 'one of those near-midnight visits from Col. Phillips' in his cabin, which confirmed his fears.[21] The Hurex Committee, however, presumably recoiling at the thought of attempting to evict Australian journalists who were covering a story from Australian soil, decided to take no action. To Tyte's disappointment, the bleak hilltop vigil was allowed to proceed.

IN LATE AUGUST and early September, despite some nagging difficulties, the senior scientists were able to report steady, satisfactory progress with the field-work, but another aspect of the preparations was in trouble. Everybody had underestimated the amount of planning needed for the final phases of the operation. A detailed timetable had to be drawn up for the activities of the last two or three days before detonation, and this would have to be vastly more complicated than the countdown rehearsed in the Thames Estuary. Many more teams were involved, with their equipment now scattered over a large number of sites, some of which were difficult to reach. Generators would have to be primed and batteries charged;

ship and boat movements would have to be co-ordinated with the scientific preparations so that the islands and the lagoon could be progressively evacuated of all personnel except the few dozen remaining in H1. Every man and every instrument would have to be accounted for. And all this would have to be geared to the predictions of the meteorologists, who were looking out for a very specific wind-pattern. Clearly it was a considerable task of co-ordination. In principle the job fell to two men, Charles Adams, the deputy technical director, and another scientist, Ted Marshall, both of whom also had onerous responsibilities in the field and found themselves swamped. Cooper and McEnhill were soon drawn in to help. The secretarial support was even more inadequate: one naval clerk who proved so lazy he had to be demoted, another who had additional duties in the messes and could never be found, and an elderly Gestetner duplicating machine with a tendency to break down at the moment of greatest need.

Somehow, they managed to construct a schedule of rehearsals of increasing scale, building up to a full-blown dress rehearsal involving all scientific and service personnel over two or more days in the second half of September. The build-up began on Tuesday, 2 September, with a large-scale test of the telemetry system. This went well. A few minor hitches were exposed and easily rectified. One of these was that some of the clocks at remote sites, which were intended to start apparatus and generators, were faulty. They had been bought in a bulk order, and it emerged that many of them did not meet the specification because poor materials had been used. A little attention, however, brought them up to scratch. A week after this, it was the turn of the gamma-ray monitoring teams and the Health Ship, the *Tracker*, to be put through their paces. This was a rehearsal of procedures after the explosion, when the levels of contamination on the islands would be remotely monitored and automatically radioed back to a control room in the *Tracker*. The ship left the lagoon to take up the position at sea it would occupy at the time of the test. The scattered transmitters were started up, and *Tracker's* aerials were oriented for the best possible reception. This test was less successful than the first, partly because some of the staff involved spent much of the morning stuck on a sandbank in Stephenson Channel, having run aground on their journey back from a weekend on the *Campania*.

The next step was a single rehearsal of all the scientific aspects of the test, and this was set for Friday, 12 September, to be completed with a dummy firing of the weapon at 9.45 a.m. the following morning. Tyte rose on the Friday at 6.30 a.m. – 'much to my steward's astonishment, and I might add my own' – to hear the weather forecast and give the go-ahead to begin the long series of procedures.[22] The early start and the fine weather seem to have brought on a feeling of well-being. 'This morning I thought I really smelt the sea, you know a really rich ozony smell such as one gets at Brighton or Shoeburyness, but the Captain disillusioned me. It was only a leak of diesel oil.' As the day unfolded, there were problems. In the *Plym's* weapon room, high humidity during the night was found to have affected some of the high-voltage equipment, and some items had to be replaced. At Cocoa Beach there was a minor panic in the afternoon when a generator serving the multiplication-rate experiments broke down. Moody was on the *Plym* at the time and could not get across to assess the trouble because the ship's boat was out of service, having lost its rudder. At H1 there were technical difficulties with the Kerr-cell cameras, again caused by generator problems. On the *Tracker*, at T5 on Trimouille and at H1 naval radio sets broke down at critical moments. The rehearsal continued. As the various sites were evacuated and the countdown progressed into the early hours of Saturday, the mood in Maddock's control room was tense, but in the event the telemetry and the firing-circuit worked perfectly, and when the decks were cleared they were able to sit down to a good lunch.

Afterwards, looking forward to a restful weekend and a hot bath on the *Campania*, they made their way down to the jetty at H2 and boarded a waiting landing-craft. The coxswain, however, informed them firmly that they had the wrong boat, as he was due to pick up two parties of scientists from the outer islands. Since all the other scientists had been evacuated from the sites as part of the rehearsal, the H1 group knew this to be impossible, but they were unable to convince him. Another landing-craft arrived, and they began to transfer to it, only to be told firmly to get back into the first boat. A heated argument broke out. By now they realised that the coxswain, in McEnhill's words, 'was acting in a fashion which suggested that he had, while waiting at H2, enjoyed some liquid refreshment at the army camp there.'[23] He was eventually convinced that he should take the scientists, although a few of them had decided they would rather wait for another boat. The drunken coxswain then wove his way up Stephenson Channel with some difficulty, as if dodging a series of large but invisible obstructions in his path, and in mid-lagoon delivered his passengers to a bigger landing-craft for transfer to the base ship. No one was lost and all arrived safely.

At Tyte's meeting on the *Campania* that Sunday the verdict on the scientific rehearsal was positive, but there was lively debate about how soon they would be ready to proceed to the next stage, which was the full-scale rehearsal involving the service side as well. This had been pencilled in for the following Friday, 19 September, but Adams made a strong plea for a deferral. Too much work remained to be done on team movements, transport and other technical matters, all of it requiring consultations with team leaders, many of whom would soon be back in the field and thus difficult to pin down. Adams was also anxious about rehearsal of the 'standby period' which might be required – that is, the period when everything would be ready except the weather. During this time, equipment would have to be kept in a state of readiness without causing serious interference to the disposition of personnel and transport, so that D-1 Day could be declared at any time. Since there was every likelihood that a standby period would occur before the real test, Adams had hoped to practise the necessary routines, and he wanted to allow a three-day delay before the full rehearsal. The planned date simply did not allow time. Tyte, for his part, wanted to push the preparations along as rapidly as possible and thought a standby rehearsal could be dispensed with. Navy planning probably had plenty of loose ends too, he argued, and the sooner both sides tested their arrangements together, the sooner they could both tidy them up. The meeting, described by Adams as 'long and heated', lasted from 10 a.m. to 5 p.m. with a break for lunch.[24] The deadlock was broken by a vote, which went in favour of proceeding with the rehearsal on the Friday.

The unfortunate Adams was thus obliged to plunge immediately into a frenzy of further meetings, lasting almost until midnight, in the attempt to complete the necessary consultations while the team leaders were still on the *Campania*. By the following evening he and Marshall were able to produce a comprehensive timetable for the rehearsal, although they warned that there had been no time for checking and it was possible that some staff might end up stranded at odd places without food. On the Wednesday rough seas intervened. The *Tracker* was unable to leave the lagoon, one of the first steps in the rehearsal procedure, so R-Day was put back to the Saturday. There was no rest for Adams and his little team, who still had to compile complete alphabetical lists of all scientific staff and their movements and circulate these for the nightly roll-calls during the rehearsal. Tyte reported them 'toiling prodigiously', and a pang of guilt drove him to help with the typing and duplicating. 'My conscience just wouldn't let me sit back when I saw Adams and the others swimming in a sea of blood, and so three not very good stencils fell to my lot to cut.'[25]

At this moment a bitter dispute broke out between the senior Ministry of Supply staff and the naval command. The period of forced politeness which followed the 'lecturette' at H1 had not lasted very long. On 9 September a number of complaints about living conditions on the *Plym* and at the Cocoa Beach camp brought Tyte's feelings of resentment welling up again. Challens called on him in his cabin to say that the facilities on the *Plym* had been run down too early and that he and his colleagues were now obliged to go ashore to Cocoa Beach to eat. They found the facilities there appalling: while they ate, rubbish was being burned just upwind, filling the Nissen hut mess with smoke and fumes, and at the same time the place was swarming with flies. 'Challens thought he had currants in his rice pudding,' Tyte wrote, 'but he was disappointed; they were only flies.'[26] He refused point-blank to eat there again, and he was not the only one. Moody had stomach trouble and pointed to bad sausages and uncooked fish, while another man had refused either to eat at Cocoa Beach or to take the sandwiches offered him instead.

For the moment, Tyte remained outwardly calm. He had already heard rumours about falling standards at Cocoa Beach and discovered that the regulars, less agitated than newcomers such as Challens, had matters in hand. They had held meetings, and the Navy had promised action, so Tyte decided to leave well alone. He did raise Challens's point about facilities on the *Plym* with the relevant naval officer, who made arrangements to restore some ·

catering on board. Privately, however, Tyte was furious. This was but one of a list of grievances that had been building up, all tending to confirm his worst suspicions. Boats and radios continued to cause trouble; Torlesse, Tyte complained, was refusing to ask the Australians for a few extra Land Rovers to ease transport problems on Trimouille, despite an offer from the Australian prime minister to help in any way he could; and Tyte believed he might not be being shown important signals from London. Doubtless he also heard the stories which reached McEnhill, that conditions in the shore camps improved magically on the occasions when naval officers spent the weekends there. The food and general services were better, and special furniture was installed to make them more comfortable. If this could be done for them, then why not for the scientists? 'Frankly,' Tyte wrote, 'I'm utterly disgusted with the Navy.' He railed against their 'sheer incompetence and utter indifference to how our people exist' and 'sheer stupidity and inability to cope with a situation outside the strict routine of their lives.'[27] The day after he wrote these words he visited the *Zeebrugge* in the lagoon and dined with the captain and Frank Morgan. He thoroughly enjoyed himself, finding the atmosphere 'free from the pomp and circumstance and trup of Admiralty' which prevailed on the *Campania*, and he revised his opinions of the Navy. It was not the whole service that was at fault, he decided, but just those in charge on the base ship. 'It's been said that our senior officers might be worse, that we were lucky we had the ones we had. That may well be true. I find it absolutely unbelievable that they could not be better.'[28]

It may have been these feelings that prompted him, on the eve of the scientific rehearsal, to raise at Torlesse's daily meeting the idea that the trial proper might be brought forward by a whole week from the notional date at the start of October. The scientific preparations had been going sufficiently well to make this a possibility, he said, and he wondered whether the Navy side might be able to cope with such a change of plan. This was, he admitted later, a 'try-on' – Adams for one would have been horrified if the trial had been brought forward – and as Tyte must have expected it did not go down well with the Navy side. Ship refuelling requirements, he was told sourly, made any advancement of the date of the test impossible. It was a needless and unhelpful piece

229

of baiting. When he was accosted after the meeting, however, it was to be confronted, not over this, but over the food problems at Cocoa Beach. Captain Cole delivered a 'furious onslaught', demanding to know why the complaints had not been made directly to the officer in charge of the camp.[29] Tyte replied bluntly that this was for the very good reason that the complainants had not been camp residents, and the conversation came to an abrupt halt.

The senior naval officers had come to dislike Tyte as cordially as he did them. Torlesse found him sour, carping and ungrateful. Writing much later, he recalled a conversation that took place on the day that the *Campania* arrived at the islands, when he laid on a small celebration in his cabin. 'I said to Dr Tyte, "Well, here we all are, at the very hour we planned more than a year ago." He [Tyte] took his face out of his lemon squash – unfortunately, he was a teetotaller – and said dryly, "Didn't you expect to?" To which it was difficult to think of a suitable answer, but I did feel that, all things considered, he might have had the grace to admit it was a matter for congratulation!' Torlesse continued: 'We never did manage to melt the difficult doctor. We did our best to do him honour; he had the best quarters in the ship after the captain, and he messed with the personal staff at my table, as the scientific chief of staff. But there was a "chip" somewhere.'[30] The personalities were obviously not well matched, but behind their differences lay practical failures. Many of the difficulties between the two men and between their respective staffs – Adams and Cooper were also involved – arose from poor co-ordination in the months before the task force sailed. Neither side, however, was prepared to take the blame for the operational problems, such as those with boats, radios and Land Rovers, which cropped up as a result, indeed they were more than keen to pin the responsibility on their opposite numbers.

It was against this background, with the naval officers in a state of some agitation and Tyte ready to erupt at any time, that a real *casus belli* emerged. Again it was, in isolation, a minor matter: Frank Morgan's living conditions aboard the *Zeebrugge*. Morgan was something of a VIP among the Ministry of Supply staff in the islands. A particularly able scientist with a rare expertise in radiochemistry, he was, as we have seen, the only senior scientist to cross over to HER from Harwell. At the Monte Bellos he had a vital job to do after the explosion, analysing the samples retrieved from the cloud, and this required rapid action and specialized laboratory facilities. Morgan had flown out separately after seeing the early stages of the casting at Aldermaston, and had already been the victim of a couple of mishaps. On the journey, he stopped over at the north-west town of Darby on what happened to be the eve of the local horse races, and found himself in a hotel packed with drunken miners and stockmen sleeping five to a room without mosquito nets. The next day he reached the islands, only to be delivered to the wrong ship. Before long, however, he and his team settled down in the *Zeebrugge*, where a laboratory had been prepared for them in a clever metal-framed structure which folded out to fill space previously occupied by stores. Unfortunately, no such ingenuity had gone into providing accommodation; indeed the whole matter had been overlooked, and they were hastily housed inside a large packing-case. This stood in a gap on the tank deck between a generator and a bulldozer, and was so cramped that only one of its four inhabitants could stand up in it at a time. There were no lockers or cupboards – they were informed that a suitcase would be perfectly adequate since they would only be wearing rough clothes. After a little more than a week of this, and just after the scientific rehearsal, Morgan mentioned it at Tyte's weekly meeting. Again, Tyte showed restraint. He raised it informally with Captain Colville of the *Zeebrugge* and was assured conversion work was under way.

The following day, however, the morning meeting with Torlesse and his staff turned into an acrimonious affair. After the premature running-down of facilities on the *Plym*, Marshall had had to intervene to prevent another piece of excessive naval 'back-loading' zeal: the removal of half the lorries and Land Rovers from Trimouille on to ships. Tyte raised this and irritated the Navy side by delivering a lecture on what was important at the trial and what was not. He then decided to mention the subject of Morgan's accommodation. 'The Admiral was already tired of his meeting and did not relish my description of the conditions that our people were asked to exist in as "appalling", and what is called in the social circles "a brisk exchange of views" promptly developed. I was silenced with the bland statement that after all this was an operation of war and we should have to put up with what we got. It was

231

undertaken that the matter would be investigated.'[31] The argument, however, did not end there. When they gathered again the next morning, the same angry cloud lowered over the meeting. It can hardly have helped that the first item on the agenda was a fresh complaint about naval radios. Then came 'a nice quiet row' about Morgan's living quarters. Torlesse's remarks of the previous day had clearly rankled with Tyte, and he started by asking the Admiral for a statement in writing that this was an 'operation of war', since this was the first he had heard of it. After this, Tyte recorded, 'I returned to the charge that the accommodation and facilities offered to the staff were appalling and what was going to be done about it? It was pointed out that we had scoured the Commonwealth for six radiochemists who were senior men and then they were housed in a dog kennel.' To this the Admiral replied that he had lived in worse conditions in his time, which Tyte dismissed as irrelevant. 'This is a matter on which I feel very strongly', Tyte wrote that night, and 'the Admiral was nearer to being batted over the bean than I suspect he has been for years. It's bad luck on him, but he is not going to bully me . . .'[32]

Skirmishing on various fronts continued for the rest of the week. On the Thursday afternoon an anxious and somewhat regretful Leonard Tyte stood on the deck of the *Campania* and watched the *Narvik*, the *Tracker* and the *Zeebrugge* leave the lagoon and enter the Parting Pool as the first stage of the full rehearsal. Frantic activity was going on all around and he was conscious that it was he who had made this haste necessary by pushing the timetable forward so vigorously. 'I felt very alone and responsible about it all. It isn't often, in fact it's very rare for such a thing to happen to me so perhaps I'm getting old. Of course you will say I have a partner – or strictly a Commanding Officer – in crime, but honestly I can't see it that way. I have just failed to effectively make my number with him and regret I have no confidence, as I should have, in him.'[33] The mood did not last. That night he went with Torlesse and Cole to the *Zeebrugge* to look at Morgan's 'dog kennels' and he was outraged by what he found. There was 'not enough room to swing a Manx cat', he wrote. No senior naval officer would ever be asked to live in such conditions, and there was no excuse for it. 'The plain fact of the case must be that CTF4 [Torlesse] completely forgot about provision of this accommodation, which he now has the audacity to say was an afterthought ...' Tyte was all the more annoyed because he was now hearing of serious overcrowding among his staff on board the *Tracker*; it appeared that they were living like sardines while two rooms with berths for twenty men each were being used to store beer. Other matters, however, were pressing: it was now the night before R-1, and Tyte was required to return to the *Campania* for the first rehearsal roll-call.

Friday found Tyte up early again, this time at 6.00 a.m., to hear the latest meteorological reports and, in consultation with Torlesse, to approve the start of operations. Conditions for boat work were, as Adams put it, 'so good as to be unrealistic', but one landing-craft none the less managed to hit rocks on North-West Island and prompt a rehearsal of the emergency salvage arrangements.[34] A few people who would in the real event be evacuated remained behind at the principal sites in case of fire or other mishap, but otherwise the procedures were as true to the plan for the real test as possible. In one respect they were more realistic than expected. R-1 day happened to be the day that Bill Moyce arrived from Britain with the plutonium core, and Tyte took the decision at the last moment that the team on the *Plym* should practise the 'live' loading of the weapon. Although Moyce and his team at Aldermaston had tested the core in an assembly designed to simulate the weapon, this was the first time it had been lowered into a real high-explosive sphere and all the old fears of accidental criticality returned. The familiar neutron counters were set up around the weapon room and the cartridge was ratcheted down millimetre by millimetre into the heart of the weapon. Every word spoken during this operation was relayed down a telephone line to H1 and recorded, in case of accidents. The procedure was watched with bemusement by the *Plym's* captain, who asked: 'What's all this ticking?' Moyce turned to him and replied: 'If that goes "Bzzzzt" you won't be 'ere any more.'[35] The job was completed safely in the early hours of Saturday morning, and the core was winched out again and placed in a safe. Only a handful of people in the task force were aware that this had happened, and it seems that one of those left in ignorance was the naval commander. Tyte's diary entry for the Friday night contains a coy passage about a decision he had taken which he 'hadn't oughter.' This is almost certainly a reference to the live loading. 'Nobody really knows about it apart from a few of our senior staff,' he wrote, 'and I don't for a moment contemplate that they would split on me.'[36]

Torlesse did not enjoy the rehearsal. If Tyte, Cooper and Adams are to be believed, most of the hitches that arose were on the naval side of the operation. The *Campania's* Action Information Centre, or AIC, which was the communications hub for much that was going on, descended into a 'complete shambles', according to Tyte, and the Rear Admiral felt that he was not kept properly informed of progress.[37] There were also problems with the evacuation of the *Plym* which led to a sharp exchange with the senior scientists. At least one of the boats carrying men off to the *Tracker*, outside the lagoon, had the greatest difficulty finding its route in the darkness. As a result, the *Tracker* was delayed in sailing to its appointed position at a safe distance from ground zero. This was important because, for safety reasons, the signal from the *Tracker* that it was in position had been chosen as a trigger for the opening of a new stage in the operation. When Tyte became impatient for the signal, Torlesse simply told him to proceed without it. 'I dare not repeat Adams's comment', wrote Tyte.[38]

Strong words were also exchanged at H1, this time between scientists. Again for safety reasons, the control panel for firing the weapons would not operate unless a number of keys had been turned in locks which formed part of the display. These keys were issued to team leaders involved in last-minute field work, who returned them to Maddock as proof that their job was complete and their men safely evacuated. In addition there was a master key, more like a plug, which was held by Challens. He and Howse were the last to leave the *Plym*, and instead of going with the others to the *Tracker*, they proceeded down the lagoon to H1, where they handed in the master key to show that everyone was safely clear of the target vessel and the countdown could continue. At first light on the Saturday morning their boat arrived at H2, they made their way up the hill by Land Rover and Challens solemnly presented the master key to Maddock. Someone remarked: 'Good thing you didn't drop that over the side!' and Challens agreed. Then a young scientist piped up: 'It wouldn't matter anyway, I've got a spare one here in the safe.' This was not part of the plan and it made a mockery of the safety procedures. Eddie Howse recalls: 'Challens blew his top completely. I think, when it came to the real test, he took the key of the safe with him.'

Despite the hiccoughs, the rehearsal was seen by the scientists as sufficiently successful to justify setting a target date for the test itself. At their Sunday meeting on 21 September, they agreed to inform Torlesse that they would be ready to take up standby positions on the night of Tuesday 30 September. If circumstances permitted, D-1 Day could be declared the next morning and the weapon could be fired on 2 October. Nine days remained.

14

The Event

ON the Monday morning after the rehearsal, the Australian destroyer HMAS *Hawkesbury* arrived in the Parting Pool, having sailed overnight from Onslow. The Admiral's barge was sent over from the *Campania* and when it returned bearing its distinguished passenger, no doubt the very best companion-way was lowered. At the top, lined up to greet him, stood Torlesse and his staff, flanked by Tyte with his. Up the steps, beaming as ever, bounded the fit and youthful form of William Penney. He shook hands all round and was shown to his quarters, resurfacing rapidly in the wardroom to mingle with sailors and scientists in his informal and jokey manner. After the tension of recent days, here was a welcome addition to Task Force Four. 'There was no doubt at all', wrote McEnhill, 'that the presence of Dr Penney on board greatly improved the morale and spirit of the entire company. This arrival was as a breath of fresh air on a somewhat jaded and slightly stale force.'[1]

Penney had remained in Britain long enough to satisfy himself that the plutonium castings were satisfactory. Then, while the core went off for its final examination, he flew out by RAF Hastings. Having left a week before Bill Moyce, he was arriving three days after him because his itinerary had included an extremely secret expedition into the Australian outback. For several months Penney had been in communication with the Australians about a possible desert site at which further British nuclear tests might be held.

These would be operations on a smaller scale than Hurricane and Penney was hoping to find a location where the logistics would be less demanding than in the Monte Bellos. The Canberra government had not given formal approval, but initial investigations suggested that a site in the northern part of the state of South Australia might be suitable. Penney was anxious to inspect it, so after stopping over in Singapore, his Hastings flew not to Onslow but to Woomera. From there, while the newspapers reported that he was due in Melbourne and Canberra, he headed instead 250 miles in the opposite direction, towards the heart of the continent. Landing at a desert airstrip, he and a small party of officials were taken in hand by an indomitable Australian surveyor and explorer called Len Beadell. They toured hundreds of miles of country by Land Rover over the next four days, sometimes sleeping in the open and sometimes under canvas at their base camp by the airstrip. When the inspection was complete Penney flew back to Woomera and then on to Onslow. Even there the Press caught no glimpse of him as he was smuggled from airfield to jetty in a covered lorry. Upon boarding the *Campania*, he promptly cabled Cherwell and Sandys to let them know that, assuming the Australians gave their assent and assuming Hurricane was a success, a place had been found to stage its sequel. This site would later be named Emu Field.

On the afternoon of his arrival at the islands Penney turned his thoughts to the present trial, calling together his senior scientists and asking each for a statement on his team's readiness. One by one they confirmed that, although certain problems remained, they expected everything to be in place for 30 September. The exception was Charles Adams, who was struggling on two fronts: the Kerr-cell cameras, for which he was responsible, were not ready, and he was still concerned about the action plans for the final days, particularly if there were to be a prolonged standby period. The high-speed cameras had come straight from the laboratory at Fort Halstead and had never really been field-tested. They were excused service during the early rehearsals while the team struggled to get them ready, and now a problem of interference had arisen between the camera electronics and the nearby recording apparatus at H1 for Moody's multiplication-rate experiments. It was hoped to eliminate this by surrounding the electronics with an aluminium screen, but no one knew with certainty whether this would work. Penney listened to the arguments and took the decision that if the problem could not be eliminated before the test, the cameras should be stood down. The result was a frantic race by the Kerr-cell team to test and prove the screens by the deadline. As to the standby period, Penney decided they would cross that bridge if they came to it.

What concerned him most was the weather. Conditions for the test had to be such that no radioactive fall-out reached the Australian mainland 'except at such a distance from the explosion that it could be regarded as innocuous.'[2] In addition, the party remaining behind at H1 had to be safe. This meant that the wind had to come, broadly speaking, from the east, the south or, just possibly, the south-west. But it was vastly more complicated than that: wind directions and speeds vary at different altitudes, and since the cloud was expected to rise to 25,000 feet or more, all the winds up to that height had to be suitable. Moreover, these winds had to be predictable more than twenty-four hours in advance to allow the D-1 preparations to be made. To make this possible, a huge meteorological operation had been mounted. A special weather post was set up at Roy Hill Cattle Station in the Australian interior, a weather ship was posted 300 miles south-west of the Monte Bellos, and observations were routinely made all along the coast. The data were fed to the *Campania*, where two Australian Meteorological Bureau officials had joined a strong naval weather team.

The results of all this investigation were depressing. During the planning phase of Operation Hurricane it was assumed that the test would take place during one of the spells of stable weather in the islands associated with the presence of a well-established anticyclone over the Australian Bight. In practice, however, it had been found that although during these spells the winds in the upper atmosphere were suitable, the lower winds were invariably so strong as to make all the boat work necessary on D-1 Day impossible. In other words, the right winds for the cloud were the wrong winds for the boats. The experts then turned their attention to the shorter periods of suitable weather which occasionally occurred at the islands, when the winds tended to be right on both counts. In a month, there might be four or five such short periods. The problem was that they usually lasted just a day, and they were very difficult to predict. To complicate matters further, particular tidal conditions were also required just before the test, to allow the ships in the lagoon to navigate the shallow channel to the open sea. Suitable tides would only arise on fourteen days in October, so taking the winds and the tides together, it was found that the number of days on which it would be possible to hold the test could be as low as two.

That the gravity of all this was only brought home to the scientists at this late stage was due in part to some mathematical homework by Herbert Pike. Before the task force had sailed, some calculations had been done to determine the characteristics and likely behaviour of the fall-out from the explosion. Pike, running over this work in his cabin on the *Campania* at Tyte's request, had discovered an important error, made by Penney himself. A figure in an equation had been placed below the line instead of above it, giving an entirely false and over-optimistic result. Pike corrected it ('I reckon I earned my keep that time'), but the consequence was to place much greater demands on the meteorologists. It is hardly surprising that a certain gloom had settled on senior staff over the matter of weather. Would they find themselves waiting for weeks, with all the hazards that implied for the sensitive equipment in the field? Would the right conditions arise at all? The task force could not remain at the islands much past the beginning of November, when the cyclone season would be due, so time was very tight. Penney went through all this with the weather team on the *Campania* and then took a firm line that all would be well. He had seen all this before at Alamogordo and Bikini, he told his colleagues. 'In the period just before preparations were completed pessimism was often rife, but it had always been unwarranted pessimism and no doubt such would be the case again.'[3] McEnhill wrote of Penney's approach: 'He appeared very optimistic, even though he may not have felt so.' This was a good guess, since in his confidential messages to London Penney was warning that the weather was 'tricky' and a delay of two weeks was possible.

Penney's authority and good humour clearly did much to improve morale, but it seems to have done nothing to repair relations between Tyte and Torlesse. Morgan's living conditions remained as before and on the day of Penney's arrival Tyte wrote in his diary: 'It is just typical of this naval force that not only will it only help with the greatest reluctance, but it will only do so under the greatest pressure and only has consideration for its own comfort.'[4] Another argument followed at Torlesse's morning meeting on the Tuesday, this time about procedures in the Action Information Centre during the final stages of the countdown. Torlesse complained that during the rehearsal he had not been kept adequately informed of progress, and he particularly wanted a clear announcement to be made when one phase of preparation ended and the next one began. Tyte resisted this on the grounds that 'the phases were purely arbitrary and in most cases their beginning and end [had] relative rather than absolute significance.' He also thought this would be a 'dangerous and misleading instrument' for Torlesse to have. These were feeble arguments, and it is difficult to escape the conclusion that Tyte was being obstructive for the sake of it. Cooper patched over the difference by proposing that instead of an announcement, the Admiral might be given a written message. 'Well, we came very near to a real row, because I was not going to budge, but this time it was not I who got annoyed. CTF4 ... was certainly pretty angry about things.'[5] As the week progressed, Tyte found excuses to skip Torlesse's meetings, which he thought were usually 'a complete waste of time from our point of view.' But there was still friction.

Early in the week, Brooking had sent an urgent message to Penney asking that, as soon as the test was over, Bill Moyce should return to Britain with the spare core. This was because some problems had arisen with the development of the horizontal loading system to be used with the production weapon when it went into service with the RAF. Further criticality experiments were needed urgently, Brooking reported. Penney agreed, and replied that arrangements would be made to fly home the spare core, cartridge and initiators seven days after the test. This flight was to leave from Onslow and before the details were settled Wing Commander John Rowlands, who would accompany it, decided that he needed to inspect the facilities there. Neither he nor Moyce had been to Onslow, having arrived at the islands by flying boat direct from Singapore, and they were concerned about safety and security in transferring their cargo from a ship or LCM through the town to the airstrip. Rowlands asked Tyte, saying he had hoped to make his reconnaissance trip in one of the *Campania's* Sea Otter aircraft but that neither of these seemed to be airworthy. Tyte called on Captain Cole, who was 'not at all helpful or sympathetic but took the line that they could land the load on the beach as though that was the whole job.'[6] When Tyte insisted, Cole suggested that the *Hawkesbury* might take Rowlands to the mainland, although this was a matter for the naval commander. Tyte duly called Torlesse on the *Campania's* internal telephone. The Admiral said firmly that he would not send the *Hawkesbury* but he might be prepared to allow a Sea Otter flight if one of the planes could be repaired in time. Tyte had his doubts and aired them. 'While I was still talking to him on this matter', Tyte claimed, 'he quite deliberately hung up the telephone.'[7] This, just three days before the test period was due to begin, provoked Tyte's bitterest and most intemperate tirade. 'I have said many rude things about the Navy in general on this trip but I was wrong. I am certain now that the prime root cause of all our troubles flow from the tone set and attitude adopted by Torlesse, who ... has no interest beyond the petty ceremonies and fruits of Rear-Admiralty ... He likes to exert his authority in petty matters, usually being discourteous to someone else in the process.' Tyte raised the question of Rowlands's visit to Onslow with Penney, who took it up with Torlesse and was promised action, but three days later, as everybody moved to standby positions, Rowlands had still not been able to make the trip. Tyte also spoke to Penney about 'the deteriorating position in relation to the Naval Commander', but to little effect.[8]

At about this time an Australian fleet comprising an aircraft-carrier, HMAS *Sydney*, and four destroyers arrived to provide air and sea cover for the test, both guarding against intruders and keeping an eye out for merchant ships which might stray into the danger area. Taken together with the *Hawkesbury* and other support ships, this brought to eleven the number of Australian naval vessels involved with Hurricane. The fleet came from Darwin and approached the islands from the north, braving uncharted shoals to come within five miles of Trimouille. Torlesse flew across by helicopter for a conference with the Australian admiral, Jack Eaton, who was 'disgusted' to learn that even he could not be told the target date for the test.[9] Considering that Eaton had essential duties to perform and plan, this seems excessively cautious. In the task force, the lowliest naval rating knew not only the target date, but the nature of the blast – souvenirs of the *Plym* were already changing hands at high prices. But by this time high-handedness towards the Australians had become a habit. They provided the site, ships and a construction team. They built up the airfields on the mainland and opened a transit camp at Onslow. They laid on communications and provisions, meteorological data and laboratory facilities for the task force. All this at their own expense, on the basis that it was a contribution to Commonwealth defence. And yet it was only at the very last moment, and with the greatest reluctance, that two senior Australian government scientists, Alan Butement, the Chief Scientist of the Department of Supply, and Leslie Martin, the scientific adviser to the Department of Defence, were invited to attend the test as observers, and they were given access exclusively to information about the effects of the explosion, not about the weapon.

Penney had two other VIP guests: the Canadian defence research chief, Omond Solandt, and his old Los Alamos friend Ernest Titterton, who had turned down the job now being done by Tyte and had since taken up a post at the Australian National University. 'I am sure you can pitch in one of the important groups and give us valuable help', Penney had written to Titterton.[10] In fact there was little opportunity in these last days for more than a tour of the principal sites, excluding of course the *Plym*. By this stage, with the exception of the Kerr-cell cameras and one or two other last-minute problems, the scientific preparations in the field were complete and most of the work to be done was packing and loading, ready for the evacuation of the islands. Penney, however, did his best to keep his distinguished party amused. Challens recalls: 'One day when we were killing time, Penney organised a shark fishing expedition with the Australian scientists, Butement and Martin. We all piled into a boat armed with hooks and lines and tins of Irish stew from the ship's store. We went off and landed on a beach and spent the afternoon shark fishing using the hunks of meat from these tins of stew. I think we caught one or two small sharks.'

In these final days, relations between Tyte and Torlesse became steadily worse and on 29 September Tyte inaugurated a 'conscious policy of non-attendance' at the Admiral's morning staff meetings. 'I fear there is far too big a risk of Torlesse and I quarrelling

violently at such a meeting ... and an open breach would be the
end as far as I am concerned.'[11] Even this was not enough to halt
the hostilities. When Torlesse convened his meeting the next morning, on the eve of the first possible D-1 Day, Tyte was absent but
Pat Cooper, as liaison officer, was in attendance. The Admiral's
attention had been drawn to a copy of a signal sent the previous
evening by Tyte to Brooking at Fort Halstead. It was a very brief
progress report, but it included the words: 'Naval communication
sets remain troublesome.'[12] Torlesse was furious about this insult
directed at naval equipment and in Tyte's absence he vented his
wrath on the best available substitute. 'Poor Cooper was subjected
to a tirade lasting some twenty minutes on the iniquities of the MoS
and of my signal in particular', Tyte wrote. 'Torlesse completely
lost his temper and was thoroughly rude to us. Cooper did not go
into details but indicated that I would also undoubtedly have lost
mine as well and let fly at him.'[13] Tyte was inclined to take this
outburst as evidence that the Admiral privately acknowledged the
radio sets were inadequate, but a signal Torlesse sent Brooking,
overriding Tyte's, suggests otherwise. The first message had been
sent without his approval, the Admiral thundered, and there was
no question of communications problems holding up the test. The
naval radio sets were 'well tried', and any difficulties were 'mainly
due to their inherent unsuitability for employment as a telephone
system by the casual user.'[14]

BY THE EVENING of Tuesday 30 September all was ready. So far
as possible, the shore camps had been run down and stores and
equipment had been loaded back on the three landing-ships, which
on the high tide made their exit from the lagoon and joined the
Campania in the Parting Pool, leaving the *Plym* alone in Bunsen
Channel. The scientific apparatus all appeared to be functioning
satisfactorily, and even the Kerr-cell camera team were happy,
having shown that their aluminium screens solved the interference
problem. Charles Adams had endured an appalling week, worrying
on the one hand about the cameras and on the other about the
plans, timetables, lists and schedules for the final stages. Now, as
he went to bed in his tent at H1, where he had taken charge, he
had just two nagging anxieties. The boat crews had been so busy
in the previous few days that there had been no opportunity to brief

them on D-1 and D-Day plans; if in the morning D-1 was declared, they would have to rely on their experience at the rehearsal. Adams's other worry was one which had been with him for some time: insufficient planning had been done for the possibility of an extended standby phase.

On the *Campania* they were keenly aware of this too. If the weather did not come right for some time, a black hole of confusion could open up before them. A delay of a fortnight, such as Penney was contemplating privately, might place the operation under intolerable strain. Apparatus could not survive the effects of heat, sand and dew for long without maintenance; maintenance could not be provided without staff on the spot; staff could not be had without camps, and so on. How many steps backward would they have to take before they could advance to the starting-line again? These worries were all the more vivid because, frustratingly, two days had just passed which would have been perfect for the test. How long would it be before such a chance came around again?

At 6.30 a.m. on 1 October Tyte and Torlesse met. Before them was the first weather-forecast of the day. A trough of low pressure ran along the coast of the mainland, accompanied by a weak anticyclone in the Australian Bight. Somewhere to the west was another anticyclone, but its location or intensity had not been established. 'It was a situation which was liable to change without much warning, and thus inherently undesirable', wrote Torlesse. 'There did not appear to be any good reason to foresee an improvement within the ensuing twenty-four hours, so it was reluctantly decided to postpone the announcement of D-1 Day.'[15] The signal 'Charlie Oboe' was sent out to all stations, meaning: 'Standby commences.' It was an anticlimax, and around the task force the gloom about the weather prospects deepened. Adams, at least, was relieved. The boat crews could now be properly briefed and other last-minute adjustments made to the action plan for D-1 and D-Day. 'A very useful, relatively quiet day was spent', he wrote.[16]

For the meteorological team it was by no means a quiet day. They were watching that coastal trough with the most intense interest. Slowly, through the day, it broke up. First there were two small low-pressure areas, then a single one, centred on Port Hedland, to the east. This was probably another transient phenomenon, but there was just a chance that it could be something more.

244

At 7.00 p.m., Tyte and Torlesse had their third weather briefing of the day. They were told that if the low at Port Hedland were to develop into a small cyclone, as seemed more than possible, it could provide the necessary stream of air to offset the high westerlies and bring the wind around to a direction suitable for the test. It was a tantalizing prospect. 'A certain amount of cautious optimism seemed justified', wrote Torlesse. And it was. By midnight the Port Hedland low was quite distinct. 'It was clear that fortune was with us ... It appeared that within the next thirty-six hours a strong southerly or south-easterly gradient would develop, and there was a reasonable chance that this southerly air stream would build up to a sufficient depth to produce a mean wind which would be within the safety limits.'[17]

At the 6.30 a.m. meeting on 2 October, with the low still developing, it was decided to bank on the forecast and go ahead. At 6.45 a.m. the signal 'Tare Dog' went out to all stations, meaning: 'Today is D-1 Day'. With this began Phase Mercury, the first stage of Adams's action plan, during which were to be completed the final preparation of scientific apparatus on remote sites and on Trimouille, the final tests and the evacuation of all personnel save those required at H1 and on the *Plym*. Activities revolved around two hubs: the *Campania*, the centre of communications where Penney, Torlesse and Tyte were in charge, and H1, where Adams and Maddock monitored the scientific build-up. Adams was still worried about the boats. The meteorologists might see in the weather the promise of favourable winds to come, but at that moment on that Thursday morning he was more impressed by the twenty-knot surface winds blowing across the islands and the three-foot waves they were whipping up. This would make progress very difficult for the two landing-craft from the *Tracker* which had the job of taking scientists on their final visits to the outlying sites. It also threatened to prevent altogether the transfer of six of the *Campania's* motor pinnaces to the safe moorings prepared for them in the Lowendal Islands, twelve miles across open sea to the south of the Monte Bellos.

The landing-craft got away early and were able to complete their missions around the islands by noon, but the sea was becoming rougher, and, in McEnhill's words, the journeys were 'exhilarating, and occasionally somewhat wet.'[18] Prospects for the pinnaces looked bleak. Then in mid-afternoon the wind suddenly eased to fifteen knots and the sea dropped. The pinnaces took their chance and completed the dash to the Lowendals without incident. What cheered the boat crews up, however, sent the meteorologists into an anxious flurry. As Torlesse put it, 'a sudden reduction in wind strength in the afternoon . . . was not in accordance with the march of events as visualized.'[19] It proved a passing worry, and the wind soon picked up again. The evacuation proceeded, and by 4.00 p.m. all sites were clear except H1 and the *Plym*, with a few men still busy at Cocoa Beach. An hour later, most of the scientists were boarding their ships and separate roll-calls were being conducted for civilians and servicemen to ensure that everybody was accounted for. In the lagoon a hitch developed when a party of sappers who were transferring Land Rovers from Trimouille to the safety of Hermite by landing-craft found the tide so low that they were unable to enter Stephenson Channel. They made their way round to Rum Cove, close to H1 on the seaward side, to discharge their vehicles. Then, while the landing-craft made for the shelter of Claret Bay near by, the four sappers went up the hill to H1 to look for somewhere to sleep. If the bomb went off successfully next morning, they would be rather closer to the explosion than they had expected. Later, another difficulty arose with two landing-craft which were heading for the Lowendals. The afternoon lull was well and truly over and the wind was now twenty-nine knots – stronger than ever. The two boats were making heavy weather of the crossing and when one began to ship water they were turned back and sent to Claret Bay for the night.

At 6.30 p.m., after another favourable weather forecast, Phase Mercury was declared at an end and Phase Venus began. With the exception of the final evacuations from the *Plym*, boat traffic was now completed and the ships of the task force withdrew from the Parting Pool. The *Campania* and the *Zeebrugge* steamed south to the Lowendals to take up their safe positions for the test, while the *Tracker* and the *Narvik*, with some duties still to perform, remained closer to hand. The camp at Cocoa Beach was deserted. On the *Plym*, the first stages of the preparation of the weapon had begun. At H1, where the population had doubled to more than sixty men and extra tents had been erected to handle the overflow, a fretful night was beginning.

H1 would be the only land site occupied when the bomb went off, and the nearest manned observation point to ground zero. Besides the forty scientists at the camp, there were now seven sappers, two naval meteorologists, a few Royal Marines from the crews of the landing-craft down the hill in Claret Bay, and the camp staff of twelve. McEnhill, the historian, was also on hand. 'It was cold and windy in the camp that evening and conditions superficially did not seem to be suitable for the trial', he wrote. 'A sense of tenseness was evident in the mood of the company. However, the repeated rehearsal of final activities was now paying dividends and there was no sign of panic or last-minute chaos.' Another guest among the scientists was John Butterfield of the Medical Research Council, who at his own suggestion and rather against naval wishes had come to H1 in case anyone needed medical assistance. 'Happily,' wrote McEnhill, 'no serious contingency arose to warrant his presence, but a few who were more "worked out" than the others or more susceptible to the nervous anxiety naturally present at this time, were treated by him. A few men looked very tired and a number were due on duty in the control laboratories for a large portion of the night.'[20] Late in the evening there was a short lecture in the mess hut, which was well attended, to explain to anybody in need of reassurance what they were likely to experience at H1 when the weapon was detonated. Then, a little before midnight, the Marines went down to Claret Bay to spend an uncomfortable night in their boats and everybody else who was not needed retired to their tents to try to sleep. It was not easy. McEnhill records: 'The night was very windy and tent flaps smacked so loudly that conditions seemed to be worse than they had ever been at H1.'[21]

The *Plym* had been stripped down to the bare essentials and only a skeleton crew remained, so the captain himself cooked the evening meal. Challens remembers it as a 'most awful concoction of tins and things that he had found around the ship.' There was plenty of joking about finishing the rum, and afterwards some dismay when the captain insisted that the dishes had to be washed – in case there was a last-minute cancellation and they all had to return. Challens, who was not immediately involved in any work, lay down in a bunk, only to be woken soon afterwards by an earsplitting noise. An able seaman with a hammer and chisel was trying to release two rifles from an armaments case. To lose a weapon in the services is a heinous offence, and he had realised at this late hour that if he could not save these rifles he might be held to account for them. Challens, sharp-tongued at the best of times, made it plain that he was none too pleased. 'It was a night of great tension', he recalls.

At half-past midnight came a critical moment, for at this stage the operation could still be suspended as it stood for twenty-four hours. If it went any farther and there was a hitch, it would have to be cancelled, meaning that the task force would return to standby stations and the whole D-1 Day routine would have to be gone through again. With the weather forecast still favourable, Tyte and Torlesse gave the order to proceed. Phase Venus was declared over and Phase Mars began. This was the loading of the weapon. On the *Plym*, Rowlands removed the cases containing the two halves of the core and the initiator from the safe and placed them in a glove box in the weapon room. Sealing the box, he put his hands into the gloves and carefully opened the containers. The nickel-coated initiator, just the size of a grape, he placed in the dimple on the flat face of one of the golden hemispheres. With Moyce watching the neutron counter for any sign of imminent criticality, Rowlands then put the other hemisphere on top and fitted the gleaming ball into the gauntlet. This he screwed on to the end of the cartridge. The plug that would complete the bomb assembly was ready.

No time was wasted. The cartridge, about two foot six inches in length, was tipped on its end and hoist above the weapon. Then, to the clicking of the neutron counters, the slow process of lowering began. Eddie Howse, whose turn in the weapon room was to come, listened from outside as Moyce called out: 'Slow . . . Slow . . . Readings going up . . . Stop . . . Wait . . . Go down . . .' Again the multiplication rate was well within safety margins and the job was simply and cleanly done. By 2.00 a.m., after ninety minutes, the cartridge had been driven home and the last aluminium plate locked in place above it.

Phase Mars was over, and Phase Jupiter now began. Challens was in charge as 'detting' – the fitting of the detonators – got under way. One by one, the thirty-two fist-sized plugs were set in place around the circumference of the weapon, their round explosive bases nestling neatly in the matching dimples carved in the outer surface of the explosive. Then came the cables. Each detonator assembly carried two bridge wires and a detector to monitor their performance. Each was in turn connected to two separate firing systems, since the whole firing procedure was being carried out in duplicate. There were in all 128 cables to be connected. The job took two hours. As before, a running commentary was being relayed to H1, where Adams and Maddock were listening. At 4.00 a.m. Challens announced that Phase Jupiter was complete and Phase Neptune could begin: the testing of the firing system and the telemetry connections between the weapon and H1.

By this stage radar wind findings by the *Campania* were showing that the conditions only just met the safety requirements, but with five hours to go the forecast was still positive. The *Narvik* and the *Tracker* still lay just clear of the islands, waiting to take on boat parties from the *Plym*. On the *Narvik*, Lt. Peter Bird was duty officer for the night. 'There was no work for the Duty Officer, but neither was there any rest; it was a time to watch and wait. Continuous rounds of the ship were necessary in such an exposed anchorage; regular visits to the wireless office to listen to the constant streams of reports and orders passing to and fro as each successive step in the final preparations was taken ... At 5.30 in the morning, just before starting to wake the ship, I recorded my own feelings: "If all continues to go well ... in a few hours the British atomic weapon will be exploded ... We still cannot be sure of the upper air of course; that may yet apply the veto. I hope not." '[22] At 6.00 a.m., Adams roused the sleeping staff at H1 with an announcement by loud hailer that D-Day was under way. 'Men arose,' wrote McEnhill, 'moved around in the cold darkness, had some sort of wash and after that a reasonably good breakfast.'[23]

On the *Plym*, Phase Saturn had begun. Two parties of men were embarking on harbour launches to make the journey out of the lagoon. These included most of the naval crew, the RAF team, Moyce and Davies. The sea was rough, the boats were small and it was not yet first light. Davies remembers it as a very unpleasant hour afloat. 'This other little boat was right behind us; if we were in the trough of a wave you could see the other one above. Moyce put a blanket over his head and sat like that all the way out.' They were very relieved when it was over. Once the passengers were on board and the boats hoisted, the landing-ships at last made their way to their safe positions, the *Narvik* to join the *Campania* off the Lowendals and the *Tracker*, the Health Ship, to its own position a little closer in.

Only a handful of men now remained on the *Plym*: Challens, Howse and a small naval party under the ship's navigation officer, Lt. Pattison. Eddie Howse recalls: 'We had to connect up the batteries which were going to charge up the power units. I was on the phone to Frank Hill and Maddock, and Challens and I took it in turns, plugging these batteries in. They were watching the telemetry at the other end, to see the battery levels coming up. When you put one of these multi-plugs in it made contact, and then again it might not make contact. At the other end they were worrying: "It's up! It's down!" until it was OK.' Challens remembers making other adjustments: 'We also had arming clocks, which were set so that nobody could possibly fire the bomb until the bracket came up in the arming clocks.' The final act was the joining of a humble plug and socket. Then the Hurricane assembly, for the first and only time, was complete in every respect. The fruit of more than five years' work, it stood in the weapon room, a massive five-foot ball plated with geometric aluminium shapes and held two feet off the ground by its stand. All around it the detonators bulged out, and from them poured forth the cables, each with a coloured label of red or green, all draped down over the ball and forming bunches on the floor which led off to the firing circuits.

The two scientists took one last look, offered up a silent prayer and then left. From the deck they clambered down the side and joined Pattison and his men in the boat. Leaving the *Plym* tugging gently on its moorings in the stiff wind, its lights ablaze and its generators humming, they made their way into the darkness of the lagoon. This final evacuation of the *Plym* and the journey to H2 comprised Phase Uranus. The boat used was a 25-foot motor cutter, towing a dory behind. It had been holed slightly the previous day in a collision with a jetty, so the pump was kept running constantly. Lt. Pattison was in charge 'to ensure its safe navigation and timely arrival' at H2.[24] The evening before, he had placed a light at H3 to indicate the entrance to Stephenson Channel in the gloom.

Challens remembers 'a fair old chop of water with the wind blowing. Water was splashing over us and we weren't feeling our best.' Pattison found his light and after an hour and a quarter tossing on the waves they reached H2, moored the boat in mid-Channel, transferred to the dory and rowed ashore. They were driven briskly up the hill to H1, where they were met by a most alarming scene of flames and smoke. Some naval stewards had been burning rubbish and the fire had spread to the spinifex, setting alight a large area of tinder-dry grass. Not only was this a danger in itself, but the smoke threatened to obscure the cameras' line of vision from H1 to the *Plym*. Every available man, scientist and serviceman alike, was turned out to beat down the flames. As this battle went on Challens delivered the master key to Adams in the control room and when it was fitted into the firing panel the announcement was made: 'Safety link in.' Phase Uranus was over.

Since everyone else was fighting the fire, Challens and Howse set off to forage for their own breakfast. Soon the blaze was extinguished and everybody returned to their stations. One more important hurdle remained: Phase Boreas. For the safety of the H1 team, the final wind check was conducted directly from their site to ensure that there was no danger of the lower winds bringing fall-out towards them. A balloon was released, its ascent carefully monitored and the figures reported to the weather centre on the *Campania*. They were greeted with horror and disbelief. Torlesse called them 'highly disturbing', so far were they removed from what was expected.[25] Rather than cancel forthwith, there was just time to repeat the experiment to ensure it was accurate. The meteorological officer at H1 was ordered to release another balloon, which he did in great haste, and although his report was cut short because he was ordered to take cover, it showed that all was well. Tyte gave the order to proceed.

It was a matter of minutes now. A little earlier, Maddock had issued a time check over the scientists' 'Channel Charlie', to which all the task force ships were tuned, allowing everybody to synchronize their watches for the countdown. At 9.10 a.m., everyone on the ships who wished to see the event and had no other duties paraded on deck to be briefed on the safety procedures they must follow. The firing sequence was about to begin. Maddock was sitting calmly at the firing panel in the gloom of the control centre, with Hill at his right hand. The desk surface was clear but for a large microphone. On the panel before them was the row of keys and the master key, all safely in place. Across the top were two rows of lights, each light indicating the state of readiness of one of the monitoring teams at work in the control centre. They were not yet all lit. In the middle of the panel were two large clock-faces, each with a single hand. One showed a time scale of eight and a half minutes; the other thirty seconds. Just above them was a sign in large, bold letters, saying: 'VETO'.

At 9.15 a.m. Maddock announced: 'Attention all stations. This is H1 control. Dog Baker has commenced. Dog Baker has commenced.'[26] On the ships the message was translated: 'Weapon will fire at some time in the next half hour.' This was the opening of the Danger Bracket. At any time within this period Maddock, under instruction from Adams, could begin the firing sequence, lasting eight minutes and twenty-five seconds. Before he could do so there was a last-minute alarm. The Kerr-cell camera team could not get the film cassettes to fit into the equipment. Adams ordered a delay. Maddock calmly announced that there would be a delay of five minutes. Almost six minutes passed as a stream of expletives poured forth from the aluminium cage now enclosing the cameras. Then they finally succeeded in pushing home the film. 'Can I have the all-ready signal, please?' asked Maddock. All the lights on the panel came on save one. 'Mr Abercrombie?' prompted Maddock, and the final bulb lit up. At a nod from Adams, he announced: 'Minus eight and a half minutes.' The firing sequence – Phase Pluto – had begun. Red flags were hoisted on all the task force ships to indicate this, in case any should have suffered a radio failure and missed the signal.

'Minus seven minutes.' Telemetry messages going out and coming back from the remote sites around the islands confirmed that the scattered apparatus was performing as required. 'Minus six minutes.' Everybody at H1 was under cover and doors had been wedged slightly open for the blast. A few men with nothing to do, including Eddie Howse, had set up crude pinhole viewers in the wall of the control centre so that they could watch the flash. 'Minus five minutes.' At Claret Bay Lt. Pattison was now in charge of the Marines. He had one of the scientists' police radios tuned in to Channel Charlie and instructed his men to stand with their backs towards the *Plym*. 'Minus four minutes.' On the task force ships the decks were full of men, lined up in the morning sunshine facing away from the islands, with their officers behind them facing in the same direction, like a reverse parade. Occasionally, amid much shuffling, they had to adjust their positions as the ships swung in the changing tide. 'Minus three minutes.' They were called to attention. All the ships, recalls Peter Bird, 'were now in a battened-down state, doors and hatches closed and clipped and the heavy steel deadlights clamped down over all ports.'[27] This was to protect men still working below from accidental exposure to the flash. 'Minus two minutes.' Bill Penney and Torlesse were together on the bridge of the *Campania*. Torlesse had a huge pair of binoculars looted from the Japanese in 1945, and these were now mounted behind him ready to view the eruption. Penney, like everyone else who wore spectacles, had been told to remove them or close his eyes, in case he might be blinded by a reflection of the flash in the inside of the lenses. 'Minus fifty-five seconds.' In the control room, oscilloscopes displayed the voltage levels of the firing apparatus in the weapon room of the *Plym*, precisely six miles and 1,283 yards away. Challens watched intently. 'I was feeling my responsibilities. If my part didn't work the whole thing would be an enormous flop.'

'Minus twenty-five seconds.' Now the last chance for a temporary delay was gone. All that could be done to halt the test was a 'veto', which would return the whole task force to standby. 'Minus twenty seconds.' The automatic fine-timing apparatus had taken over. 'Fifteen seconds.' To Challens's relief, the voltage levels were perfect and steady. 'Ten seconds.' The voice going out on Channel Charlie was still calm. 'Five. Four. Three. Two. One. NOW.'

THE TIME WAS twenty-nine minutes and twenty-four seconds past nine, Monte Bello Islands time, which was thirty-six seconds to eight Perth time or thirty-six seconds before 1.00 a.m. London time. In the weapon room in the hull of HMS *Plym*, the trigatrons in the twin firing-circuits unleashed the high-voltage current from the capacitors, allowing it to surge down the cables and scatter into the thirty-two detonator assemblies that surrounded the sphere. The microscopic bridge wires in each assembly were vaporized and ignited the PETN explosive in which they were packed. With that, detonation waves took shape in the RDX outer shells of the high-explosive lenses. As these thirty-two separate convex waves raced inwards towards the core, the lenses did their work. Each wave, striking the point of the Baratol cone, began to slow and change shape. Passing through the thickest part of the cone, the leading point of the wave slowed most, and the edges least. The convex wave straightened and then bent backwards until it was concave. Now there was a single inward-moving spherical detonation wave. Reaching the massive supercharge of pure, fast RDX, the wave leapt forward until it struck the next layer, the uranium tamper. This in turn crashed, with incredible violence, against the core. The effect was to transform the plutonium into a sphere of hot, thick liquid, no longer the size of a grapefruit but of an orange, and in another instant of a plum. Inside that was the initiator. It too become a molten mass, and in that moment the essential first nuclear reaction took place. Alpha particles emitted by the polonium struck nuclei of the beryllium surrounding it. The result was a spray of neutrons, which scattered into the plutonium like machine-gun fire. Reduced to this compressed and molten state, the plutonium was supercritical, and the neutrons set in motion the fission chain reaction. When a neutron struck a plutonium nucleus that nucleus split into two and released both a surge of energy and more neutrons. These neutrons in turn struck other nuclei, and the process was repeated. The multiplication rate of these fissions was such that within a dozen or so generations, billions were taking place. Then billions of billions. A race was now under way between the chain reaction and the cumulative eruption of energy – light, heat and blast – bursting forth from the fissions. Soon the energy won, the inward shock wave was thrown backwards and outwards and the nuclear explosion took place.

The first evidence of this was observed by a Kerr-cell camera at H1 twenty-three millionths of a second after the detonation. A ball of fire was emerging from the centre of the bomb, nine feet below the waterline, and what the camera captured at that instant was a segment of that fireball that had broken through the hull of HMS *Plym*. Beside this could be seen the bows of the frigate, silhouetted against a similar eruption of light on the far side. The fireball grew with unimaginable speed. After thirty-five millionths of a second it had risen to a height of more than twenty feet. After less than a hundredth of a second it was 350 feet high and 500 feet wide.

The *Plym* had disappeared. In just over half a second the fireball was one-third of a mile across, after which it started to contract. At the control centre six miles away this sudden and intense flash of light, passing through the merest cracks in the timber walls, was enough to bring the brightness of day to the darkened firing-room for one instant. Frank Hill recalls feeling the heat flash on the back of his neck at the same moment. On the *Narvik*, Peter Bird wrote that 'despite a blazing tropical sun intensified by reflection from the water all round, a blinding light bathed the ships and the ocean from horizon to horizon.'[28]

After about one-tenth of a second, the cameras recorded that water began to shoot outwards and upwards from the fireball. Then a column of water began to form, its base distorted by the previous presence of the *Plym*. When a whole second had passed the familiar mushroom shape emerged, about 1,800 feet high and with a cloud at its head. Around this central feature was a wider secondary eruption, which heaved into the air a huge mass of water more than half a mile across, to a height of 550 feet. Also thrown upwards by these upheavals were thousands of tons of coral sand swept up from the sea-bed, so that afterwards an underwater crater remained beneath where the *Plym* had lain that was 300 yards across and twenty feet deep at the middle.

Three seconds passed. Those lined up on the ships were required to remain with their backs to the blast but at H1 a stream of men came charging out of the control centre to attend to their equipment. As they climbed the camera gantries or rounded the corners of the building, McEnhill wrote, 'they could see the vast, crisply-outlined water column rising rapidly in the stillness. This was the most impressive feature of these early seconds – the vastness of the upheaval, its splendid symmetry, and the stillness.'[29] Butterfield, the doctor, watched as 'a grey and white column rose from the lagoon ... capped by a white cloud shaped like a cauliflower.'[30] On the ships no one had yet seen this. The count continued upwards: 'Six. Seven. Eight. Nine. Ten.' Then a voice declared: 'You may look now', and a thousand men turned on their heels to see the atomic destruction. 'The sight that met our eyes as we turned was vastly more terrifying than can be appreciated from any photograph', wrote Bird. 'The great, grey-black mass, just flowering at the top like a tremendous cauliflower, appeared, even at a distance, to be towering right over us.'[31]

When thirty seconds had passed at H1 the ground shook, and almost immediately there was the crash of the blast wave. 'Like the pressure from an express train passing close by', thought Butterfield. McEnhill noted that it was 'a little more impressive than many had bargained for' and indeed a few inside the control centre got a fright when everything suddenly went black – yards of blackout cloth that had been stuffed into cracks in the wall were blown out and thrown over their heads. By now the wind was at work, and its behaviour was every bit as complex as the meteorologists had anticipated. At ground level it was southerly, but by 6,000 feet it was easterly. Then it came suddenly round to the south again at 8,000 feet, becoming a south-westerly at 12,000 feet and a westerly at 20,000 feet. Slowly, as the murky, boiling mass surged upwards, these corkscrew winds twisted the mushroom out of shape and the splendid symmetry was lost. The stiff easterlies around 6,000 feet seemed to knock most of the cloud sideways and downwards as a gale would a rotten tree, while higher up the gentler southerlies were catching the top of the cloud and pushing it to the north. As the hundreds of seamen and scientists on the broad flight deck of the *Campania* gazed up at this in awed fascination, a double shock wave struck them. Penney said later: 'It seemed ages before we heard the bang but, in fact, it was only a minute. Somewhat to our surprise, a second bang – at least as loud as the first – followed a few seconds later. At the same time we felt a peculiar sensation in our ears such as one has in an aircraft losing height rapidly. We were feeling the suction, or reduced pressure, which always follows a blast wave. All the time the cloud was getting higher and higher and assuming fantastic shapes . . .'[32] The second bang, which mystified many who experienced it, was caused by reflection from a layer of warm air two miles up.

Farther afield, on Mount Potter, the Press team had been ready, alerted by rumour that the test was imminent and brought to action stations by the light flash. Dan O'Sullivan was on duty. He picked up the field telephone and passed the message to a young colleague, Peter Barnett, who was waiting in the communications truck at the base camp below. With him were two telegraphists, selected as the quickest in Western Australia. Barnett gave the first signal

256

to one of these, who swiftly encoded it in Morse and transmitted it to Perth. The British bomb had been detonated. Then O'Sullivan came on the line with more and, as Barnett typed, the telegraphists took it in turns to rattle out the code. Within the hour, copies of the *Perth Daily News* were rolling from the presses bearing the front-page news. O'Sullivan's full report that day announced: 'With a brief, lightning-like flash, Britain's first atomic weapon was exploded at 8 a.m. today in the Monte Bello Islands, off the north-west coast of Western Australia. The flash was followed by a huge expanding cloud which reached a height of 12,000ft within about three minutes of the explosion. By that time it was a mile across at its widest part. Although no official announcement has been made it is believed that the explosion was from a tower either at Flag Island or at Hermite Island – the largest in the Monte Bello group. The Press observation point is on the highest point in Rough Range, north of the Fortescue River, and is only fifty-five miles from the Monte Bello Islands. Observers here did not feel a ground shock, but a heavy air-pressure pulse hit the mainland four minutes and fifteen seconds after the flash of the explosion, which occurred on the tick of 8 o'clock. At the same time pressmen heard a report like a clap of thunder, followed by a prolonged rumble like that of a train going through a tunnel. The air and ground shocks were sufficiently intense to cause slight pain in the ears. The immediate flash resembled the top quarter of a setting sun.'[33]

On the *Campania* too, there was a rush to get the message out. Within three minutes of the detonation a signal was transmitted to London carrying the priority 'emergency'. It was addressed to the Admiralty and it said simply: 'DOUBLOON repetition DOUBLOON.'[34] It was 1.17 a.m. before this landed on the desk of the Admiralty duty officer in London. The codeword 'Doubloon' meant that the task force commander had approved the release of a Press statement saying that a British atomic weapon had been successfully tested. But before he told the newspapers, the duty officer had a list of other people who had to be informed, including Evans-Lombe, Morgan, Cherwell, Sandys and Churchill. The call to Downing Street did not go as planned. The Prime Minister was staying with the Queen at Balmoral and the man on duty at Number Ten was a private secretary, Anthony Montague Browne, a former fighter pilot who had just started work for

Churchill. The caller from the Admiralty 'suggested that I should wake the Prime Minister at Balmoral and inform him,' Montague Browne recalled much later, 'but even at this early stage I concluded that this would be imprudent.'[35] Churchill, then seventy-eight years old, learned of the success at breakfast time and offered no complaint at having been allowed to slumber on. It was not the only hitch of the night for the Admiralty Duty Office, and there were ill-tempered *post mortems* afterwards about why it took fourteen minutes for the news to reach London, why Reuters had the news (from Mount Potter) six minutes ahead of the Admiralty, and why it took more than an hour to tell the Ministry of Supply. The Government had been 'scooped' by the Press with its own story.

Back in the islands, many of the scientists were experiencing a sense of anticlimax. Eddie Howse, who had observed the blast through his pinhole viewer at H1 recalls: 'That was just a flash, and not a very good impression.' Then he went outside. 'I was disappointed, because it was so far away. It was a long time before you heard the bang and felt the shock wave.' Many others felt the same. Why? They were certainly a long way from the blast, and the shapeless, mud-laden cloud rose only half as high as expected. Their weapon had lost its mystery and become an ugly blot on the sky. They may also have been struck by the contrast with the film footage from the Bikini tests, which was taken by long-lensed cameras and had the sound of the explosion cut and re-dubbed to coincide with the fireball. Or they may simply have been feeling the reaction that often goes with completing a task that has absorbed years of commitment and effort. John Challens was so unimpressed by the explosion he believed it was a failure. 'I thought, "Oh God, it hasn't gone off right." The bang wasn't all that much – it was a fair old thud but it didn't look that impressive – and I felt absolutely down. I thought, "My God, it hasn't really worked." About mid-morning, we all got into a tank landing-craft back to *Campania*. It was a very rough ride, with the thing pitching up and down, and I was getting more and more down. Then I went up the companionway and Penney was at the top and he said, "Congratulations, it's beautiful." Then I realized it must have been all right.'

H1 was evacuated twenty minutes after the explosion, the

scientists turning off their equipment, gathering up their records and heading down to Rum Cove to be picked up by the landing-craft which had spent the night in Claret Bay. Pattison was in charge. Adams reported to him when everybody was aboard and swiftly they headed out round Attlee Point and made for the *Campania*. Behind them the cloud was now sprawled across fifty miles of sky, and from the surface of Trimouille rose the smoke of hundreds of spinifex fires. Three hours after the blast, Torlesse cabled London: 'Penney pleased with result of explosion as observed from *Campania*. Evacuation completed. No casualties.'[36] A further message followed, from Penney: 'We have records in all important scientific experiments. We have fully met our commitment to the Australians that no harmful contamination will be deposited on the mainland. All contamination went northwards and will stay there for at least another 10 hours. It is possible that no contamination whatever will reach the mainland. The dispersion is already sufficient to eliminate all danger from fall-out now taking place. The meteorological conditions were extraordinarily fortunate for us and I am sure that no estimate of the power of the bomb can be made from photographs from the mainland. I think that we can rest assured that no significant dust samples can be collected by foreigners. We alone will know the power and efficiency of our weapon.'[37]

In the hours that followed, messages of congratulations arrived from Evans-Lombe, the Hurex chairman, from the Board of Admiralty, from Cherwell, from Sandys and from Churchill. Cherwell told Penney warmly: 'Knowing you, I never had any doubts myself, but am delighted it has all gone well.' Churchill was more formal: 'Congratulations on your successful achievement. Please convey to those concerned at Montebello and at home the thanks of Her Majesty's Government for all their toil and skill which have carried this great enterprise to fruition.'[38]

There were parties over the next few nights, and the wardroom bar on the *Campania*, with its duty-free prices, was extremely busy. The refugees from the now-vanished *Plym*, who all along had been a relatively happy band, appear to have led the celebrations. Their party was, as Challens was later to tell Tyte, 'a truly combined operation consisting of some of the Naval officers, the RAF officers [from the weapon-loading team] and some of our civilians', and there was 'song-singing and general uproarious conduct.' John Davies recalls watching a squadron leader climb atop a table in the wardroom and proceed to demonstrate 'some sort of dance', while Bill Moyce remembers the RAF singing a song to the tune of 'The wee deoch an doris': 'Goodbye *Campania*, Goodbye toodle-oo/ Goodbye *Campania*, It's a long time since we came to you/Your ladders are a failure/Your wardroom is a farce/And as for your atomic bomb . . .' Just as they sang the last line, Penney appeared, and asked: 'What's that they're saying about the bomb?' Moyce says: 'I like to believe I said I couldn't hear it because of the noise.' Eddie Howse witnessed another incident: 'One of the admin. chaps, a tall youngster who came to Aldermaston afterwards, got slightly drunk. Now as you went into the wardroom, the officers used to hang their hats just inside on a hook by the door. This chap – I think he had had enough of the Navy by then – stood there and threw all the hats overboard until someone stopped him.' Rivalry, however, seems to have taken second place to revelry, and McEnhill noticed that naval officers joined lustily in the 'denouncements of *Campania* and all her appendages.'[39] Soon there was another cause for celebration, for Penney was informed from London that he was to be knighted.

15

The Aftermath

WITHIN a few hours it was evident that by all known standards this had been a very dirty explosion. Far more radioactive fall-out was deposited on the islands than anyone had expected. The fireball and the eruption which accompanied it lifted thousands of tons of water and sand into the air. There they were mixed with the 'fission products' of the nuclear reaction – the radioactive residues from the splitting of billions of plutonium atoms – into a dense and deadly cloud of contaminating particles. Some of this blew away over the sea and was scattered over many thousands of miles in the weeks to come, but the tricks of the wind and the sheer weight of matter brought much of it down on the islands and the lagoon as a torrent of toxic rain.

The *Plym* had vanished, mostly turned to vapour in the fireball. Here and there, the shore of Trimouille was streaked with a gluey black substance. At first this was thought to come from a layer of mud beneath the sea-bed but after closer examination it was identified as the remains of the frigate. Some larger fragments survived, scattered far and wide, and these were probably responsible for many of the spinifex fires that occurred.

There had been no base surge worthy of the name; the process may have begun, but if it did it was drowned by the rainstorm, which started a minute after the detonation and lasted for nine minutes. It left a great, broad footprint of contamination stamped across the map, with its heel at the point in the Bunsen Channel

261

where the *Plym* had been anchored. The side of the foot covered much of the northern half of Trimouille, while the toes lay to the west, over the water, so that a grey-and-black stain covered a swathe of little islands whose names were now less appropriate than ever: Bluebell, Carnation, Gardenia, Kingcup and Jonquil.

The first to visit this scene were the helicopter crews. Two aircraft took off from the *Campania* at 11.30 a.m., two hours after the detonation. While one stood off, monitoring radiation from a distance and ready to intervene in case of accident, the other flew deep into the contaminated part of the lagoon, as close to ground zero as its radiation readings permitted, to lower a container and collect a sample of sea-water. This was quickly delivered to HMS *Zeebrugge*, where Frank Morgan and his team were waiting to begin their analysis.

While the helicopter mission was under way, the first of the six motor pinnaces which had been dispatched to the Lowendals moved up to join HMS *Tracker* about five miles from the islands. The Health Ship was now effectively in charge of operations. It was linked by telemetry to unmanned radiation-monitoring posts scattered over the islands, and for the rest of the day, on a large map in the health-control room, it maintained a picture of the changing state of contamination. The *Tracker* also contained the decontamination and health-monitoring facilities through which would pass all personnel engaged in 're-entry' to the Monte Bellos over the coming four weeks. Here, the re-entry teams were carefully briefed. They then dressed in their protective gear – cotton underwear, woollen socks, heavy overalls with double thickness below the elbow and the knee and elasticated cuffs at ankle and wrist, rubber boots, rubber gloves, sweatrags for around the neck and 'jungle hats'. At 12.35 p.m., gathering up their gas masks and the dosimeters and film badges which would measure their exposure to radiation, they set off in conditions now perfectly calm and sunny.

The pinnaces had been covered with canopies to prevent contaminated sea spray or dust being blown in, and the crews – also in full protective gear – had received basic training in radiological safety procedures. Through the afternoon they completed a number of missions, testing the water at various points, removing samples from collectors on buoys moored in the lagoon and landing in areas considered relatively safe. One boat tried to penetrate to Gladstone

Beach, to the north of ground zero, but found it too 'hot' to approach. Another boat landed at the southern end of Trimouille to deliver a party whose job was to find some of the rockets which had been fired through the cloud from North-West Island. Four rockets were found and were dispatched by helicopter to the *Zeebrugge*. Once these arrived, the *Zeebrugge* steamed south to Sandy Island, forty miles away, so that Morgan's analysis could be conducted in calm waters, free from contamination. A tent was set up ashore for micro-balance work. Further samples were soon delivered which had been collected from the cloud by an RAAF flight of Lincoln aircraft operating from Broome.

By the evening of D-Day, the team on the *Tracker* was able to describe the extent of the radioactive contamination: 'The whole of Trimouille, Alpha and North-West Islands, and all islands between, must be considered "dirty" for purposes of re-entry. Hermite is almost certainly "clean" but must be checked. The indications are that the northern half of Trimouille is heavily contaminated, but little over the southern half; from T1 for about one mile north there is only slight contamination and most of that appears to be due to pieces of *Plym*.'[1]

The day had seen three radiation scares. The rocket-recovery team, on their return from Trimouille to the *Tracker*, were found to have contaminated hands. Repeated washing was enough to clean them. One of the helicopters became contaminated after passing through a cloud of smoke from a fire on Trimouille. It was sent to the *Tracker*, where the crew, too, were found to be slightly contaminated. Again, showering was enough. In the evening a more dramatic event occurred. The *Tracker* had moved as close to the islands as was thought safe, reaching a point to the south of the Parting Pool, a mile from Flag Island. What had been an extremely busy day on the Health Ship was just drawing to a close when the alarm was raised. One of the scientists describes what happened: 'At 1900 hours the radioactive background on *Tracker* rose by a factor of about 500. This completely put out of operation all the beta-gamma personnel-monitoring equipment on board. The trouble was brought about by a change of wind which had brought airborne contamination down on *Tracker*, probably from the grass fires which had burnt throughout the day and continued to burn that night. *Tracker* soon steamed clear and it was evident that residual contamination from this dry activity was very small.'[2]

The following day the wind got up and very little boat work was possible. In the evening, just before 11.00 p.m., fall-out was detected over both the *Tracker* and the *Campania*. Again, the danger was slight and passed quickly, but Torlesse was becoming concerned. He and Penney were due to leave the islands for London in a few days to brief the Prime Minister and senior ministers and officials, and to give a Press conference. Torlesse wondered whether he would be better employed at the islands. Besides the succession of worrying incidents, a variety of other considerations were weighing on the Admiral's mind. The scientists were unanimous in their verdict that the general contamination of the islands and of the sites where records and equipment remained to be recovered was far worse than anticipated. The contamination of the sea-water was impeding ship movements and causing difficulties for boat traffic. Problems had been encountered finding a safe place to moor boats at night. The weather was unstable and had already cost the re-entry teams a day's work. Worse still, a large, intact and active portion of the radioactive cloud was lingering out at sea, some way to the north-west but still in the general area of the islands. The fear remained that it might drift back over the task force, or towards some inhabited part of the Australian coast.

After discussions with Penney, Torlesse cabled London. 'Contamination over the greater part of Trimouille and northern half of the lagoon is extensive and severe', he reported. 'Limited experience so far indicates that large-scale recovery of records and examination of test equipment on Trimouille will involve much contamination of personnel and boats and possibly some very responsible decisions. We are not dealing with exactly calculable risks. In circumstances and in view of explicit responsibility of the Naval Commander for safety, I could not advise my leaving Monte Bello with Penney on D+5 Day, or the absence of at least fourteen days which this journey would entail. Dr Penney concurs.'[3] Torlesse sought permission to remain at his post with the task force to oversee re-entry work, and to send Commander Willan, the captain of HMS *Narvik*, to London in his place. The request was circulated at the highest levels in Whitehall before receiving approval. When the Press conference in London eventually took place, Torlesse's apologies were presented and the impression was given to the journalists that the explanation for his absence was bad weather. The 'extensive and severe' fall-out over the islands was not mentioned.

The test had been conducted in the form that it took to allow the scientists to assess the effects of an atomic explosion on a ship in harbour. The lessons were clear: even though there had been no base surge, this was far dirtier and deadlier than any other known form of explosion. The final report, completed two years later after all the data had been processed and interpreted, set this out in civil-defence terms. With an explosion of the Monte Bello type, the area in which everyone could be expected to receive a lethal dose of gamma radiation was between twice and four times as great as with a similar weapon exploded in the air. The conclusion was that 'the residual contamination due to the deposited fission products provides a major contribution to the effect of a weapon detonated in this way'.[4] If London or Liverpool suffered such an attack, a larger number of people – perhaps a far larger number – would probably be killed by radiation than at Hiroshima or Nagasaki.

After the enforced pause on D+1 Day, the re-entry work proceeded rapidly for a week, was interrupted by unfavourable weather for four days, and then continued briskly until completion on 23 October. In the event, Torlesse did not face any 'very responsible decisions' regarding safety risks. One man was killed in this phase of the operation, but not by radiation. He was a sapper whose bulldozer turned over on him. The cloud ultimately dispersed without grave incident; one part did cross the coast of Australia at high altitude but the resultant deposits of radioactivity were negligible. At the islands, the team on the *Tracker* proved highly efficient both at anticipating and avoiding dangerous situations and at the business of health-monitoring and decontamination. In total, 940 man-sorties were made into the contaminated areas over thirteen working days, and everyone involved was required to pass through the *Tracker*'s decontamination procedures at the end of each day. This 'conveyor belt' is described by McEnhill: 'One part of the deck had been roped off as a dirty area and men entered this as they disembarked from the pinnaces after having come from the islands. Here decontamination teams relieved them of contaminated records, or instruments, which were placed in special sections for subsequent monitoring. Their overalls, gloves, boots, etc., were removed, monitored and placed in appropriate bins to be dealt with later. The men, clad in underpants, now passed below to the dirty side of the decontamination control. Further monitoring of various parts of their bodies was made and then they passed into showers, after which they were remonitored. If clean, they passed into the clean side of the Health Control, were weighed, given a drink and some salt tablets, and then they dressed.'[5]

In 82 per cent of cases, no significant contamination was found after the first shower. Of those who remained, most had suffered contamination of the neck, face and hair, an indication that the gas mask, sweatrag and hat together did not provide adequate protection around the head. A second shower was sufficient for 5 per cent. Treatment of the skin with chemical agents followed by further washing left a further 12 per cent clean. In the remaining cases, involving eight men, 'slight residual contamination' persisted.[6]

Measured another way, the safety record appears in the same light. Before the test, acting on the advice of the Medical Research Council and the medical staff of the Ministry of Supply, Penney had established three dose levels: a normal working rate at which men could safely enter and re-enter contaminated areas day after day; a 'lower integrated dose' which, if received, would bar a man from further work involving exposure to radiation for six weeks; and finally a 'higher integrated dose'. Exposure at this last level could only be risked in an emergency and with the personal authorization of the naval commander, and any man who received so high a dose would not be subjected to any further radiation for a year. These standards were compatible with internationally recommended procedures at the time. On Operation Hurricane, no one was exposed to the higher integrated dose and thirty-one people received the lower integrated dose, thus ruling themselves out of further re-entry work at the islands.

In 1985, the safety of the British nuclear tests in Australia was examined by an Australian Royal Commission amidst public concern over possible health damage to test veterans and to the

Australian public, particularly Aborigines. The broad conclusions reached about Hurricane were that health and safety regulations were observed, that personnel were not exposed to radiation beyond the set limits and that decontamination procedures were 'tediously and thoroughly' carried out.[7] Some lapses were identified. The crews of the RAAF Lincoln aircraft which took samples from the cloud were exposed to external radiation, although they had not been informed of the risks or provided with monitoring equipment. And naval divers who were involved in salvaging a landing-craft which sank off Daisy Island in stormy weather during the re-entry phase were exposed to the risk of swallowing contaminated water.

This is by no means the last word on the safety. Just because the standards set were generally observed does not mean that the standards themselves were the correct ones. The relationship between radiation dosage and health damage is highly complex and even today is imperfectly understood. The Royal Commission, which heard evidence from a number of Hurricane veterans who alleged that they had suffered illness as a result of their involvement with the test, looked into it in considerable detail. It drew three important conclusions. The first was that the policy adopted on exposure to radiation was 'reasonable and compatible with the international recommendations applicable at the time.'[8] In 1952, scientists still believed in the notion of a safe dose of radiation, and their efforts were devoted to identifying the dose levels which lay at the threshold between safety and danger. This idea of a threshold is no longer accepted: there is no such thing as a safe dose, only one which is relatively less dangerous. Another conclusion from the Royal Commission declares: 'The measures taken before and at the time of the tests for protecting persons against exposure to the harmful effects of radiation, based as they were on the concept that any dose below a certain level was "safe", must be regarded as inadequate in the light of radiation standards at the present time.'[9] The third relevant conclusion flows from the second: 'Their exposure to radiation as participants in the trial programme has increased the risk of cancer among "nuclear veterans".'[10]

This view has been tested statistically. In 1983 the Ministry of Defence, responding to public concern about the health of test veterans, commissioned a detailed study by the National

Radiological Protection Board. It identified 21,300 men who had taken part in the twenty-one British nuclear tests that were carried out in Australia and the Pacific between 1952 and 1958, and in a variety of lesser experiments involving nuclear materials. Their health records in the years that followed were compared with those of a 'control group' composed of a similar number of men of similar birth dates who had not taken part in tests. If the health of the veterans had suffered because of their involvement in the tests, then their records would be likely to show a higher incidence of certain radiation-related diseases than among the men in the control group. The first results were published in 1988. 'It is concluded', the report said, 'that participation in the nuclear weapons test programme has not had a detectable effect on the participants' expectation of life nor on their total risk of developing cancer ...'[11] The study found among the veterans a slightly higher incidence of two forms of cancer, multiple myeloma and leukaemia. This could not be directly attributed to radiation, for it was discovered that the incidence of these diseases among the control group was surprisingly low and the suspicion was that it was not the higher finding, but the lower, that was abnormal. Further investigation was undertaken and in 1993, after ten years of work, the results were reported: 'The possibility that the participants experienced a small risk of developing leukaemia in the first twenty-five years after the tests cannot be ruled out but, as the risk was not concentrated in those involved in any particular test, those known to have been exposed to radiation, or those with any particular job, possible explanations for such a risk are unknown and it is concluded that the excess of leukaemia in test participants compared with controls that was noted in the previous report is likely to have been a chance finding.'[12]

In short, a thorough statistical examination of the medical evidence, conducted by a scientific body with impeccable credentials, could find no evidence of any general failure of policy or practice. There matters rest. Veterans' groups continue to press the cases of some individuals who claim to be victims of particular errors or oversights, but at this distance in time it is all but impossible for them to prove cause and effect. With the Ministry of Defence still denying responsibility for health damage, and in the absence of any case-by-case arbitration procedure which might settle claims on the basis of probabilities and without allocating blame, it seems that there is little hope for the aggrieved veterans. In the meantime, the passing years take their toll; if some new evidence emerges or the official policy is changed, it will come too late for most of those who might have benefited.

WHAT ABOUT THE islands? It was certain long before the test that some areas would remain contaminated for far longer than the three years which Attlee had unwisely mentioned to Menzies in March 1951. After the task force had left the site an Australian presence was maintained for three months and then the islands were abandoned. A small British party returned in late 1953 and reported: 'The islands are still very contaminated and, because further decay is at a very slow rate, the conditions are not likely to change significantly over the next ten years.'[13] Just over a year later, Penney tried to allay Australian concerns: 'A man could walk about for fifty hours in the most heavily contaminated areas with safety and would certainly not experience any harmful effects ... A man who spent 200 hours now in the most contaminated areas would probably begin to show signs of sickness ... We have made the statement that contamination will persist for ten years. This is scientifically true, but envisages something which is most unlikely to happen – that somebody will spend weeks or months in the contaminated areas.'[14] In 1956 Penney's scientists returned to carry out two more nuclear tests on the islands, one on Trimouille and the other on Alpha Island. After this, parts of the Monte Bellos were fenced off and marked with signs in five languages saying: 'Danger – Radioactive. Keep Out.' They remained in any case a prohibited area, although the people of the north-west coast, steadily stripping the sites of whatever hardware and scrap was worth salvaging, paid no attention to that. The man who was Onslow's police officer in the early 1960s testified later that not only was he unaware that the islands were out of bounds but he had himself visited them to collect copper cables left behind by the British. The Australian Royal Commission concluded that no one visiting the islands in the years after the tests had received a hazardous exposure to radiation. Forty years after Hurricane, they remained technically a prohibited area, although yachts were said to call there occasionally.

269

The Aftermath

The wildlife undoubtedly suffered. Many animals and birds, particularly on Trimouille, were killed by the Hurricane explosion and some suffered slow and painful deaths from radiation sickness. In terms of the destruction of rare species, however, it seems clear that the task force did less damage than the earlier visitors who introduced the rats and cats. The wallabies and bandicoots, the native mammals which had been present at the beginning of the century, had been wiped out long before 1952, and the two rare varieties of bird thought to have been present, the spinifex bird and the black-and-white fairy wren, were never seen in the months of build-up to the test. In all, twenty-seven varieties of bird were spotted, and all were seen again after the explosion save two, of which there had previously been only one sighting each. Frank Hill, who had combined his work in Maddock's team with the collection of natural history samples from the islands, later read a paper on the Monte Bellos to the Linnaean Society in London and listed more than 350 varieties of flora and fauna which had been identified. One of his discoveries, a water beetle, proved to be entirely new to science and was named, in his honour, *Halobates hilliella*. No comparable audit has been conducted since, so it is impossible to say whether all the species fared as well as the birds, although that seems likely.

William Penney left the islands for London on 9 October. On the previous day he had seen all the senior team leaders to hear their preliminary reports on the explosion. Some had met with disappointment: one of the Kerr-cell cameras had failed, and Moody's multiplication-rate experiment had fallen victim to the phenomenon known as electro-magnetic pulse, which played havoc with its complex electronics. The great majority of the equipment, however, had functioned exactly as planned. There was general agreement on the yield, which was the principal piece of information that Penney wanted to set before the Prime Minister. This was calculated at first at twenty kilotons, similar to the yield of the Nagasaki weapon, Penney's original model. Some years later this figure was revised to twenty-five kilotons. This means that the Hurricane device exploded with a force equivalent to 25,000 tons of TNT – twice as powerful as the uranium weapon dropped over Hiroshima and roughly ten per cent more powerful than Fat Man.

Penney returned to Britain to find himself the object of curiosity and excitement bordering on adulation. For the first few days his home was besieged and Joan Penney was forced to come and go by a back door. For several weeks every public appearance he made was reported in the Press, and every sentence he uttered was analyzed for what it might reveal about the weapon or its maker. In the absence of official information, speculation and conjecture reigned. The weapon had been exploded on a tower; the operation bore the typically Churchillian name of 'Operation Havoc;'[15] Penney himself was 'easily the best mind in the world on atoms and hydrogen bomb research';[16] he had developed a weapon that could spread destruction over a wider area than American bombs; the bomb was 'smaller and more compact than the standard bombs in the U.S. stockpile', and employed a 'novel mechanism to set off the plutonium' (this last, by accident or design, was actually true).[17] The *Daily Graphic* trumped all by declaring: 'Britain now has what is believed to be the world's most powerful atomic weapon.'[18]

On 23 October, with the members of the House of Commons back from the party conferences, Churchill at last gave a statement on the test which put an end to much of the nonsense: 'The object of the test was to investigate the effects of an atomic explosion in a harbour. The weapon was accordingly placed in HMS *Plym*, a frigate of 1,450 tons, which was anchored in the Monte Bello Islands. Conditions were favourable and care was taken to wait for southerly winds so as to avoid the possibility of any significant concentration of radioactive particles spreading over the Australian mainland. Specimen structures of importance to civil defence and to the armed services were erected at various distances. Instruments were set up to record the effect of contamination, blast, heat flash, gamma-ray flash and other features of interest. The weapon was exploded in the morning of 3 October. Thousands of tons of water and of mud and rock from the sea bottom were thrown many thousands of feet into the air and a high tidal wave was caused. The effects of blast and radioactive contamination extended over a wide area and HMS *Plym* was vaporized except for some red-hot fragments which were scattered over one of the islands and started fires in the dry vegetation. Very soon after the explosion two naval officers undertook the dangerous task of flying helicopters over the heavily contaminated lagoon where *Plym* had lain. This was in order to take samples of the water so that its radioactivity could be measured. After a longer interval, scientists and service personnel in protective clothing entered the contaminated area to examine the effect and to recover records. Technical descriptions of the performance of the bomb cannot, of course, be given. It may, however, be said that the weapon behaved exactly as expected and forecast in many precise details by Dr W. G. Penney, whose services were of the highest order. Scientific observations and measurements show that the weapon does not contradict the natural expectation that progress in this sphere would be continual. To give some idea of the character of the explosion might I say this. Normal blood temperature is ninety-eight and two-fifths degrees – many of us go higher than that. (Laughter) When the flash first burst through the hull of *Plym* the temperature was nearly one million degrees. It was of course far higher at the point of explosion. The explosion caused no casualties to the personnel of the expedition. No animals were used in the test. Apart from some local rats which were killed, no mammals were seen in the affected area and such birds as there were had mostly been frightened away by the earlier preparations. Her Majesty's Government in the United Kingdom wish to express their indebtedness for all the help received from Australia. Not only did the Australian Commonwealth allow us to use their territory for the test, but all branches of their Government, and particularly the Navy, Army and Air Force, gave us the most valuable collaboration in the preparation and execution of this important experiment. All those concerned in the production of the first British atomic bomb are to be warmly congratulated on the successful outcome of an historic episode, and I should no doubt pay my compliments to the Leader of the Opposition and the Party opposite for initiating it.'[19]

A fortnight later, Penney himself spoke on BBC radio, giving his own description of the background and circumstances of the test and dispelling some more of the myths. The Z shape of the cloud, which had given rise to speculation about a 'Z-weapon', was simply explained as the result of contrary winds, and the second bang was a reflection from the upper atmosphere. He spoke of the 'harmonious way in which scientists and servicemen have worked together', adding a little more honestly that the services had had much to put up with and 'the ordeal was not as bad as they feared'. He concluded: 'Mr Churchill has said that the results of our atomic weapon programme should be beneficial to public safety. As a scientist, I should like most strongly to agree with this view. The energy and enthusiasm which have gone into the making of this new weapon stemmed essentially from the sober hope that it would bring us nearer the day when world war is universally seen to be unthinkable.'[20]

The Hurricane device was not a deliverable air-force weapon: it lacked the necessary fusing and arming equipment and the ballistic case. Work had been under way on these components for some time at Fort Halstead and in industrial firms including Vickers and Percivals, and in the course of 1953 they were subjected to field trials. In addition, the various wrinkles in the design of the Hurricane components had to be ironed out, full-scale production facilities had to be established and RAF training and maintenance procedures had to be organized. It was not until November 1953 that the first Mark I bomb, a great steel whale five feet across and nearly twenty feet long, was finally delivered to the RAF.

IN 1951, REFLECTING on the war of propaganda over atomic weapons then raging between the United States and the Soviet Union, Penney had written that Britain was 'in the position of either having to produce the atomic weapon or admit that for one reason or another we cannot afford to. The discriminative test for a first-class power is whether it has made an atomic bomb and we have either got to pass the test or suffer a serious loss in prestige both inside this country and internationally.'[21]

In a sense, Penney was wrong; this was not a test that would be passed or failed, but the beginning of a race of indefinite duration and enormous cost. Less than a month after Hurricane, sensational news broke in the United States. On 1 November, on the tiny island of Elugelab in the Eniwetok atoll, the Americans had detonated a thermonuclear explosion with a yield more than a hundred times greater than Hurricane. It was not a bomb – in fact the device was bigger than a house – but it was proof that the hydrogen bomb was feasible. Just at the moment when Britain appeared to have caught up, it fell behind again, and the Government faced the choice of renewing the effort of competition or retiring. Having come so far, it decided to press on, and Penney, who had long been sceptical about Britain's ability to support a hydrogen-weapons programme, soon found himself overseeing one. But the race did not stop with the hydrogen bomb, for attention soon switched to the development of ever more sophisticated delivery systems, and ultimately Britain was unable to stay with the pace.

Penney was right, however, to see the possession of the bomb as a measure of prestige. His weapon may not have halted Britain's decline as a world power, but it slowed that decline. History had given Britain a seat at the top table of international affairs but in the late 1940s the lease on that seat had been running out. The atomic bomb extended the lease. Empire and wealth would slip away and the leadership of the West would become established in Washington, but so long as Britain remained a nuclear power it remained a power. The symbol of this status was permanent membership of the Security Council of the United Nations; it was no accident that, as the Cold War ended, the five permanent members were the five nations acknowledged to have nuclear weapons: the United States, the Soviet Union, Britain, France and China.

Although it may not have seemed so to those involved, this extension of the lease was cheaply bought. Detailed comparison with the American or the Soviet bomb-development programmes is impossible, but in broad terms there can be no doubt that Britain was required to invest far less to develop its weapon. That its success came later – seven years after the Trinity Test and three after Joe One – was in retrospect of little consequence. Of course at the time the price seemed desperately high: scientists and engineers with rare and precious skills had to be diverted from other work by the hundred, while scarce materials were diverted from industry. In cash terms, the final bill for the bomb has been estimated at £150 million, a sum equivalent to twenty per cent of all British defence spending in the single year 1948 (or ten per cent in 1952, when rearmament was under way). This was Britain's age of austerity, the age of Cripps, spivs and snoek, of bread rationing and endless sterling crises. The national mood of emergency and of make-do permeated both the planning and execution of the weapon programme, and if the margin between success and failure was narrow it is hard to see how it could have been otherwise.

In ideal conditions HER might have been independent from the start, but the conditions were anything but ideal. Penney's instinct told him that he would need the expertise and manpower of the Armament Research Department. There, in the laboratories and workshops of Fort Halstead and Woolwich, the atomic cuckoo fed and grew until it was ready for flight. Many administrative and political difficulties flowed from this choice, notably the lateness of the decision to establish Aldermaston and the bitter feud over the divorce from ARE, but there can be no doubt that it was the right choice. Penney's recruitment problems demonstrated that he could not have started independently as Cockcroft did at Harwell; he had to have a core staff with the necessary qualities of 'skill and silence', as he put it. As it was, he was most fortunate in the men he found at ARD and the men he picked to join them. From Corner the mathematician to Bunce the engineer, and from Pilgrim the field trials specialist to Willows the metallurgist, across a range of hundreds of people in dozens of disciplines, he was ably and often ingeniously supported and served. Some credit for this is due to the education system which produced these scientists. Penney did not have access to the cream of British science; he was not in a position to take his pick of university professors and Fellows of the Royal Society. Instead, he took what he could get and it is a measure of the strength of the scientific establishment that men of such high calibre were available. This prompts a question: if British science in the 1940s and 1950s could muster the expertise to make an atomic bomb, despite so many constraints, how many other countries must have the potential to do so four decades later?

As for Operation Hurricane, it was the most melodramatic of all Britain's nuclear trials in the 1950s. We know now that no site is a good site for an atmospheric nuclear explosion, but even by the standards of 1952 the Monte Bellos were an ill-judged choice for the first British test. Their remoteness, their choppy waters and their unpredictable weather raised obstacles which proved almost too great for such a small task force to overcome. The clash of personalities between Tyte and Torlesse and the clash of cultures between scientists and sailors only compounded this mistake. Had the opportunity of 3 October been missed, it is open to doubt whether it would have been possible to wait until the next suitable day, 23 October. But a fiasco was avoided, by however narrow a margin. The bomb exploded satisfactorily, the results were successfully recorded and, despite unexpectedly severe contamination, there were no dreadful accidents. Tyte and Torlesse, as much as Penney, deserve credit for that. Their differences were in large measure the result of failures of planning for which a great many people shared responsibility.

William Penney had become Sir William, and late in life Sir William was to become Lord Penney, OM, KBE, FRS. After the atomic bomb came the hydrogen-bomb programme, and as that approached its successful climax he helped to hammer out the long-sought agreement that re-opened weapons co-operation with the United States. Later, he threw himself into the negotiations for a comprehensive nuclear test ban, and was bitterly disappointed with the failure to outlaw all tests. (Atmospheric explosions like Hurricane were prohibited, but testing continued underground.) Penney took over Harwell, rose to be chairman of the United Kingdom Atomic Energy Authority and later became Rector of his *alma mater*, Imperial College. In 1985, at the age of seventy-six, he emerged from retirement to testify before the Australian Royal Commission on nuclear tests, reliving his experiences of the 1940s and 1950s. He was deeply affected and distressed by the hostile questioning and the hostile publicity that this entailed. He died in 1991.

In one of the most trying moments of his appearance before the Royal Commission, Penney snapped at a questioner: 'I thought we were going to have a nuclear war. The only hope I saw was that there should be a balance between East and West. That is why I did this job, not to make money. I did not make any money. What I really wanted to do was to be a professor.'[22] This was the persistent tension in Penney's life from the day in November 1945, during his Gloucestershire honeymoon, when he decided to accept the post of CSAR. His work had its rewards and he was capable of savouring them, but he could never forget that he was capable of other, perhaps better things. Back in the HER days, when he was often required to travel up and down from Fort Halstead to Whitehall by official car, he was sometimes accompanied by John Rowlands, the RAF officer attached to his staff. Rowlands recalls one conversation they had. They were talking about their plans for the future, and Penney remarked: 'I would rather be remembered for other things than for making the atomic bomb.' Rowlands replied with a shake of the head: 'You will never shake that off.'

Notes

The principal sources for this book fall under three headings: published material, official documents and the recollections of some of those involved. The published works are listed in the bibliography or, in some cases, are identified in the notes that follow. The official documents are scattered through many files in the Public Record Office in London but the main groupings are in the records of the Ministry of Supply, the Admiralty and the Cabinet Office. A further, very large collection of papers relating to Operation Hurricane is to be found in file DEFE16, assembled for the Australian Royal Commission into British Nuclear Tests in Australia in 1984-5. The recollections of veterans of the Manhattan Project, HER and Operation Hurricane, and of others associated with them, were gathered largely in a series of interviews and in correspondence during 1991-3. In a few cases, unpublished memoirs or diaries were made available. No private Penney papers survive; he did not keep records systematically, and destroyed what he had before his death in 1991.

Prologue

1. PRO DEFE16/412
2. Ibid.

1. A New World Order

1. PRO CAB130/3.
2. PRO CAB130/2.
3. PRO CAB130/3.
4. Williams, *A Prime Minister Remembers* (London, 1961), p. 97.
5. Richards, *Portal of Hungerford* (London, 1977), p. 167.
6. Churchill, *The Second World War*, vol. 2 (London, 1949), p. 405.

7. Gowing and Arnold, *Independence and Deterrence*, vol. 1 (London, 1974), p. 169.
8. Gowing, *Britain and Atomic Energy* (London, 1964), p. 447.
9. Truman, *Memoirs: Year of Decisions* (New York, 1955), p. 534.
10. *Independence and Deterrence*, vol. 1, p. 76.
11. Owen, 'Nuclear Engineering in the United Kingdom – The First Ten Years', in *Journal of the British Nuclear Engineering Society*, vol. 2 (London, 1963), p. 23.
12. Michael Perrin, quoted in 'A Bloody Union Jack on Top of It', programme one, BBC Radio 4, 5/5/88.
13. PRO AB16/1905.
14. Ibid.
15. Ibid.
16. PRO CAB130/16.
17. Williams, op. cit., pp. 118–19.

2. Penney

1. Interview given by Lord Penney to Denis Richards in 1974 for his book, *Portal of Hungerford*. Quoted by kind permission of Mr Richards.
2. Imperial College biography, compiled on the occasion of Lord Penney's retirement as Rector in 1973.
3. Testimonial by John van Vleck, 2 February 1933, from the records of the 1851 Commission.
4. Testimonial by Sydney Chapman, Professor of Mathematics at Imperial College, 7 April 1933, from the records of the 1851 Commission.
5. Lady Penney, interview with author.
6. Bertin, *Atom Harvest* (London, 1955), p. 142.
7. H. Jones, writing of Sir Geoffrey Taylor in *Biographical Memoirs of Fellows of the Royal Society*, vol. 22 (London, 1976), p. 598.
8. Penney, contributing to the same memoir, p. 603.
9. PRO AB1/481.
10. Ibid.
11. Jungk, *Brighter Than A Thousand Suns* (London, 1982), p. 113.
12. Written answers by Lord Penney to questions submitted by Ferenc Morton Szasz in July 1988 for his book *British Scientists and the Manhattan Project*. Quoted by kind permission of Professor Szasz.
13. PRO AB1/615.
14. Penney to Szasz. See note 12.
15. Peierls, *Bird of Passage* (Princeton, 1985), p. 201.
16. Peierls, letter to author.
17. PRO AB1/615.
18. 'Notes on initial meeting of Target Committee', Los Alamos National Laboratory Archives.
19. Peierls, op. cit., p. 203.
20. Philip Morrison, quoted in Rhodes, *The Making of the Atomic Bomb* (London, 1986), p. 678.
21. Groves, *Now It Can Be Told* (London, 1963), p. 343.

22. Quoted in Boyle, *No Passing Glory: The Full and Authentic Biography of Group Captain Cheshire VC, DSO, DFC* (London, 1955), p. 261.
23. Lord Penney, D. E. J. Samuels and G. C. Scorgie, 'The Nuclear Explosive Yields at Hiroshima and Nagasaki', *Transactions of the Royal Society of London*, 1970, A266, p. 259.
24. Bertin, op. cit., p. 145.
25. Penney interview with Richards. See note 1.
26. Broadcast on ABC radio, Australia, 2 September 1956.
27. Goodchild, *Oppenheimer, The Father of the Atom Bomb* (London, 1983), p. 166.
28. Interview with author.
29. Gowing, *Britain and Atomic Energy* (London, 1964), p. 386.
30. *Sunday Times*, 15/9/67.
31. *Liverpool Echo*, 1/8/53.
32. Bertin, op. cit., p. 147.
33. *Sunday Times*, 15/9/67.
34. *Independence and Deterrence*, vol. 1, p. 180.
35. Hartcup and Allibone, *Cockcroft and the Atom* (Bristol, 1984), p. 142.
36. PRO AB1/353.
37. PRO AB16/346.
38. PRO AB16/1905.
39. PRO AB16/346.
40. Ibid.
41. Portal interview with Alfred Goldberg, 1963. From the papers of Denis Richards.

3. First Steps

1. Letter from John Tomblin to author.
2. Penney interview with Richards.
3. PRO AB16/1905.
4. Hennessy, *Whitehall* (London, 1990), p. 718.
5. PRO AB16/1905.
6. PRO AB16/586.
7. Ibid.
8. PRO AB16/242.
9. PRO AB16/586.
10. PRO AB16/243.
11. Penney interview with Richards.
12. PRO AB16/243.
13. Ibid.
14. Ibid.

4. To Work

Most of the quotations in this chapter come from the author's interviews with HER veterans. Speakers not named in the text are identified below.

1. PRO AB16/586.
2. Ibid.
3. Challens.
4. PRO AB16/586.
5. Pat Cachia.
6. Len Bunce.
7. Bunce, quoting Gallie.

5. The Task is Doubled

1. PRO AB16/586.
2. Hinton interview with Richards.
3. Pincher, *Into the Atomic Age* (London, 1947), p. 104.
4. House of Commons Debates, vol. 450, col. 2117.
5. *New Statesman*, 17/5/63.
6. PRO AB16/251.
7. Ibid.
8. *Independence and Deterrence*, vol. 2, p. 449.
9. Penney interview with Richards.
10. PRO AB16/245.
11. Ibid.
12. Ibid.
13. PRO AB16/790.
14. PRO AB16/245.
15. Penney interview with Richards.
16. Ibid.
17. *Independence and Deterrence*, vol. 2, p. 450.

6. Lightning Strikes Twice

1. Montgomery Hyde, *The Atom Bomb Spies* (London, 1982), pp. 142-3.
2. Szasz, op. cit., p. 92.
3. *Independence and Deterrence*, vol. 2, p. 147.
4. Ibid. p. 149.
5. Moss, *Klaus Fuchs: The Man Who Stole the Atom Bomb* (London, 1987), p. 200.
6. This and subsequent quotations from Dr Corner are from letters to the author.
7. Letter from Peierls to author.
8. Moss, op. cit., p. 92.
9. PRO AB16/586.
10. Botti, *The Long Wait* (Westport, Conn., 1987), p. 58.
11. Hartcup and Allibone, op. cit., pp. 157-8.
12. Moorehead, *The Traitors* (London, 1952), p. 133.
13. Ibid. p. 138.

7. Annus Horrendus

1. PRO AB16/788.
2. PRO AB16/1127.
3. Ibid.
4. Ibid.
5. Ibid.
6. Ibid.
7. Ibid.
8. *Independence and Deterrence*, vol. 1, p. 230.
9. PRO DEFE32/1.
10. Ibid.
11. PRO AB16/245.
12. PRO AB16/1127.
13. PRO AB16/586.
14. Ibid.
15. *Independence and Deterrence*, vol. 2, p. 73.

8. Aldermaston

1. 'The Site Takes Shape', *A WRE News*, April 1971, reprinted in *Independence and Deterrence*, vol. 2, pp. 194–5.
2. Ibid.
3. Ibid.
4. Owen, 'Crabbed Age and Youth', *A WRE News*, April 1971.
5. PRO AB16/586.
6. Ibid.
7. This and subsequent quotations from William Lord are from his unpublished memoir, *A Gentle Puff*.
8. Alvarez, *Alvarez, Adventures of a Physicist* (New York, 1987), pp. 127–8.
9. PRO AB16/835.
10. 'The Site Takes Shape', op cit., pp. 198.
11. *Independence and Deterrence*, vol. 2, p. 459.
12. Ibid., p. 451.
13. PRO AB16/942.
14. Ibid.
15. Hothersall, quoted by Aubrey Thomas in interview with author.

9. Trial

1. PRO AB16/1132.
2. Ibid.
3. W. G. Penney *et al.*, 'Some gravity wave problems in the motion of perfect liquids', *Transactions of the Royal Society of London*, 1952, A244, p. 233.
4. PRO AB16/88.
5. PRO AB16/1132.
6. Ibid.

7. Ibid.
8. Milliken, *No Conceivable Injury* (London, 1986), p. 54.
9. Jeremy N. Green, 'Australia's Oldest Wreck', *British Archaeological Reports*, Supplementary series 27 (Oxford, 1977), p. 18.
10. Ida Lee, 'The First Sighting of Australia by the English', *Geographical Journal*, vol. 83 (1934), p. 319.
11. Ibid.
12. Green, op. cit., p. 21.
13. Louis Freycinet, *Voyages des Découvertes* (Paris, 1815), p. 224.
14. Ibid.
15. Phillip Parker King, *Narrative of a Survey*, vol. 2 (London, 1827), p. 364.
16. John Lort Stokes, *Discoveries in Australia*, vol. 2 (London, 1846), p. 207.
17. Ibid., p. 211.
18. Ibid.
19. Hill, *Ports of Sunset* (Melbourne, 1946), p. 27.
20. PRO DEFE32/2.
21. *Report of the Royal Commission into British Nuclear Tests in Australia*, vol. 1 (Canberra, 1985), p. 13.
22. Ibid., p. 11.
23. PRO AB16/586.
24. A. D. Torlesse, *Some Account of My Life* (private memoir), p. 165.
25. Ibid., p. 167.
26. PRO DEFE32/2.
27. Ibid.
28. Ibid.
29. Ibid.

10. Final Preparations

1. PRO AB16/570 and *Independence and Deterrence*, vol. 2, p. 137.
2. PRO AB16/571.
3. Symonds, *A History of British Atomic Tests in Australia* (Canberra, 1985), p. 31.
4. Torlesse, p. 168.
5. Bird, *Operation Hurricane* (Worcester, 1989), p. 23.
6. Royal Commission Report, vol. 1, p. 449.
7. Torlesse, p. 169.
8. Gilbert, *Never Despair: Winston S. Churchill 1945–1965* (London, 1990), p. 199.
9. Ibid., p. 467.
10. Herbert Nicholas, *The British General Election of 1950* (London, 1951), p. 102.
11. Gilbert, op. cit., p. 538.
12. Richards, op. cit., p. 358.
13. Morgan, *Peace and War, A Soldier's Life* (London, 1961), p. 286.
14. Richards interview with Friston How.
15. Morgan, op. cit., p. 290.
16. Ibid.

17. Birkenhead, *The Prof in Two Worlds* (London, 1961), p. 300.
18. Ibid., p. 301.
19. *Independence and Deterrence*, vol. 1, p. 432.
20. Morgan, op. cit., p. 297.
21. Arnold, *A Very Special Relationship* (London, 1987), pp. 14–15.
22. Torlesse, p. 169.
23. PRO ADM116/6088.
24. PRO ADM116/6087.
25. Morgan, op. cit., p. 297.
26. Torlesse, p. 169.
27. Lord Sherfield, interview with author.
28. *The Times*, 2/4/52.
29. *Daily Express*, 2/4/52.
30. Bird, op. cit., p. 51.
31. Ibid., p. 46.
32. Ibid. p. 56.
33. Leonard Tyte's Hurricane Diary, PRO DEFE16/187, 22/8/52, and Operation Hurricane, Report of the Naval Commander, p. 14.
34. Torlesse, p. 172.
35. *The Times*, 21/5/52.
36. *The Times*, 22/5/52.
37. *The Times*, 24/7/52.
38. Frank Hill, private memoir, p. 8.
39. *Independence and Deterrence*, vol. 2, p. 473.

11. The Voyage Out

1. Noah Pearce, 'Australia Ahoy!', a private diary of the voyage and early stages of Operation Hurricane. Quoted by kind permission of Mr Pearce.
2. PRO AB16/1132.
3. *Independence and Deterrence*, vol. 2, p. 483.
4. Ibid., p. 486.
5. PRO DEFE16/296, J. J. McEnhill, 'The Story of Operation Hurricane', p. 2.
6. Ibid., p. 6.
7. Ibid., p. 11.
8. PRO DEFE16/187. Although this takes the form of a diary and is referred to as such, the entries were intended as reports to HER in Britain and were sent in batches every few days to Penney or, after his departure, Brooking. This entry is from 24 June.
9. Ibid.
10. McEnhill, p. 8.
11. Ibid.
12. Ibid., p. 13.
13. Ibid., p. 14.
14. Ibid., p. 10.
15. Ibid., p. 25.
16. Ibid., pp. 12–13.

17. Ibid., p. 12.
18. Ibid., p. 14.
19. PRO DEFE16/197, P. F. Cooper, 'A General Account of the Operation', section 5, para 32.
20. Ibid., 5.18.
21. Tyte, 23 September.
22. Ibid., 30 July.
23. McEnhill, p. 17.
24. Ibid., p. 12.
25. Ibid., p. 11.
26. Ibid., p. 12.
27. Ibid.
28. Ibid.
29. Cooper, 5.35.
30. McEnhill, p. 14.
31. Ibid., p. 15.
32. Ibid., p. 21.
33. Ibid.
34. Ibid., p. 22.
35. Ibid., p. 25.
36. Ibid., p. 26.
37. Tyte, 28 July.
38. Ibid., 29 July.
39. Ibid., 31 July.
40. Ibid., 1 August.
41. Bird, op. cit., p. 62.

12. The Core

The information for this chapter is drawn primarily from the evidence of men who were involved: David Deverell, James Hole, William Lord, William Moyce, Frank Roberts, Sir John Rowlands, Aubrey Thomas.

1. Interview with James Hole.
2. Lord letter to author.
3. *Independence and Deterrence*, vol. 2, p. 468.
4. Ibid., p. 467.
5. Lord, 'A Gentle Puff'.
6. James Hole interview.

13. Rehearsals

1. Cooper, 7.4.
2. Pearce, 11 August.
3. Ibid., 18 August.
4. McEnhill, p. 46.
5. Ibid., p. 54.
6. Tyte, 25 August.

7. Ibid., 23 August.
8. McEnhill, p. 35.
9. Letter to author.
10. Tyte, 26 August.
11. McEnhill, p. 45.
12. Ibid.
13. Hill, private memoir, p. 12.
14. Tyte, 1 September.
15. Cooper, 7.4.
16. Tyte, 24 August.
17. Ibid., 4 September.
18. Bird, op. cit., p. 65.
19. Tyte, 5 September.
20. Ibid., 4 September.
21. Ibid., 11 September.
22. Ibid., 12 September.
23. McEnhill, pp. 53–4.
24. PRO DEFE16/197.
25. Tyte, 16 September.
26. Ibid., 9 September.
27. Ibid.
28. Ibid., 10 September.
29. Ibid., 11 September.
30. Torlesse, pp. 173–4.
31. Tyte, 15 September.
32. Ibid., 16 September.
33. Ibid., 18 September.
34. Ibid., 19 September.
35. William Moyce, interview with author.
36. Tyte, 19 September.
37. Ibid. 20 September.
38. Ibid.

14. The Event

1. McEnhill, p. 59.
2. Naval Commander's Report, p. 63.
3. McEnhill, p. 59.
4. Tyte, 22 September.
5. Ibid., 23 September.
6. Ibid., 27 September.
7. Ibid.
8. Ibid., 28 September.
9. Torlesse, p. 175.
10. PRO DEFE16/235.
11. Tyte, 29 September.
12. PRO ADM116/6093.
13. Tyte, 30 September.

14. PRO ADM116/6093.
15. Naval Commander's Report, p. 64.
16. PRO DEFE16/197 Appendix F, 'Hurricane – Action Organisation'.
17. Naval Commander's Report, p. 64.
18. McEnhill, p. 64.
19. Naval Commander's Report, p. 65.
20. McEnhill, p. 64.
21. Ibid.
22. Bird, op. cit., p. 75.
23. McEnhill, p. 65.
24. Naval Commander's Report, p. 112.
25. Ibid., p. 65.
26. Details of the countdown are from Naval Commander's Report, pp. 98–100, and the official film, 'Operation Hurricane', made by the Crown Film Unit. Some of the events in the film were staged after the operation was complete, using the appropriate HER scientists, but there is no reason to believe the procedure shown was not correct.
27. Bird, op. cit., p. 76.
28. Ibid., p. 77.
29. McEnhill, p. 66.
30. PRO DEFE16/192.
31. Bird, op. cit., p. 77.
32. Penney, 'The Montebello Explosion', a BBC broadcast made on 7/11/52 and reprinted in *Atomic Scientists' News*, vol. 2, no. 3 (January 1953).
33. *West Australian*, 4/10/52.
34. PRO ADM116/6087.
35. Gilbert, op. cit., p. 764.
36. PRO ADM116/6087.
37. Ibid.
38. PRO ADM/116/6093. The story is told that Churchill had prepared two messages, one saying 'Thank you, Dr Penney', in case of failure, and the other saying 'Well done, Sir William'. This was certainly not the content of Churchill's first communication with Penney and it seems that it was some time later that he had news of his knighthood.
39. McEnhill, p. 71.

15. Aftermath

1. Naval Commander's Report, p. 28.
2. PRO DEFE16/671.
3. PRO AB16/570.
4. PRO AIR8/2309, Operation Hurricane, Director's Report, Top Secret Section, p. 3.
5. McEnhill, p. 69.
6. Director's Report, p. 33.
7. Report of the Royal Commission, Conclusions and Recommendations, conclusion 84.
8. Conclusion 51.

9. Conclusion 53.
10. Conclusion 74.
11. Darby *et al.*, *Mortality and Cancer Incidence in UK Participants in UK Atmospheric Nuclear Weapon Tests and Experimental Programmes*, National Radiological Protection Board (Chilton, Oxon, 1988), p. 85.
12. Darby *et al.*, *Mortality and Cancer Incidence 1952–1990 in UK Participants in the UK Atmospheric Nuclear Weapon Tests and Experimental Programmes*, National Radiological Protection Board (Chilton, Oxon, 1993), p. 53.
13. PRO DEFE16/211.
14. PRO DEFE16/426.
15. *The Times*, 4/10/52.
16. Ibid., 3/10/52.
17. *Daily Express*, 3/10/52.
18. Smith, *Clouds of Deceit* (London, 1985), p. 78.
19. The text is printed in Bird, op. cit., pp. 96–7.
20. BBC broadcast, 7/11/52.
21. *Independence and Deterrence*, vol. 2, p. 500.
22. Milliken, op. cit., p. 24.

Bibliography

Alvarez, Luis W., *Alvarez, Adventures of a Physicist* (New York, 1987)
Arnold, Lorna, *A Very Special Relationship: British Atomic Weapon Trials in Australia* (London, 1987)
Baylis, John, *Anglo-American Defence Relations, 1939-1984* (London, 1984)
Beadell, Len, *Blast the Bush* (London, 1967)
Bertin, Leonard, *Atom Harvest* (London, 1955)
Bird, Peter B., *Operation Hurricane* (Worcester, 1989)
Birkenhead, The Earl of, *The Prof in Two Worlds: The Official Life of Professor F. A. Lindemann, Viscount Cherwell* (London, 1961)
Blakeway, Denys, and Lloyd-Roberts, Sue, *Fields of Thunder: Testing Britain's Bomb* (London, 1985).
Botti, Timothy J., *The Long Wait: The forging of the Anglo-American Nuclear Alliance, 1945-1958* (Westport, Conn., 1987)
Boyle, Andrew, *No Passing Glory: The Full and Authentic Biography of Group Captain Cheshire VC, DSO, DFC* (London, 1955)
Bullock, Alan, *Ernest Bevin, Foreign Secretary* (Oxford, 1985)
Clark, Ronald W., *The Greatest Power on Earth* (London, 1980)
—— *Tizard* (London, 1965)
Costello, John, *Mask of Treachery* (London, 1988)
Darby, S. G. *et al.*, *Mortality and Cancer Incidence in UK Participants in UK Atmospheric Nuclear Weapon Tests and Experimental Programmes*, National Radiological Protection Board (Chilton, Oxon, 1988)
Elphick, B. L., 'First Bomb', *AWRE News*, February 1991
Gilbert, Martin, *Never Despair: Winston S. Churchill 1945-1965* (London, 1990)
Goldberg, Alfred, 'The Atomic Origins of the British Nuclear Deterrent', *International Affairs*, July 1964
Goodchild, Peter, *Oppenheimer: The Father of the Atom Bomb* (London, 1983)

Bibliography

Gowing, Margaret, *Britain and Atomic Energy 1939–1945* (London, 1964)
—— assisted by Arnold, Lorna, *Independence and Deterrence: Britain and Atomic Energy 1945–52* (London, 1974)
Graves, Howard, *British Atomic Weapons Development 1945–51* (Oxford University B.Litt. thesis, 1971)
Groves, Leslie, *Now It Can Be Told* (London, 1963)
Harris, Kenneth, *Attlee* (London, 1982)
Hartcup, Guy, and Allibone, T. E., *Cockcroft and the Atom* (Bristol, 1984)
Hayward, Keith, *The British Nuclear Weapon Programme 1945–47* (Manchester University M. A. thesis, 1972)
Hecht, Selig, and Rabinowitch, Eugene, *Explaining the Atom* (London, 1957)
Hennessy, Peter, *Whitehall* (London, 1990)
—— *A Bloody Union Jack On Top Of It*, BBC Radio 4 documentary, two programmes, broadcast May 1988
Herken, Greg, *The Winning Weapon: The Atomic Bomb in the Cold War 1945–1950* (Princeton, 1988)
Hewlett, Richard G., and Anderson, Oscar E., *The New World, 1939–1946* (Pennsylvania, 1962)
—— and Duncan, Francis, *Atomic Shield, 1947–52* (California, 1990)
Hill, Ernestine, *Ports of Sunset* (Melbourne, 1946)
Jones, Peter, *British Attitudes to Nuclear Defence* (London, 1990)
Jungk, Robert, *Brighter Than A Thousand Suns: A Personal History of the Atomic Scientists* (London, 1982)
Milliken, Robert, *No Conceivable Injury: The Story of Britain and Australia's Nuclear Cover-Up* (London, 1986)
Montgomery Hyde, H., *The Atom Bomb Spies* (London, 1982)
Moorehead, Alan, *The Traitors* (London, 1952)
Morgan, General Sir Frederick, *Peace and War: A Soldier's Life* (London, 1961)
Moss, Norman, *Klaus Fuchs: The Man Who Stole The Atom Bomb* (London, 1987)
Newton, Verne W., *The Cambridge Spies: The Untold Story of Maclean, Philby and Burgess in America* (New York, 1991)
Owen, Leonard, 'Nuclear Engineering in the United Kingdom – The First Ten Years', *Journal of the British Nuclear Engineering Society*, vol. 2 (London, 1963)
Owen, W. Charles, 'Crabbed Age and Youth', *AWRE News*, April 1971
Peierls, Sir Rudolf, *Bird of Passage: Recollections of a Physicist* (Princeton, 1985)
Pincher, Chapman, *Into the Atomic Age* (London, 1947)
—— *Too Secret Too Long* (London, 1984)
—— 'Sir William Penney', *Discovery*, November 1955
Rhodes, Richard, *The Making of the Atomic Bomb* (London, 1986)
Richards, Denis, *Portal of Hungerford* (London, 1977)
Robinson, Derek, *Just Testing* (London, 1985)
Shurcliff, W. A., *Bombs at Bikini: The Official Report of Operation Crossroads* (New York, 1947)
Simpson, John, *The Independent Nuclear State* (London, 1986)

Bibliography

Smith, Alice Kimball, *A Peril and a Hope: The Scientists' Movement in America 1945–47* (Cambridge, Mass., 1971)

Smith, Joan, *Clouds of Deceit: The Deadly Legacy of Britain's Bomb Tests* (London, 1985)

Smyth, Henry deWolf, *Atomic Energy for Military Purposes* (Princeton, 1948)

Symonds, J. L., *A History of British Atomic Tests in Australia* (Canberra, 1985)

Szasz, Ferenc Morton, *British Scientists and the Manhattan Project* (London, 1992)

—— *The Day The Sun Rose Twice: The Story of the Trinity Site Nuclear Explosion, July 16, 1945* (Albuquerque, 1984)

Williams, Francis, *A Prime Minister Remembers* (London, 1961)

Williams, Robert Chadwell, *Klaus Fuchs, Atom Spy* (London, 1987)

Wyden, Peter, *Day One: Before Hiroshima and After* (New York, 1984)

Index

Index

Abercrombie, S. D., 252
Acheson, Dean, 111
Adams, Charles, 2, 5, 156, 159,
 216, 217–18, 225, 227, 228, 229,
 230, 234, 237, 243–4, 245, 249,
 251, 252, 259; *quoted* 233
Addison, Viscount, 23
Admiralty, 31, 116, 149, 151, 153,
 179, 189, 193, 199, 229, 258,
 259
Air Ministry, 87, 147
Aldermaston, 91, 96, 97, 113, 115,
 117, 121, 122, 124, 126, 127–44,
 166, 202–10, 231, 233, 260, 275
Aldermaston Committee, 130
Alexander, Albert, 23, 24, 88, 111,
 164, 166
Alexander, Earl, 172, 173
Alvarez, Luis, 33, 133, 134; *quoted*
 133–4
Apex Committee, 172–4
Argonne Laboratory, Chicago, 13
Armament Research Department
 see Armament Research
 Establishment
Armament Research Establishment,
 22–275 *passim*
Arnold, Henry, 114
Ashworth, Bill, 72

Atomic Energy Commission (USA),
 110, 162
Atomic Energy Council, 89, 90, 91,
 93, 107
Atomic Energy (Defence Research)
 Committee, 61–2, 66, 120
Atomic Energy Research
 Establishment, Harwell, 14, 16,
 22, 45, 63, 86, 90, 91, 96, 99,
 101, 103, 106, 110, 111, 124,
 125, 129, 132, 143, 174, 177,
 208, 230, 275, 276
Atomic Scientists' News, 89
Attlee, Clement, 8, 10, 11, 12, 13,
 14, 18, 19, 21, 23, 24, 25, 56,
 62, 81, 83, 85–6, 87, 89, 93, 94,
 95, 97, 115, 119, 120, 150, 157,
 169, 171–2, 173, 269, 272;
 quoted 8–9, 94–5; *see also*
 Cabinet committees
Australian Broadcasting
 Commission, 3
Australian Meteorological Bureau,
 238
Australian Security and Intelligence
 Organization, 2

Barnes, David, 135–6, 141, 202,
 211

Barnett, Peter, 256–7
Basic High Explosive Research *see* High Explosive Research
Beadell, Len, 237
Bean, Cecil, 70, 131, 166
Beeching, Richard, 116–17
Berkshire Chronicle, 129
Berlin, 94, 111, 170
Bethe, Hans, 33, 103; *quoted* 99
Bevin, Ernest, 12–13, 23, 24, 94, 121; *quoted* 21
Bird, Peter, 249; *quoted* 177, 178–9, 222, 249, 253, 255–6
Blackman, W., 116, 123
Bohr, Niels and Aage, 33
Bretscher, Egon, 105
Bridges, Edward, 61
British-Canadian nuclear reactor research project, 16
British Embassy, Washington, 99, 101, 107–8
British High Commission, Canberra, 150
Brooking, Patrick, 117–18, 122, 123, 142, 179, 186, 187, 210, 240, 243
Bunce, Len, 77, 78, 181, 182, 275; *quoted* 73, 82, 167
Burgess, Guy, 163
Butement, Alan, 242
Butterfield, John, 247; *quoted* 255, 256
Byrnes, James, 21

Cabinet committees: Attlee's committees on atomic energy, 8, 10, 15, 21, 24 (GEN 75), 23–4, 26, 46, 84 (GEN 163); Attlee's Defence Committee, 121
Cachia, Pat, 75–6, 77; *quoted* 78, 82, 83
Cadogan, Alexander, 45
Campaign for Nuclear Disarmament, 83
Campania, HMS, 160–1, 176, 179, 184–264 *passim*; *Campania* Action Information Centre, 234, 240

Canadian Defence Research Board, 147
Capenhurst gaseous diffusion plant, Cheshire, 20–1, 94, 106, 112
Chadwick, James, 16, 24, 34, 40, 42, 45, 98, 105, 107; *quoted* 35
Chalk River, Ontario (British-Canadian research reactor), 13, 20, 45, 124, 134, 143
Challens, John, 66, 67–8, 70, 71, 72–3, 80, 103, 104, 118, 119, 122, 123, 131, 159, 168, 198, 216, 228, 234–5, 247–58 *passim*; *quoted* 68–9, 242, 259–60
Chatham Dockyard, 57, 175, 176, 179, 182
Cherwell, Viscount, 40, 42, 171, 172, 173, 237, 257, 259
Cheshire, Leonard, 37–8, 42
Chiefs of Staff Sub-Committee on the Strategic Aspects of Atomic Energy, 146, 147, 148
China, 109, 274
Chivers, Messrs. W. E., 128
Churchill, Winston, 15, 17, 24–5, 62, 163, 165, 169, 170, 171, 172–4, 179–80, 181, 186, 257–8, 259, 264, 270, 273; *quoted* 271–2
Civil Service Commission, 125
Cockburn, Robert, and 'Cockburn Project', 107, 147
Cockcroft, John, 16, 22, 45, 86, 89, 90, 91, 92, 101, 111–12, 113, 114, 117, 125, 142, 148, 275; *quoted* 93
Cold War, the, 94, 274
Cole, A. B., 194, 230, 232, 242
Colville, G. C., 231
Cook, William, 116, 117
Cooper, Pat, 186, 187, 192–3, 194, 196, 212, 219, 221, 225, 230, 234, 240, 243; *quoted* 213
Cooper, Tony, 2, 5
Corner, John, 39, 104, 105, 106, 113, 123, 130, 135, 136, 138, 139, 275
Crabb, Lionel 'Buster', 140

Cripps, Stafford, 23, 274
Crossman, Richard, 89
Curie, Marie and Pierre, 132

Daily Express, 87, 89, 174
Daily Graphic, 86, 271
Daily Mail, 165
Daily Mirror, 174
Daily Telegraph, 89, 164
Dalton, Hugh, 23, 115
Davies, John, 79, 82, 249-50, 260;
  quoted 80, 176
Davis, A. H., 116, 123, 136
Davis, Edward 'Dizzy', 2, 5, 57,
  59, 97, 137, 146, 147, 149, 151,
  154, 185; *quoted* 6, 93
Deverell, David, 177, 207, 208
D-notice Committee, 87, 164
D-notices, 87, 89, 164, 165

Eaton, Jack, 241
Eden, Anthony, 165, 172
Eisenhower, Dwight D., 170
Ellis, Geoffrey, 132, 208
Eniwetok (US trials base), 146,
  147, 149, 150, 273
Evans-Lombe, Edward, 161, 165,
  172, 257, 259
Experimental Establishment, 73

Federal Bureau of Investigation,
  99, 101, 102, 106, 111
Fermi, Enrico, 33
Ferranti, 135
Feynman, Richard, 33
Foreign Office, 147, 174
Fort Churchill (military research
  station, Hudson Bay), 147,
  150-1
Foulness range, Essex, 79-81, 84,
  115, 119, 176, 182
Franks, Oliver, 112
Fraser, Baron, 116, 120, 156
Frisch, Otto, 33, 40, 100
Fuchs, Klaus, 40, 55, 99-107, 111,
  113-14, 115, 120, 135, 138-9,
  146, 147, 162

Gallie, George, 76, 78, 182, 183
Garner, Harry, 118, 119, 122;
  quoted 123
Ginns, Dennis, 20
Goble, Alfred, 33
Gouzenko, Igor, 13, 102
Grange, Alan, 94, 207
Greatbach, Percy, 123
Grove, W. P., 123
Groves, Leslie, 20, 35, 43, 46;
  quoted 33, 37

Harris, Arthur 'Bomber', 15
Hawkesbury, HMAS, 236, 241
Hickenlooper, Bourke B., 110
Hicks, Ernest, 118
High Explosive Research, 24,
  48-276 *passim*
Highfield, Alfred, 116, 123
Hill, Frank, 180-1, 215, 216, 250,
  252, 255, 270; *quoted* 221
Hillan, Bernard, 66, 80
Hinton, Christopher, 16, 20, 21,
  22, 45, 84, 85, 89-90, 91,
  92, 93, 98, 120, 142; *quoted*
  87
Hiroshima, 8, 9, 24, 37-9, 41, 43,
  71, 83, 130, 145, 146;
  Hiroshima bomb, 39, 50, 270
Hole, James ('Jimmy'), 141-2, 202,
  211
Home Office, 217
Hopkin, Graham, 123, 130, 132,
  144, 203, 205, 206, 207, 210
Hothersall, A. W., 123
House of Commons, 88, 89, 164,
  169, 171, 174, 175, 179, 180,
  271
House of Lords, 171
Howse, Edward, 65-6, 67, 70, 83,
  215, 216, 234, 248, 250, 251,
  252, 258; *quoted* 66-7, 80-1,
  234-5, 260
Hughes, Emrys, 179-80
Hurricane Executive Committee
  (Hurex), 161, 165, 173, 193,
  224, 259
Hurricane Panel, 161

Hydrogen bomb, 83, 102, 104, 105, 117, 273, 274, 276

Imperial Chemical Industries, 16, 63, 98, 116, 117
Imperial College, 27, 29, 32, 39, 97, 276

Japan, 8, 17, 36
Jeger, George, 88
Joint Intelligence Committee, 147

Karangi, HMAS, 3, 4, 5, 201
King, Mackenzie, 18
Kistiakowsky, George, 33
Knight, Arthur, 143, 205, 206
Kokura, 38
Kronig, R. de L., 27–8

Lennard-Jones, John, 40, 130
Lewis, David, 123, 125, 130, 131, 203; *quoted* 204
Littler, Derrik, 105
Lockspeiser, Ben, 62–3, 64, 66, 81, 93, 94, 113, 118
Long Range Weapons Organization, 5
Lord, Bill, 133, 134, 143–4, 203, 206–7, 208, 210; *quoted* 204
Los Alamos National Laboratory, 32, 33–4, 50, 52–4, 74, 75, 82, 83, 92, 100–6 *passim*, 112, 115, 132, 133–4, 135, 136, 138, 168, 209; British Los Alamos team, 26, 32, 33, 34, 37, 40, 51, 81, 99, 105, 133, 159

Maccoll, J. W., 123
McEnhill, John, 71, 72, 118, 122, 148, 187, 192, 194, 197, 225; *quoted* 188–98 and 214–29 *passim*, 238, 239, 245, 247, 249, 255, 256, 260, 265–6
Maclean, Donald, 88, 106, 109, 162–3
McMahon, Brien, 19; *quoted* 109
McMahon Act (1946), 20, 46, 55, 109, 110, 132, 133, 134, 163

Maddock, Ieuan, 71, 72, 80, 175, 176, 178, 213, 215, 216, 217, 221, 222, 226, 234, 245, 249, 250, 251–2, 270
Makins, Roger, 174
Manhattan Project, 17, 20, 34–6, 37, 41, 49, 50, 81, 82, 99, 100, 112, 133; Manhattan Project Target Committee, 35–6, 41
Marley, Greg, 55, 103, 159
Marriott, A. J., 118, 122
Marshall, Ted, 225, 228, 231
Martin, Leslie, 242
Maxwell-Fyfe, David, 174
May, Alan Nunn, 13, 20, 99
Medical Research Council, 217, 247, 266
Menzies, Robert, 150, 157–8, 163, 165, 229, 269
MI5, 99, 102, 111, 114
MI6, 108
Military College of Science, 63
Ministry of Civil Aviation, 96
Ministry of Defence, 88, 267–9
Ministry of Health, 97
Ministry of Labour, 97
Ministry of Supply, 2, 16, 22, 24, 58, 59, 60, 61, 62, 63, 81, 86, 87, 94, 118, 122, 129, 142–3, 171, 172, 174, 180, 197, 210, 228, 230, 243, 258, 266
Ministry of Transport, 127
Ministry of Works, 96, 97, 127, 128, 141, 142, 143, 144
'Modus Vivendi' (British-American accord), 109, 110, 111, 115
Molotov, Vyacheslav, 13
Montague Browne, Anthony, 257–8
Monte Bello Islands, 1, 3–6, 149, 150–63, 166, 175, 177–81 and 184–8 *passim*, 196, 199–272 *passim*; early exploration of the Islands, 151–6
Moody, N. F., 124, 125, 216, 226, 228, 237, 270
Morgan, Frank, 125, 177, 208, 229, 230–1, 232, 239, 262, 263
Morgan, Frederick, 170–1, 172, 257

Morgan, William, 170
Morrison, Herbert, 23
Mott, Ernest, 73–4, 75, 77, 79, 82, 123, 131, 167, 182, 183
Moyce, Bill, 71–2, 73, 103, 136, 148, 208–9, 210–11, 212, 233, 236, 240, 248, 249–50, 260; *quoted* 72–3, 82, 103–4
Muggeridge, Malcolm, 164

Nagasaki, 8, 9, 37–9, 41, 43, 71, 83, 130, 145, 146; Nagasaki bomb, 39, 50, 103, 104, 108, 131, 135, 137, 138, 139, 145, 270
Napier, Stanley, 70
Narvik, HMS, 161, 165, 177, 201, 212, 222, 232, 246–55 *passim*, 264
National Radiological Protection Board, 267–8
Nato, 25
Neumann, John van, 33, 36, 37
New York Herald Tribune, 164
Nicoll, Jack, 223
Nuclear arms race, 111, 273–4
Nuclear weapons test ban, 276
Nuclear weapons tests: Trinity Test (Alamogordo, New Mexico, 1945), 36–7, 38, 41, 138, 139, 145, 146, 239, 274; Operation Crossroads (Bikini atoll, Marshall Islands, Pacific, 1946), 43–4, 45, 55, 71, 78, 138, 139, 145–6, 148, 150, 217, 239, 258; tests at Eniwetok, Marshall Islands (1948), 146; tests at Eniwetok and Nevada Desert (1951), 150; 'Joe One' (Stalin's first atomic test, 1949), 109, 111, 115, 120, 169, 274: *see under* Operation Hurricane for British tests (1952–8)

Operation Epicure (survey expedition for Operation Hurricane), 1–5, 7, 150, 151, 156, 201; Epicure Report, 5–6, 185
Operation Hurricane (British nuclear weapon test, Monte Bello Islands, 1952): preparations, 156–83, 202–11; UK rehearsals, 175–7; site rehearsals 212–35; action plan, 245–53; detonation, 253–6; radioactive fall-out, 261–6, 271–2; health-monitoring and de-contamination, 265–6; health damage to test veterans and Australian public, 158, 266–9; contamination of site and visitors to site, 269–70, 271–2, 276; cost, 274–5; consequences for Britain, 273–6; subsequent British tests (1952–8), 157, 236–7, 266, 268, 269, 275
Operation Spoofer, 173
Oppenheimer, J. Robert, 33, 34, 37, 82, 83; *quoted* 41
Orr-Ewing, Charles, 174
O'Sullivan, Dan, 256, 257; *quoted* 224
Owen, Leonard, 20, 98

Parsons, William, 37
Pearce, Noah, 158, 190, 212, 216; *quoted* 82, 184, 188, 213–14
Peierls, Rudolf, 33, 36, 40, 100, 101; *quoted* 35, 105
Penney, William, 22–277 *passim*
Percival Engineering, 182, 273
Perrin, Michael, 16, 21, 22, 89, 90, 92, 95, 98–9, 100, 101, 102, 107–8, 114; *quoted* 59
Perth Daily News, 223, 257
Phillips, Max, 2, 3, 5, 224
Physics of Explosives Committee (Physex), 31, 78
Pike, Herbert, 39, 82, 104, 105, 106, 118, 122, 135, 139, 167, 219, 239
Pilgrim, Roy, 43, 78–9, 80, 113, 123, 158, 211, 217, 275
Pincher, Chapman, 87

Index

Plym, HMS, 161, 166, 175, 176, 178, 179, 183, 185, 188, 198–272 *passim*
Pontecorvo, Bruno, 162
Poole, H. J., 119, 122, 124
Portal, Viscount, 14–16, 21, 22, 23, 24, 45, 46, 57, 58, 59–60, 61, 63, 81, 85–97 *passim*, 98, 102–3, 113, 115–25 *passim*, 143, 149, 169–70, 171; *quoted* 22–3, 23–4, 46–7, 62, 149–50

Rabi, Isidor, 33
Ramsey, Norman, 37
Reading Mercury, 129
Reuters, 258
Risley industrial complex, Lancs, 16, 84, 90, 91
Road Research Laboratory, 123
Roberts, Frank, 144
Rolls-Royce, 117
Roosevelt, Franklin D., 17, 20
Rowlands, John, 136–8, 210, 240–1, 248, 277; *quoted* 211; Rowlands' RAF team, 137–8, 139, 210
Royal Air Force, 15, 57, 94, 108, 136, 137, 185, 210, 240, 249, 259, 260, 273: *see also under* Rowlands, John
Royal Aircraft Establishment, Farnborough, 57, 123, 137
Royal Arsenal, Woolwich, 48, 57, 70–1, 73–8, 79, 82, 84, 86, 131, 135, 166–7, 182, 208, 210, 275
Royal Australian Air Force, 1, 2, 158–9, 177, 212, 263, 267
Royal Australian Navy, 2, 5, 157
Royal College of Science, 27
Royal Commission into British Nuclear Tests in Australia (1985), 158, 266–7, 269, 276
Royal Engineers, 156, 158, 165, 177–9, 200, 212, 213, 221, 222, 246, 247, 265
Royal Institution, 72
Royal Marines, 219, 247, 252–3
Royal Navy, 15, 31, 137, 148–9,

152, 153, 160, 186, 187, 189, 191, 192, 194, 219, 220, 221–2, 223, 228, 229, 241, 259, 260
Royal Ordnance Factories, 77, 167, 182
Royal Society, 28, 148, 275

Sandys, Duncan, 172, 173, 237, 257, 259
Scotland Yard, 174
Scott, Charles, 2, 5
Segre, Emilio, 33
Sellafield *see* Windscale
Shinwell, Emanuel, 121–2
Shoeburyness ranges, Essex, 59, 79, 175
Skardon, William James, 114
Skinner, Herbert, 107
Smith, Cyril, 110–11
Smith, Pat, 158, 222
Smith, Wilfred, 123
Smyth Report, 20
Snow, C. P., 39, 40, 41, 42, 66, 81, 133
Solandt, Omond, 242
Soviet Union, 8, 10, 13, 83, 86, 89, 99, 101, 106, 108, 109, 110, 114, 120, 121, 134, 148, 162, 164, 171, 173, 273, 274
Springfields industrial complex, Preston, 20, 84, 86, 91
Stalin, Josef, 9, 12, 13, 88, 108
Strauss, George, 87
Strauss, Lewis, 110
Sydney, HMAS, 241

Task Force Four, 160–1, 166, 177, 184–201, 212–65 *passim*
Taylor, Geoffrey, 30 32, 33, 40, 55, 90, 91, 93, 102, 107
Tedder, Baron, 94, 95
Teller, Edward, 33
Thermonuclear test, Eniwetok atoll (1952), 273
The Times, 89, 166, 174, 180
Thomas, Aubrey, 209; *quoted* 210
Thornhill, Ken, 118, 122

Titterton, Ernest, 43, 55, 68, 69, 70, 103, 159, 242
Tizard, Henry, 62, 63, 93, 94, 95, 107, 113, 119–20, 121, 146, 147
Tomblin, John, 212, 216
Torlesse, David, 160, 161, 165, 166, 172, 173, 179, 185–201 and 220–59 *passim*, 264, 265, 275, 276; *quoted* 173–4, 246, 251
Tracker, HMS, 161, 179, 188, 200, 201, 225–34 *passim*, 245, 246, 249, 250, 262, 263, 264
Treasury, the, 172
Truman, Harry S., 17, 18, 20, 108, 110, 111
Tube Alloys, 16, 17, 98
Tuck, James, 43, 55, 102, 103
Tyte, Leonard, 123, 159–60, 179, 181, 189, 190, 191, 193, 194, 199, 200, 216, 219–48 *passim*, 251, 275, 276

Undex Committee, 31
United Kingdom Atomic Energy Authority, 276
United Nations, 11, 19, 25, 169, 170; Atomic Energy Commission, 12, 18, 45; Security Council, 274
United States, 7, 9, 10, 17, 18, 19, 25, 32, 89, 97, 100, 101, 108–13, 119–20, 121, 138, 145, 146, 147, 148, 150, 157, 161–2, 163, 169, 271, 273, 274, 276; Air Force, 108; Congress, 18, 19, 110, 111, 163; State Department, 88; Defense Department, 35, 108; Embassy, London, 108

Vickers, 273
Vleck, John van, 33

Warrego, HMAS, 157, 158
Washington Agreement, 18, 19
Weapons Scientific and Technical Committee, 90
Wedd, G., 181
West Australian, 223
White, Dick, 99
Willan, D. P., 264
Willows, Richard 'Guv', 143, 144, 167, 203, 206, 275
Wilmot, John, 23, 24
Wilson, Harold, 97
Wilson, N., 128, 141–2
Windscale, Cumberland (nuclear reactor and industrial complex), 11, 16, 20, 84, 86, 94, 106, 112, 129, 132, 134, 166, 202, 208
Woomera, 5, 166, 177, 237

Zeebrugge, HMS 161, 165, 177, 201, 212, 229, 230, 231, 232, 246, 251, 252, 253, 262, 263